The Open University

MST326 Mathema
and fluid mechanics

# Block 2

The cover image is of a two-dimensional Kármán vortex street (courtesy of the Institute of Computational Fluid Dynamics, Tokyo, Japan).

This publication forms part of an Open University course. Details of this and other Open University courses can be obtained from the Student Registration and Enquiry Service, The Open University, PO Box 197, Milton Keynes MK7 6BJ, United Kingdom: tel. +44 (0)845 300 6090, email general-enquiries@open.ac.uk

Alternatively, you may visit the Open University website at http://www.open.ac.uk where you can learn more about the wide range of courses and packs offered at all levels by The Open University.

To purchase a selection of Open University course materials visit http://www.ouw.co.uk, or contact Open University Worldwide, Walton Hall, Milton Keynes MK7 6AA, United Kingdom, for a brochure: tel. +44 (0)1908 858793, fax +44 (0)1908 858787, email ouw-customer-services@open.ac.uk

The Open University, Walton Hall, Milton Keynes, MK7 6AA.

First published 2009.

Edited, designed and typeset by The Open University, using the Open University TeX System.

Printed and bound in the United Kingdom by Henry Ling Limited, at the Dorset Press, Dorchester DT1 1HD

ISBN 978 0 7492 2311 3

1.1

*The Open University has had Woodland Carbon Code Pending Issuance Units assigned from Doddington North forest creation project (IHS ID103/26819) that will, as the trees grow, compensate for the greenhouse gas emissions from the manufacture of the paper in MST326 Block 2. More information can be found at https://www.woodlandcarboncode.org.uk/*

# Contents

# UNIT 5    Kinematics of fluids

## Study guide

This unit, which starts Block 2 of the course, depends significantly on the vector calculus that was covered in *Unit 4*, and to some extent on the solution of first-order partial differential equations and a version of the Chain Rule from *Unit 3*.

The unit is relatively long, though this will be balanced by a shorter *Unit 6*. The first four sections here will probably take roughly equal times to complete, with Section 5 requiring a bit less. This last section departs from the general theme of the rest of the unit, but underpins *Unit 6* and much of the rest of the block.

There is a multimedia session associated with Subsection 3.2, for which you are referred to the *Media Guide*. There is no audio activity associated with this unit.

## Introduction

*Unit 1* introduced some of the basic properties of fluids, such as the physical ideas of viscosity and compressibility, and some of the measurable quantities like flow velocity, density and pressure. It also introduced the fundamental idea of the continuum model. Although in reality the fluid is composed of discrete molecules, the model is a continuous one in which, for instance, the density is defined at each point in a fluid. Some of the basic ideas were then used to solve problems involving fluids at rest.

Now we start to investigate fluids in motion. In this unit and in *Unit 6*, the fluid under investigation is assumed to be inviscid. All real fluids possess viscosity, and it is important to be aware of this fact in interpreting every solution obtained. However, the inviscid model does provide much insight into the actual behaviour of fluids in many cases. We noted in *Unit 1* that the flow of a real fluid past an object can be considered in two regions, one adjacent to the boundary, where the viscosity has a considerable effect (the boundary layer), and an outer region where the viscous effects are negligible. Thus *Units 5* and *6* relate principally to the outer region. *Units 7* and *8* consider a more complicated model which includes the effects of viscosity.

The strategy for solving fluid flow problems is often different from the familiar approach in solid mechanics. There, we start with a particle as a model of a body in motion subject to certain forces. These forces are modelled by vectors, and using the laws of vector algebra we obtain the total force on the particle. Newton's Second Law then provides a relationship between the acceleration of the particle and the total force acting on it, and this relationship is used to find the velocity and position of the particle at any instant of time, given the position and velocity at one instant. So the problem-solving strategy in particle mechanics may be summarised as in Figure 0.1.

There are some occasions when we go in the opposite direction — from the position or velocity to the total force.

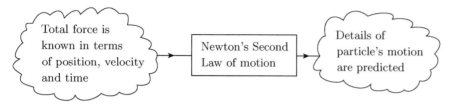

*Figure 0.1*

Many of the problems to be solved in fluid mechanics require a different approach, so it is important to identify at the outset the way in which to approach the subject. In a fluid flow problem, there are two main aims:

- to find the velocity field describing the velocity of the fluid at each of the points in the region occupied by the fluid, and
- to find the total force on any solid boundary in contact with the fluid.

In the *inviscid* case, there are two equations that enable us to achieve these aims. The *continuity equation* places a constraint on the velocity field; then the appropriate version of Newton's Second Law (called *Euler's equation* for the inviscid fluid model) provides both details of the velocity and also the pressure distribution in the fluid. The effect on any solid boundaries in the fluid can then be expressed in terms of the net surface force, which is obtained by integrating the pressure distribution over the boundary surface. This approach (for an inviscid fluid) is summarised in Figure 0.2.

The continuity equation was introduced in *Unit 4* Subsection 3.3. Euler's equation is derived in Section 5 of this unit.

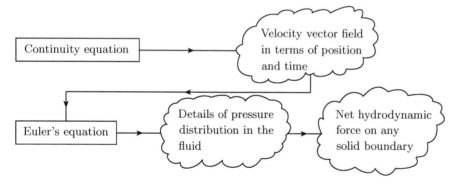

*Figure 0.2*

The initial and boundary conditions, not indicated in Figure 0.2, place additional constraints on the velocity field.

The last two steps in this problem-solving strategy were put to use in *Unit 1*, when evaluating the net force on a flat plate immersed in a static liquid. Since the liquid was at rest, the velocity field was zero, so the pressure distribution could be found without the use of Euler's equation (i.e. Newton's Second Law for an inviscid fluid).

You will see in Section 5 that the basic equation of fluid statics is just a special case of Euler's equation.

In general, the flow of a fluid is three-dimensional and unsteady. Mathematically, this means that the flow parameters, such as velocity and density, may depend on all three space coordinates and time; for example, in Cartesian coordinates, the velocity $\mathbf{u}$ may depend on $x$, $y$, $z$ and $t$.

However, there are many physical situations in which, owing to the symmetry of the problem, the flow parameters depend on only one or two space coordinates. A flow is said to be *two-dimensional* if the flow parameters depend on only two space coordinates. Using Cartesian coordinates ($x$, $y$ and $z$) or cylindrical polar coordinates ($r$, $\theta$ and $z$), the flow pattern for such a flow is the same in any plane $z = $ constant. The flow of water past a long circular cylinder is an example of a flow that can be modelled as two-dimensional. In practice, of course, all bodies and fluid regions are finite, so that the two-dimensional assumption applies only to that part of the cylinder where we can ignore 'end-effects'.

In Sections 1–3, all of the velocity fields to be considered are two-dimensional. To specify such a flow, we require:

- a plane $z = c$ (a constant) such that at no point on the plane is there a velocity component perpendicular to the plane, and
- the flow pattern to be identical in all planes parallel to the plane $z = c$.

Usually, we choose the plane $z = 0$ as a reference plane and the Cartesian coordinates $x$ and $y$, or plane polar coordinates $r$ and $\theta$, as convenient space coordinates. This means that any solid boundaries in the flow must have a uniform cross-section which can be drawn as a curve in the plane $z = 0$. For example, the flow past a circular cylinder is represented diagrammatically as the flow past a circle. Also, all of the flow parameters will be functions of $x$, $y$ and $t$ or $r$, $\theta$ and $t$.

Sections 1–3 deal with the basic kinematics of two-dimensional fluid flows. Section 1 introduces the differential equations for *pathlines* and *streamlines*. Section 2 introduces a scalar field, called the *stream function*, which for an incompressible fluid provides an alternative method of modelling the flow and finding the streamlines. Sections 2 and 3 derive the stream functions for several simple two-dimensional flow types (the *uniform flow*, *source*, *doublet* and *vortex*), and suitable combinations of these are used to model more complicated flows.

Section 4 introduces the idea of *differentiation following the motion*, which is necessary for the development of *Euler's equation* in Section 5.

# 1   *Pathlines and streamlines*

Much of the fluid mechanics component of this course is concerned with finding the velocity vector fields for fluids in motion. With this in mind, we first investigate ways of visualising the velocity field. Clearly, when we predict a velocity field from mathematical theory, we shall require a means of validating the results by comparison with the actual flow under investigation. The visualisation of a real fluid flow is important for the modelling process, and many new modelling ideas owe their origin to some form of flow visualisation. Two methods of visualising fluid flows relate to the *pathlines* and *streamlines* of the flow. This section develops the mathematical equations for each of these.

You saw the use of pathlines and streamlines while studying *Unit 1*.

# 1.1   Visualisation of the flow field

In *Unit 1* Subsection 1.4, you saw some of the many methods that are used to give a pictorial representation of fluid flows. Such visualisations are often vital to the formulation of a mathematical model for the fluid flow. For example, the streamlines past an aerofoil at high incidence are quite different from those for the low-incidence case (see Figure 1.1), and so we might expect that different mathematical models would be needed for the two cases.

See the corresponding *Media Guide* section.

Here 'incidence' refers to the angle at which the aerofoil faces the stream.

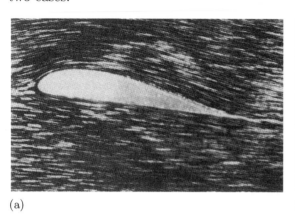
(a)

(b)

*Figure 1.1*   Flow from left to right past an aerofoil at (a) low incidence, and (b) high incidence

We now introduce the concepts of *pathline*, *streamline* and *streakline* on which flow visualisation methods are based.

## Pathlines

Imagine that, at an instant of time, a particle of smoke is injected into a fluid (a gas) at a fixed point $P$, with the velocity of the fluid at $P$. It is reasonable to assume that this particle will move with the fluid, that is, it will have the velocity of the fluid at each point it occupies. Figure 1.2 shows the position of the smoke particle at several instants of time ($t = 0, 1, 2, 3$) for a two-dimensional flow.

For a liquid, a dye would replace smoke. Ideally the particle of smoke or dye has the same density as the fluid.

The set of all positions of the particle from $t = 0$ to $t = 3$ is a continuous path. A **pathline** is the path traced out by an individual fluid particle during a specified time interval.

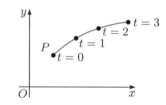

*Figure 1.2*

If another particle is injected at $P$, at time $t = 1$ say, then, in general, the pathline for this particle will differ from that for the original particle. However, if the flow is *steady* (that is, at each point all conditions are independent of time), the pathline (for $t = 1$ to $t = 4$) of the second particle will be the same as that of the first particle (for $t = 0$ to $t = 3$); in fact, for steady flow, every particle passing through $P$ has the same pathline.

Steady flow was defined in *Unit 1* Subsection 1.4.

By injecting smoke particles at several points at the same time, we can obtain a pathline visualisation of a flow.

Subsection 1.2 explains how to obtain the equations of pathlines of a flow for which the velocity field **u** is given.

## Streamlines

Imagine that aluminium powder is scattered evenly over the region of interest in a particular flow, and that a photograph is taken with an exposure just long enough for the particles of powder to have made short trails. Each trail will be in the direction of the velocity of the particle (see Figure 1.3), and so the photograph represents the directions of the whole flow (the velocity direction field) at a given instant of time. We can sketch

*Figure 1.3*   Trails and velocity vectors

on the photograph the trajectories of this direction field by drawing smooth curves which have the trails as tangents. Since the trails are everywhere parallel to the velocity vectors, the trajectories of the direction field are the field lines of the velocity vector field.

In fluid mechanics, the field lines of the velocity vector field are called *streamlines*. In more basic terms, a **streamline** at an instant of time is a curve such that, at each point along the curve, the tangent vector to the curve is parallel to the fluid velocity vector.

In general, if we take another photograph of the particle trails at some later time, the streamline pattern revealed will be different from that obtained before. At each instant of time there is a corresponding streamline pattern. Figure 1.4 shows a set of streamlines at one instant of time, for flow past a plate that oscillates back and forth about its central axis (directed into the page). This pattern alters as the plate moves.

Direction fields are discussed in MST209 *Unit 2*, and vector fields (including field lines) are discussed in MST209 *Unit 23*.

Streamlines are sometimes called *flowlines* or *lines of flow*.

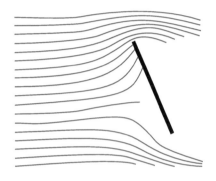

*Figure 1.4*   Streamlines at one instant for oscillating plate flow

*Figure 1.5*   Comparison of (dashed) streamline and (solid) pathline

Figure 1.5 shows a streamline and a pathline through the same point for the oscillating plate flow; note that they are different curves, because this is an unsteady flow. If the flow is steady, then the streamlines do not change with time and, moreover, the streamline through a point $P$ is the same *geometrically* as any pathline through $P$. In some cases, the pathlines and streamlines can coincide even if the flow is not steady.

The equations of streamlines are considered in Subsection 1.3, and the above remarks concerning steady flow are illustrated.

## Streaklines

*Unit 1* explained how *streaklines* were created by the continuous injection of dye into a fluid at a particular point. Streaklines differ in general both from streamlines (since the instantaneous fluid velocity vector may not be tangent to a streakline at a given time) and from pathlines (since a continuous stream of particles is involved, rather than the path of a single particle). However, for a steady flow the pathlines, streamlines and streaklines all coincide.

If the pathline of a particle, starting from a fixed point $P$ at time $\tau$, is given by $\mathbf{r}(t, \tau)$ for $t \geq \tau$, this position function can be regarded as varying with the starting time $\tau$ as well as with $t$. For each fixed value of $\tau$, the function describes a pathline, with variable $t$. For each fixed value of $t$, the function describes a streakline, with variable $\tau$.

We shall not pursue further the mathematical equations for streaklines, concentrating instead on pathlines and streamlines.

A visual comparison between pathlines, streamlines and streaklines, which refers to the oscillating plate of Figures 1.4 and 1.5, can be found via the *Media Guide*.

## 1.2 Pathlines

### Motion of a single particle

To illustrate the idea of pathlines, consider the motion of a shot in athletics. The set of points through which the shot passes is the *path* of the shot.

Projectile motion is discussed in MST209 *Unit 14*.

To find this path, we start by deriving the equation of motion. Assuming that there is no air resistance, and that the only force acting on the shot is its weight, $\mathbf{W}$, the force diagram and choice of axes are as shown in Figure 1.6. The equation of motion is

$$ m\mathbf{a} = m\frac{d^2\mathbf{r}}{dt^2} = \mathbf{W} = -mg\mathbf{j}, \qquad \text{so that} \qquad \frac{d^2\mathbf{r}}{dt^2} = -g\mathbf{j}, \tag{1.1} $$

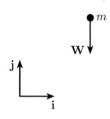

*Figure 1.6*   The forces acting on the shot

where $\mathbf{r} = x\mathbf{i} + y\mathbf{j}$ is the position vector of the shot at any time, $\mathbf{a}$ is its acceleration, $m$ is the mass of the shot and $g$ is the magnitude of the acceleration due to gravity. Suppose that the shot is projected from height $h$ above the horizontal ground with speed $v_0$ and at an angle $\theta_0$ above the horizontal. Then the initial conditions are

$$ \mathbf{r}(0) = h\mathbf{j}, \qquad \frac{d\mathbf{r}}{dt}(0) = v_0 \cos\theta_0\, \mathbf{i} + v_0 \sin\theta_0\, \mathbf{j}. $$

Integrating Equation (1.1), and substituting in the second initial condition, gives

$$ \frac{d\mathbf{r}}{dt} = v_0 \cos\theta_0\, \mathbf{i} + (-gt + v_0 \sin\theta_0)\, \mathbf{j} = \mathbf{v}, $$

where $\mathbf{v}$ is the velocity vector at time $t$. Integrating this equation, and substituting in the first initial condition, gives

$$ \mathbf{r} = v_0 \cos\theta_0\, t\,\mathbf{i} + (-\tfrac{1}{2}gt^2 + v_0 \sin\theta_0\, t + h)\,\mathbf{j}, $$

from which the $x$- and $y$-coordinates of the position of the shot at any time $t$ are obtained as

$$ x = v_0 \cos\theta_0\, t \qquad \text{and} \qquad y = -\tfrac{1}{2}gt^2 + v_0 \sin\theta_0\, t + h. \tag{1.2} $$

The time $t$ provides a natural parameter for the path of the shot. The shape of the path is found by eliminating $t$ between the two equations (1.2), to obtain

$$ y = -\frac{g}{2v_0^2 \cos^2\theta_0}\, x^2 + \tan\theta_0\, x + h, $$

which is the equation of a parabola (see Figure 1.7). This curve is the path along which the shot travels before hitting the ground; it is a pictorial record of the shot's motion.

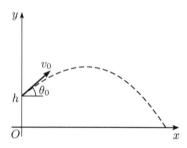

*Figure 1.7*   Path of a shot

### Motion of many particles in a fluid

For a fluid in motion, there are infinitely many fluid particles that we could choose to follow, so there will be infinitely many pathlines. Suppose that we take one particular fluid particle that travels along a path through the point $Q$, shown in Figure 1.8. If the position vector of the fluid particle when at $Q$ is $\mathbf{r}$, then its velocity $\mathbf{v}$ is given in terms of $\mathbf{r}$ by

*Figure 1.8*

$$ \mathbf{v} = \frac{d\mathbf{r}}{dt}. $$

The velocity $\mathbf{v}$ of the fluid particle when at $Q$ is the same as the velocity vector field $\mathbf{u}$ of the fluid at $Q$. Thus

$$ \frac{d\mathbf{r}}{dt} = \mathbf{u}. \tag{1.3} $$

In general, $\mathbf{u}$ depends on position and time, so that this vector equation represents coupled scalar differential equations linking $x$, $y$ and $t$. The following example shows how the equations of the pathlines for a flow are found from this vector equation when $\mathbf{u}$ is known.

*This vector equation also applies for three-dimensional flow problems, but here we deal with the two-dimensional case.*

### Example 1.1

Find the equations of the pathlines for a fluid flow with velocity field

$$\mathbf{u} = ay\,\mathbf{i} + bt\,\mathbf{j}, \qquad \text{where } a, b \text{ are positive constants.}$$

Sketch the pathlines of the fluid particles which pass through the points $(X, 0)$ at time $t = 0$, for $X = -1, 0, 1, 2, 3$.

### Solution

The vector differential equation (1.3) for a pathline is

$$\frac{d\mathbf{r}}{dt} = \mathbf{u} = ay\,\mathbf{i} + bt\,\mathbf{j},$$

and since by definition

$$\frac{d\mathbf{r}}{dt} = \frac{dx}{dt}\,\mathbf{i} + \frac{dy}{dt}\,\mathbf{j},$$

*See MST209 Unit 6 for the definition of the derivative of a vector function.*

we have

$$\frac{dx}{dt} = ay, \qquad \frac{dy}{dt} = bt.$$

The second equation integrates to give

$$y = \tfrac{1}{2}bt^2 + C, \qquad \text{where } C \text{ is an arbitrary constant.}$$

Then from the first equation, we have

$$\frac{dx}{dt} = ay = \tfrac{1}{2}abt^2 + aC.$$

This integrates to give

$$x = \tfrac{1}{6}abt^3 + aCt + D, \qquad \text{where } D \text{ is an arbitrary constant.}$$

These equations for $x$ and $y$ in terms of $t$ represent infinitely many curves in the region of fluid. For each pair of values for $C$ and $D$ we obtain a different pathline, depending on the fluid particle we choose to follow. The pathline of the particle which passes through the point $(X, 0)$ at time $t = 0$ must be such that $x = X$ and $y = 0$ at $t = 0$, that is,

*We now have $x = x(t)$ and $y = y(t)$, with $t$ as a parameter. We can, in principle, eliminate $t$ to obtain an equation relating $y$ directly to $x$. This is done for the specific case below.*

$$y(0) = C = 0 \qquad \text{and} \qquad x(0) = D = X.$$

The pathline equations for this particle are then

$$x = \tfrac{1}{6}abt^3 + X, \qquad y = \tfrac{1}{2}bt^2.$$

*These equations define the pathline for any specified time interval.*

We can eliminate the parameter $t$ from these two equations to obtain an explicit equation for the pathline:

$$(x - X)^2 = \frac{2a^2}{9b}y^3.$$

The pathlines corresponding to $X = -1, 0, 1, 2, 3$ are shown in Figure 1.9 (in which, for convenience, we have taken $b/a^2 = 16/9$).

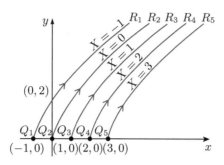

*Figure 1.9*

With $b/a^2 = 16/9$, the pathline $Q_1 R_1$ crosses the $y$-axis at $y = 2$, as indicated. More generally, $Q_1 R_1$ crosses the $y$-axis at $y = (9b/2a^2)^{1/3}$.

The direction of flow, shown by arrowheads, can be deduced from the sign of either component of $\mathbf{u}$. For example, $u_1 = ay$ is positive in the upper half-plane, where $y > 0$, so the flow is from left to right. Only the flow for $t \geq 0$ is shown here.

Note that the particle which travels along the pathline $Q_1 R_1$, for example, was at the point $Q_1$ when $t = 0$. Note also that the same scales should be used for the $x$- and $y$-axes, since we wish the pathlines to be a visual representation of the real flow. ■

## Exercise 1.1

Find the equations of pathlines for the two-dimensional flow with $\mathbf{u} = U\mathbf{i}$, where $U$ is a positive constant. Sketch some of these pathlines.

The next example involves the use of plane polar coordinates, $r$ and $\theta$.

## Example 1.2

Find the equations of pathlines for a fluid flow with velocity field

$$\mathbf{u} = \frac{m}{r}\,\mathbf{e}_r \qquad (r \neq 0),$$

where $m$ is a positive constant. Find the pathline of the particle which passes through the point $r = 1$, $\theta = \frac{1}{4}\pi$ at time $t = 0$.

Does the particle speed up or slow down as time passes?

### Solution

The polar form of the differential equation (1.3) for the pathlines, $d\mathbf{r}/dt = \mathbf{u}$, is

$$\frac{dr}{dt}\,\mathbf{e}_r + r\frac{d\theta}{dt}\,\mathbf{e}_\theta = \mathbf{u}.$$

In this example $\mathbf{u} = (m/r)\,\mathbf{e}_r$, and hence

$$\frac{dr}{dt} = \frac{m}{r}, \qquad r\frac{d\theta}{dt} = 0 \qquad (r \neq 0).$$

It follows that

$$r\frac{dr}{dt} = m \qquad \text{and} \qquad \frac{d\theta}{dt} = 0,$$

which integrate to give

$$r^2 = 2mt + C, \qquad \theta = D, \qquad \text{where } C \text{ and } D \text{ are arbitrary constants.}$$

The ranges for $r$ and $\theta$ are

$$r \geq 0, \quad -\pi < \theta \leq \pi.$$

The unit vectors $\mathbf{e}_r$, $\mathbf{e}_\theta$ for plane polar coordinates are the same as those for cylindrical polar coordinates in *Unit 4* Subsection 1.1. They were defined for the plane polar case in MST209 *Unit 20* and used in MST209 *Units 27* and *28*.

The polar form of the velocity vector is given in MST209 *Unit 28* as

$$\dot{\mathbf{r}} = \dot{r}\,\mathbf{e}_r + r\dot{\theta}\,\mathbf{e}_\theta.$$

This is the derivative with respect to time $t$ of the position vector, $\mathbf{r} = r\,\mathbf{e}_r$.

The pathline of the particle which passes through the point
$P_0$ ($r = 1$, $\theta = \frac{1}{4}\pi$) at time $t = 0$ has $C = 1$ and $D = \frac{1}{4}\pi$, so the pathline
equation in this case is

$$r^2 = 2mt + 1, \qquad \theta = \tfrac{1}{4}\pi.$$

(Note that, since $\theta$ is constant on each pathline, the elimination of $t$
between these two equations does not apply here.)

This is a ray $OP_0P_1P_2$, coming out from the origin $O$ at the constant
angle $\frac{1}{4}\pi$ (see Figure 1.10). Since $r$ is an increasing function of $t$, or
equivalently, since $dr/dt > 0$, the direction of flow along the pathline is
outwards, as indicated by the arrowhead. (Note that $O$ itself is excluded
from the pathline, since $r \neq 0$, and that the motion occurs only for
$t > -1/(2m)$.)

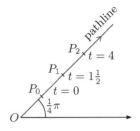

*Figure 1.10*

As time goes by, the particle slows down; after $1\frac{1}{2}$ seconds (with $m = 1$), it
reaches $P_1$ ($r = 2$), and after 4 seconds it reaches $P_2$ ($r = 3$).

The full set of pathlines includes all equations of the form
$\theta = D$ ($-\pi < D \leq \pi$). Some of these rays starting from the origin $O$ are
shown in Figure 1.11, with $O$ itself excluded in each case.  ■

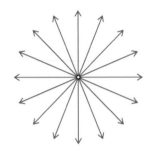

*Figure 1.11*

The velocity vector field in Example 1.2 is one of the basic models that can
be used to describe many real fluid flow problems. Fluid particles emerge
from the origin, $O$, and follow radial pathlines. We say that the flow field
$\mathbf{u} = (m/r)\,\mathbf{e}_r$ represents a **source** of fluid at $O$. A source can be thought of
as providing an injection of fluid along an axis perpendicular to the plane
of the flow (and hence into the page in Figure 1.11). The fluid flows out
equally in all directions perpendicular to this axis. We can interpret the
constant $m$ by considering the rate at which fluid crosses a circle of
radius $a$ (see Figure 1.12), representing a cylinder whose axis coincides
with the line of the source. At any point on the circle, the speed of the
fluid is $m/a$. The total volume of fluid flowing across the circumference of
the circle in unit time and per unit depth into the paper is therefore

$$(2\pi a)\frac{m}{a} = 2\pi m.$$

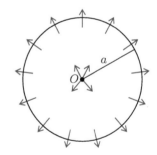

*Figure 1.12*

Since the flow is steady, this volume of fluid must be provided in unit time
by the inflow of fluid per unit length along the line of the source
through $O$. So $m$ is proportional to the rate at which fluid (by volume) is
delivered into the flow region, per unit length of the source line, and $2\pi m$
(the volume flow rate across any circle containing $O$) is called the
**strength** of the source.

The velocity field

$$\mathbf{u} = -\frac{m}{r}\,\mathbf{e}_r \qquad (r \neq 0,\ m > 0)$$

is said to represent a **sink** of fluid at $O$. Its **strength** is also $2\pi m$. Both the
source and the sink are basic flow patterns that will recur later in this unit.

The following procedure can be used for finding the equations of pathlines.

### Procedure 1.1

To find pathlines for a two-dimensional flow, for which the velocity field **u** has been determined, proceed as follows.

(a) Write down the differential equation for the pathlines, either in vector form as

$$\frac{d\mathbf{r}}{dt} = \mathbf{u} \tag{1.3}$$

or in component form, with

$$\frac{d\mathbf{r}}{dt} = \frac{dx}{dt}\,\mathbf{i} + \frac{dy}{dt}\,\mathbf{j} = \frac{dr}{dt}\,\mathbf{e}_r + r\frac{d\theta}{dt}\,\mathbf{e}_\theta. \tag{1.4}$$

(b) Solve these differential equations, if possible, to obtain the parametric equations

$$x = x(t), \quad y = y(t) \qquad \text{or} \qquad r = r(t), \quad \theta = \theta(t).$$

It may then be possible to eliminate $t$ in order to obtain an equation relating $x$ and $y$ (or $r$ and $\theta$).

Integration of these equations can be achieved by any appropriate method.

The parametric equations in terms of $t$ show a particle's progress along the pathline.

(c) Use a given initial point (if any) to determine the particular pathline required.

(d) If a sketch of pathlines is required, the direction of flow along each pathline (denoted by an arrowhead) can be found by considering the sign of a velocity component, $dx/dt$ or $dy/dt$ (or $dr/dt$ or $d\theta/dt$), at any point on the pathline.

Use this procedure to solve the following exercise.

### Exercise 1.2

Find the equations of pathlines for the following flows:

(a) a flow with velocity

$$\mathbf{u} = \frac{k}{r}\,\mathbf{e}_\theta \qquad (r \neq 0), \qquad \text{where } k \text{ is a positive constant};$$

(b) a flow with velocity

$$\mathbf{u} = x(3t+1)\,\mathbf{i} + 2y\,\mathbf{j} \qquad (x > 0,\ y > 0).$$

Sketch some pathlines for part (a) only, and comment on how the fluid speed varies as $r$ increases.

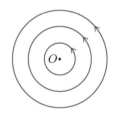

*Figure 1.13*

The velocity vector field $\mathbf{u} = (k/r)\,\mathbf{e}_\theta$ in Exercise 1.2(a) is another of the basic flow patterns that will be used to model more complicated fluid flow problems. In contrast to the source, whose pathlines radiate from one point, the pathlines are circles centred on the origin, and fluid particles move along these circles (see Figure 1.13). The further the circle is from the origin, the lower is the speed. This type of flow is called a **vortex** of **strength** $2\pi k$, and is studied further in *Unit 7*. The flow along pathlines is anticlockwise if $k > 0$ (as in Exercise 1.2(a)) and clockwise if $k < 0$.

As with the source, a vortex should be thought of as extending along a line through $O$, perpendicular to the plane of the flow. The reason for the factor $2\pi$ in the definition of vortex strength will be seen in *Unit 7*.

The talcum powder particles in the flow round the plughole, in the bath experiment of *Unit 1* Section 2, travel along almost circular paths. A vortex could be used to model the flow near the plughole.

# 1.3 Streamlines

## Important properties of streamlines

Subsection 1.1 explained that the field lines of the velocity vector field at a given instant of time are called streamlines, and that the flow visualisation method associated with streamlines is to photograph particle trails over a short time interval. By 'joining up' the trails with smooth curves, the resulting curves give a good approximation to the streamlines. (Also, the relative lengths of the trails indicate the variation in magnitude of the velocity field.)

If the velocity field depends on time, then the streamline pattern will change each instant (because the direction of the velocity vector at each point changes). However, for steady flows (those which do not depend on time), the streamline pattern remains the same. In steady flow, the fluid particles travel along the streamlines so that the pathlines and streamlines then coincide.

This is illustrated in Example 1.4 below.

It is often useful to imagine streamlines being drawn in the real fluid, and we often speak of them as if they were. Further, for any streamline at an instant of time, at each point of it we can picture the fluid velocity vector as tangential to the curve. An important property of streamlines can be deduced from this characterisation. At any point, the flow is tangential to the local streamlines. Hence the following is also true.

At any instant of time, there is no fluid crossing any streamline.

This follows because, at any point on a streamline, the velocity vector is perpendicular to $\mathbf{n}$, a vector normal to the streamline. Hence $\mathbf{u} \cdot \mathbf{n} = 0$, and $\mathbf{u} \cdot \mathbf{n}$ provides a measure of the flow rate across a curve or surface in the fluid.

In *Unit 4* we derived the volume flow rate across a surface $S$ as $\int_S \mathbf{u} \cdot \mathbf{n} \, dA$.

A second important property of streamlines is the following.

At any instant of time, distinct streamlines cannot cross.

We establish this fact by using a contradiction argument. Suppose that two streamlines do cross at a point, $A$ say. Then, since at each point of a streamline the velocity vector is parallel to the tangent to the streamline, the velocity vector at $A$ has two different directions (see Figure 1.14), and so the velocity field is not uniquely defined. This contradiction establishes the result. (Nor can $\mathbf{u}$ physically have two directions at a point.)

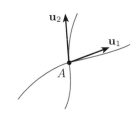

A streamline may *appear* to cross itself, or to divide into more than one branch, at a point where the velocity is zero; see Figure 2.15 on page 31. Such cases are not covered above.

*Figure 1.14*

## Finding the streamline equations

In order to derive the streamline equations, we use the condition that at any instant of time the velocity vector **u** is parallel to the instantaneous streamline.

If $P$ and $Q$ are neighbouring points on the same streamline (see Figure 1.15), then the velocity vector **u** at $P$ is approximately parallel to the chord $PQ$. As $Q$ approaches $P$ then, in the limit, the slope of the tangent to the streamline at $P$ is equal to the slope of the velocity vector at $P$. If the streamline has equation $y = f(x)$ and $\mathbf{u} = u_1\,\mathbf{i} + u_2\,\mathbf{j}$, then

$$\frac{dy}{dx} = \frac{u_2}{u_1} \qquad (u_1 \neq 0). \tag{1.5}$$

Both sides of this equation represent the instantaneous slope of the streamline at $P$ at time $t$.

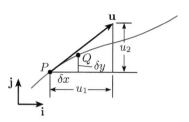

*Figure 1.15*

Similar equations hold in plane polar coordinates (see Figure 1.16), for which $\mathbf{u} = u_r\,\mathbf{e}_r + u_\theta\,\mathbf{e}_\theta$; the 'slope' of the tangent to the streamline at $P$ ($= r\,d\theta/dr$) is equal to the 'slope' of the velocity vector at $P$ ($= u_\theta/u_r$), and so

$$r\frac{d\theta}{dr} = \frac{u_\theta}{u_r} \qquad (u_r \neq 0).$$

More conventionally, the polar coordinate form is written as

$$\frac{1}{r}\frac{dr}{d\theta} = \frac{u_r}{u_\theta} \qquad (u_\theta \neq 0). \tag{1.6}$$

The streamline example below uses the flow field of Example 1.1.

In this case, 'slope' is referred to the unit vectors $\mathbf{e}_r$ and $\mathbf{e}_\theta$ at the point $P$.

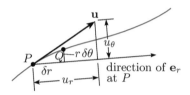

*Figure 1.16*

### Example 1.3

Find the streamlines through the point $(x_0, y_0)$ for the following two-dimensional flow field:

$$\mathbf{u} = ay\,\mathbf{i} + bt\,\mathbf{j}, \qquad \text{where } a, b \text{ are positive constants.}$$

### Solution

In this unsteady flow, Equation (1.5) defining the streamlines is

$$\frac{dy}{dx} = \frac{u_2}{u_1} = \frac{bt}{ay} \qquad (y \neq 0), \qquad \text{or} \qquad ay\frac{dy}{dx} = bt.$$

In this differential equation, $t$ is held constant, because a set of streamlines is defined at each instant of time. Integrating with respect to $x$, we obtain

$$\tfrac{1}{2}ay^2 = btx + C, \qquad \text{where } C \text{ is a constant.}$$

The point $(x_0, y_0)$ lies on this streamline if

$$\tfrac{1}{2}ay_0^2 = btx_0 + C,$$

and so, by subtraction of the last equation from the one before,

$$\tfrac{1}{2}a(y^2 - y_0^2) = bt(x - x_0).$$

These streamlines are parabolas; for example, if $x_0 = y_0 = 0$ and $b/a = 2$, then the streamlines are given by $y^2 = 4tx$. The streamlines through $(x_0, 0)$ at time $t = 1$ are $y^2 = 4(x - x_0)$, some of which are shown in Figure 1.17.

These equations are quite different from those for the pathlines derived in Example 1.1 and shown in Figure 1.9. When the flow is unsteady, the pathlines and streamlines will normally be different, as in this case. ■

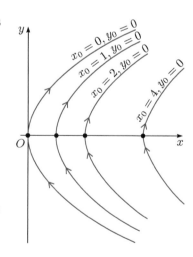

*Figure 1.17*  Streamlines at time $t = 1$ (with $b/a = 2$)

Note that the direction of flow has been shown on the streamlines in Figure 1.17. This may be found by considering a point $(x, y)$ on a streamline. At this point, $\mathbf{u} = ay\,\mathbf{i} + bt\,\mathbf{j}$. Now $u_1 = ay$ has the same sign as $y$, and $u_2$ is positive. This information is shown in Figure 1.18, and justifies the direction of arrowheads shown in Figure 1.17. Note also that the same scale should be used on each axis in order that the streamlines represent the real flow.

Three-dimensional direction fields can model fluid flows, and these also lead to streamlines, but we shall deal only with two-dimensional flows.

For many simple flows, the direction of flow is obvious from other considerations.

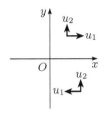

### Exercise 1.3

Find the streamlines through the point $(x_0, y_0)$ for the two-dimensional vector field

$$\mathbf{u} = U \cos\alpha\,\mathbf{i} + U \sin\alpha\,\mathbf{j}, \qquad \text{where } U, \alpha \text{ are constants.}$$

*Figure 1.18*

(This vector field represents a uniform flow at angle $\alpha$ to the $x$-axis.)

---

The next example requires use of the polar coordinate form of the streamline equations.

### Example 1.4

Find the streamlines for the fluid flow with velocity field

$$\mathbf{u} = \frac{m}{r}\,\mathbf{e}_r \qquad (r \neq 0),$$

where $m$ is a positive constant.

The pathlines for this flow were found in Example 1.2.

### Solution

In this case of the flow due to a source, $\mathbf{u} = (m/r)\,\mathbf{e}_r$ implies that

$$u_r = \frac{m}{r} \qquad \text{and} \qquad u_\theta = 0.$$

We use the first form of the streamline equation,

$$r\frac{d\theta}{dr} = \frac{u_\theta}{u_r} = \frac{0}{m/r} = 0,$$

which integrates to give $\theta = \text{constant}$. Thus, the streamlines are rays from the origin, and are identical to the pathlines obtained in Example 1.2 (see Figure 1.11). This illustrates the fact that for steady flow, streamlines and pathlines are identical. ∎

The second form of this equation, which is Equation (1.6), is not defined when $u_\theta = 0$.

These examples suggest the following procedure for determining streamlines. A major point, which makes this an easier process than that for pathlines, is that for unsteady flows, $t$ is taken as constant during the integration.

### Procedure 1.2

To find streamlines for two-dimensional flows, for which the velocity field $\mathbf{u}$ has been determined, either as $\mathbf{u} = u_1\,\mathbf{i} + u_2\,\mathbf{j}$ or as $\mathbf{u} = u_r\,\mathbf{e}_r + u_\theta\,\mathbf{e}_\theta$, proceed as follows.

(a) Write down the differential equation for the streamlines either as

$$\frac{dy}{dx} = \frac{u_2}{u_1} \qquad (u_1 \neq 0) \tag{1.5}$$

or as

$$\frac{1}{r}\frac{dr}{d\theta} = \frac{u_r}{u_\theta} \qquad (u_\theta \neq 0). \tag{1.6}$$

(b) Solve this differential equation, regarding $t$ as a constant.

(c) Substitute one point, $(x_0, y_0)$ say, which is on the streamline of interest, to obtain its equation.

(d) Sketch the graphs of several typical streamlines at a selected time $t$; this gives an instantaneous picture of the flow at time $t$. The direction of flow along each streamline (denoted by an arrowhead) can be found by considering the sign of a velocity component, $u_1$ or $u_2$ (or $u_r$ or $u_\theta$), at any point on the streamline for the given time.

The cases for which $u_1 = 0$ or $u_\theta = 0$ at all points are discussed below.

Each of Equations (1.5) and (1.6) can be used also in the 'upside down' form, that is,

$$\frac{dx}{dy} = \frac{u_1}{u_2} \qquad (u_2 \neq 0),$$

$$r\frac{d\theta}{dr} = \frac{u_\theta}{u_r} \qquad (u_r \neq 0).$$

If a velocity component is zero everywhere, then the equation of streamlines is easy to write down. For example, if $u_1 = 0$, then the velocity is parallel to the $y$-axis, and so the streamlines are given by $x = $ constant. Similarly,

if $u_2 = 0$, the streamlines are given by $y = $ constant;

if $u_r = 0$, the streamlines are given by $r = $ constant;

if $u_\theta = 0$, the streamlines are given by $\theta = $ constant.

This case arose in Example 1.4.

### Exercise 1.4

Find the equations of the streamlines for the following flows:

(a) $\mathbf{u} = \dfrac{k}{r}\,\mathbf{e}_\theta \qquad (r \neq 0)$;

(b) $\mathbf{u} = x(3t+1)\,\mathbf{i} + 2y\,\mathbf{j} \qquad (x > 0,\ y > 0)$.

For part (b), sketch the streamlines which pass through the point $(1,1)$ for times $t = 0$, $t = \frac{1}{3}$ and $t = 1$.

At this stage, you might ask which of pathlines and streamlines are the more relevant. The answer is that, while pathlines have a role to play, streamlines are usually more relevant since they depict the flowlines of a region of fluid at a particular instant of time. This is what can most conveniently be photographed, and most pictures of fluid flows show the positions of coloured particles over a small interval of time.

For more on pathlines, streamlines and streaklines, see the *Media Guide*.

The flow in Exercise 1.4(a) is the vortex flow discussed after Exercise 1.2. You have seen that for a source and for a vortex (each of which is a steady flow), the streamlines and the pathlines coincide. These flow patterns, together with that for a uniform flow, are very important in attempts at modelling real fluid flows in Section 3 of this unit and in *Unit 7*. The results for these flows are summarised as follows.

## Summary of results

(a) The velocity field of *a source of strength* $2\pi m$ at the origin is

$$\mathbf{u} = \frac{m}{r}\,\mathbf{e}_r \qquad (r \neq 0,\ m > 0),$$

and the streamline pattern is the set of all radial lines

$$\theta = \text{constant} \qquad (\text{see Figure 1.19}).$$

The strength, $2\pi m$, is the volume rate of inflow of fluid into the region.

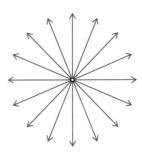

*Figure 1.19*  Source at origin

(b) The velocity field of *a sink of strength* $2\pi m$ at the origin is

$$\mathbf{u} = -\frac{m}{r}\,\mathbf{e}_r \qquad (r \neq 0,\ m > 0),$$

and the streamline pattern is the set of all radial lines

$$\theta = \text{constant}.$$

The strength, $2\pi m$, is the volume rate of outflow of fluid from the region.

(c) The velocity field of *a vortex of strength* $2\pi k$ at the origin is

$$\mathbf{u} = \frac{k}{r}\,\mathbf{e}_\theta \qquad (r \neq 0),$$

and the streamline pattern is the set of all circles

$$r = \text{constant} \qquad (\text{see Figure 1.20}).$$

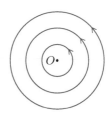

*Figure 1.20*  Vortex at origin

(d) The velocity field of a *uniform flow* of speed $U$ at an angle $\alpha$ to the $x$-axis is

$$\mathbf{u} = U\cos\alpha\,\mathbf{i} + U\sin\alpha\,\mathbf{j},$$

and the streamline pattern is the set of all (parallel) lines making an angle $\alpha$ with the $x$-axis (see Figure 1.21).

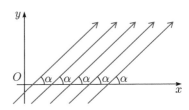

*Figure 1.21*  Uniform flow

# End-of-section exercises

### Exercise 1.5

Determine the pathline and the streamline which pass through the origin at $t = 0$ for the velocity field

$$\mathbf{u} = a\cos(\omega t)\,\mathbf{i} + a\sin(\omega t)\,\mathbf{j}, \qquad \text{where } a, \omega \text{ are positive constants.}$$

### Exercise 1.6

Find the equations of the pathlines and the streamlines, in the form $r = f(\theta)$, for the velocity field

$$\mathbf{u} = r\cos(\tfrac{1}{2}\theta)\,\mathbf{e}_r + r\sin(\tfrac{1}{2}\theta)\,\mathbf{e}_\theta.$$

*Hint:* First find the streamlines.

# 2 The stream function

Section 1 showed that streamlines provide a pictorial method of representing the velocity field of a fluid flow.

Any velocity field **u** which represents a fluid flow must satisfy the continuity equation. Starting from this equation, we shall define a scalar field called the *stream function*. This scalar field specifies a fluid flow, and its contours are the streamlines of the flow.

One advantage of working with the stream function rather than the velocity field is that we have to find one scalar function rather than two ($u_1$ and $u_2$). In this section we obtain the stream functions for certain basic flows, and Section 3 explains how to use combinations of these basic flows to model more complicated flows.

As in Section 1, this section concerns two-dimensional flows (see page 9). The definition of the stream function depends on the flow being two-dimensional.

## 2.1 Introducing the stream function

We begin with the continuity equation for the two-dimensional flow of a constant-density fluid. In Cartesian coordinates, this equation is

$$\nabla \cdot \mathbf{u} = \frac{\partial u_1}{\partial x} + \frac{\partial u_2}{\partial y} = 0,$$

where $\mathbf{u} = u_1 \mathbf{i} + u_2 \mathbf{j}$. If we introduce the scalar field $\psi(x, y)$, such that

$$u_1 = \frac{\partial \psi}{\partial y} \qquad \text{and} \qquad u_2 = -\frac{\partial \psi}{\partial x}, \tag{2.1}$$

then, for any such function $\psi$, the continuity equation is automatically satisfied, because

$$\nabla \cdot \mathbf{u} = \frac{\partial}{\partial x}\left(\frac{\partial \psi}{\partial y}\right) + \frac{\partial}{\partial y}\left(-\frac{\partial \psi}{\partial x}\right)$$

$$= \frac{\partial^2 \psi}{\partial x \partial y} - \frac{\partial^2 \psi}{\partial y \partial x}$$

$$= 0, \qquad \text{by the commutative property of partial differentation.}$$

This version of the continuity equation was derived in *Unit 4*, Exercise 3.8(a). The operator $\nabla$ was introduced in *Unit 4* Subsection 5.1.

What is more, it can be shown that the equation $\nabla \cdot \mathbf{u} = 0$ guarantees the existence of such a scalar field $\psi(x, y)$.

The scalar field $\psi(x, y)$ is called the **stream function** of **u**. The following example shows how we can find the stream function from the velocity vector field of a uniform flow, and that the contour lines for the scalar field $\psi$ (that is, the curves $\psi$ = constant) are the streamlines for the velocity field.

This property is satisfied by all the functions $\psi$ that we deal with. In MST209 *Unit 12*, this was called the Mixed Derivative Theorem.

### Example 2.1

Find the stream function $\psi(x, y)$ for the uniform flow with velocity field

$$\mathbf{u} = U \cos \alpha \, \mathbf{i} + U \sin \alpha \, \mathbf{j}, \qquad \text{where } U, \alpha \text{ are constants.}$$

Show that the contour lines $\psi$ = constant are the streamlines of this flow, as found in Exercise 1.3 on page 19.

### Solution

For the uniform flow, Equation (2.1) gives

$$u_1 = \frac{\partial \psi}{\partial y} = U \cos \alpha \qquad \text{and} \qquad u_2 = -\frac{\partial \psi}{\partial x} = U \sin \alpha.$$

Integrate the second equation to give

$$\psi(x,y) = -Ux\sin\alpha + f(y),$$

where $f$ is an arbitrary function. Differentiating this equation with respect to $y$, we have

$$\frac{\partial\psi}{\partial y} = 0 + f'(y)$$

$$= U\cos\alpha,$$

from the first equation. Integrating $f'(y) = U\cos\alpha$ gives

$$f(y) = Uy\cos\alpha + A,$$

where $A$ is an arbitrary constant. Hence the stream function is

$$\psi(x,y) = -Ux\sin\alpha + Uy\cos\alpha + A.$$

The lines $\psi = $ constant are defined by the equation

$$-Ux\sin\alpha + Uy\cos\alpha + A = \text{constant} = B, \text{ say}.$$

Write $(B-A)/(U\cos\alpha) = C$ (also a constant), to obtain

$$y - x\tan\alpha = C.$$

These equations are the same as those of the streamlines found in Exercise 1.3. They are parallel lines making an angle $\alpha$ with the $x$-axis. Figure 2.1 shows four of these streamlines. (The directions shown are for $U > 0$.) ∎

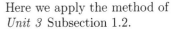

Here we apply the method of *Unit 3* Subsection 1.2.

We assume that $\cos\alpha \neq 0$ here. If $\cos\alpha = 0$ then

$$\mathbf{u} = \pm U\mathbf{j}, \quad \psi = \mp Ux + A,$$

with contours $x = $ constant.

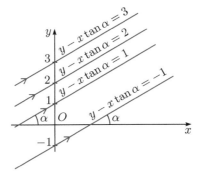

*Figure 2.1*

### Exercise 2.1

Find the stream function $\psi(x,y)$ for the flow with velocity field

$$\mathbf{u} = ay\,\mathbf{i}, \qquad \text{where } a \text{ is a positive constant.}$$

Sketch several contour lines for $\psi(x,y)$.

This flow is called a *shear flow*, because the velocity component in the $x$-direction increases linearly with $y$, as shown in Figure 2.2.

For the shear flow in Exercise 2.1, the velocity vector field is parallel to the $x$-axis, so that the streamlines are lines parallel to the $x$-axis. As in Example 2.1, the contour lines, $\psi = $ constant, are the streamlines. We now show that, for any velocity field $\mathbf{u}$, the streamlines are always the curves $\psi = $ constant, where $\psi(x,y)$ is the stream function of $\mathbf{u}$.

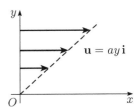

*Figure 2.2*

23

Figure 2.3 shows part of a streamline. Suppose that the streamline has parametric equations $x = x(s)$ and $y = y(s)$, for some parameter $s$. Then, if $\mathbf{r}$ is the position vector of any point $P$ on the streamline, $d\mathbf{r}/ds$ is a tangent vector to the streamline. Since at every point of a streamline $\mathbf{u}$ is parallel to the tangent, we have

$$\mathbf{u} \times \frac{d\mathbf{r}}{ds} = \mathbf{0}.$$

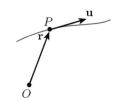

Now

$$\mathbf{u} = \frac{\partial \psi}{\partial y} \mathbf{i} - \frac{\partial \psi}{\partial x} \mathbf{j} \quad \text{and} \quad \frac{d\mathbf{r}}{ds} = \frac{dx}{ds} \mathbf{i} + \frac{dy}{ds} \mathbf{j},$$

*Figure 2.3*

so that

$$\mathbf{u} \times \frac{d\mathbf{r}}{ds} = \left( \frac{\partial \psi}{\partial y} \frac{dy}{ds} + \frac{\partial \psi}{\partial x} \frac{dx}{ds} \right) \mathbf{k} = \mathbf{0}.$$

Using the Chain Rule for a function of two variables,

$$\left( \frac{\partial \psi}{\partial y} \frac{dy}{ds} + \frac{\partial \psi}{\partial x} \frac{dx}{ds} \right) \mathbf{k} = \frac{d\psi}{ds} \mathbf{k} = \mathbf{0}.$$

This version of the Chain Rule was introduced in MST209 *Unit 12*, and put to use in *Units 3* and *4* of this course.

Therefore $d\psi/ds = 0$ along a streamline, and hence $\psi$ is constant along a streamline.

Each streamline is therefore a contour line for the stream function $\psi(x, y)$. This argument applies at each instant of time, since both the streamline and the stream function may be time-dependent for an unsteady flow.

The stream function provides a second method of finding the equations of the streamlines, which is often more convenient than using Procedure 1.2 on page 20.

As you will see in Section 3, the stream function for a complicated flow can be found by adding together the stream functions for several basic flows. The velocity field and the streamlines for the more complicated flow are then obtained directly from this stream function.

The next example shows how the plane polar coordinate form for the stream function can be derived.

### Example 2.2

Suppose that $\psi(x, y)$ is the stream function for the velocity field $\mathbf{u} = u_1 \mathbf{i} + u_2 \mathbf{j}$. Show that:

(a) $\boldsymbol{\nabla} \psi$ is perpendicular to $\mathbf{u}$;

(b) $\mathbf{u} = \boldsymbol{\nabla} \psi \times \mathbf{k}$.

(c) Hence obtain the equations defining the stream function $\psi(r, \theta)$, where $\mathbf{u}$ is given in plane polar coordinates.

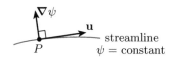

*Figure 2.4*

### Solution

(a) Two vectors are perpendicular when their scalar product is zero and neither is the zero vector. From the defining equations for $\psi$, we have

$$u_1 = \frac{\partial \psi}{\partial y} \quad \text{and} \quad u_2 = -\frac{\partial \psi}{\partial x}.$$

Hence

$$(\boldsymbol{\nabla} \psi) \cdot \mathbf{u} = \left( \frac{\partial \psi}{\partial x} \mathbf{i} + \frac{\partial \psi}{\partial y} \mathbf{j} \right) \cdot (u_1 \mathbf{i} + u_2 \mathbf{j})$$

$$= (-u_2 \mathbf{i} + u_1 \mathbf{j}) \cdot (u_1 \mathbf{i} + u_2 \mathbf{j}) = 0,$$

and thus $\boldsymbol{\nabla} \psi$ and $\mathbf{u}$ are perpendicular.

An alternative argument is based on the contours for $\psi$. Since these are streamlines, at any point $P$ on a contour line, the velocity vector $\mathbf{u}$ is parallel to the tangent. One property of the gradient vector $\boldsymbol{\nabla} \psi$ is that it is directed normal to a contour (see *Unit 4* Subsection 1.3). Hence $\boldsymbol{\nabla} \psi$ is perpendicular to $\mathbf{u}$ (see Figure 2.4 above).

(b) The vector product of $\boldsymbol{\nabla}\psi$ with $\mathbf{k}$ is

$$\boldsymbol{\nabla}\psi \times \mathbf{k} = \left( \frac{\partial \psi}{\partial x}\mathbf{i} + \frac{\partial \psi}{\partial y}\mathbf{j} \right) \times \mathbf{k}$$

$$= \frac{\partial \psi}{\partial y}\mathbf{i} - \frac{\partial \psi}{\partial x}\mathbf{j}$$

$$= u_1\mathbf{i} + u_2\mathbf{j} = \mathbf{u}.$$

(c) In plane polar coordinates,

$$\boldsymbol{\nabla}\psi = \frac{\partial \psi}{\partial r}\mathbf{e}_r + \frac{1}{r}\frac{\partial \psi}{\partial \theta}\mathbf{e}_\theta,$$

This is the expression for **grad** $\psi$ in cylindrical polar coordinates (see *Unit 4* Subsection 1.3), with $\partial\psi/\partial z = 0$ since the flow is two-dimensional.

and the equation from part (b), $\mathbf{u} = \boldsymbol{\nabla}\psi \times \mathbf{k}$, becomes

$$\mathbf{u} = u_r\mathbf{e}_r + u_\theta\mathbf{e}_\theta$$

$$= \left( \frac{\partial \psi}{\partial r}\mathbf{e}_r + \frac{1}{r}\frac{\partial \psi}{\partial \theta}\mathbf{e}_\theta \right) \times \mathbf{k}$$

$$= \frac{1}{r}\frac{\partial \psi}{\partial \theta}\mathbf{e}_r - \frac{\partial \psi}{\partial r}\mathbf{e}_\theta.$$

The cross products between the unit vectors $\mathbf{e}_r$, $\mathbf{e}_\theta$ and $\mathbf{e}_z = \mathbf{k}$ were given in *Unit 4* Subsection 1.1.

Hence the equations

$$u_r = \frac{1}{r}\frac{\partial \psi}{\partial \theta} \qquad \text{and} \qquad u_\theta = -\frac{\partial \psi}{\partial r} \tag{2.2}$$

define the stream function $\psi(r,\theta)$ in polar coordinates. ∎

The strategy of this solution is worth noting. Starting from a definition in Cartesian coordinates, we derive a vector result, $\mathbf{u} = \boldsymbol{\nabla}\psi \times \mathbf{k}$, which holds in any coordinate system. Then we deduce from this the corresponding form of the definition in plane polar coordinates.

## Example 2.3

Find the stream function and the equation of the streamlines for the flow with velocity vector field

$$\mathbf{u} = U\cos\theta\left(1 - \frac{a^2}{r^2}\right)\mathbf{e}_r - U\sin\theta\left(1 + \frac{a^2}{r^2}\right)\mathbf{e}_\theta.$$

### Solution

Using Equations (2.2), we have

$$\frac{1}{r}\frac{\partial \psi}{\partial \theta} = u_r = U\cos\theta\left(1 - \frac{a^2}{r^2}\right), \tag{2.3}$$

$$-\frac{\partial \psi}{\partial r} = u_\theta = -U\sin\theta\left(1 + \frac{a^2}{r^2}\right). \tag{2.4}$$

Integrating Equation (2.4) with respect to $r$ gives

$$\psi(r,\theta) = U\sin\theta\left(r - \frac{a^2}{r}\right) + f(\theta),$$

where $f$ is an arbitrary function. Substituting into Equation (2.3) gives

$$\frac{1}{r}\left[U\cos\theta\left(r - \frac{a^2}{r}\right)\right] + \frac{1}{r}f'(\theta) = U\cos\theta\left(1 - \frac{a^2}{r^2}\right).$$

Thus $f'(\theta) = 0$ and so $f(\theta) = C$, where $C$ is an arbitrary constant. The stream function is then

$$\psi(r,\theta) = U\sin\theta\left(r - \frac{a^2}{r}\right) + C.$$

The streamlines are the lines of constant $\psi$, given by

$$U\sin\theta\left(r - \frac{a^2}{r}\right) = \text{constant}. \quad∎$$

### Exercise 2.2

Find the stream functions for the following velocity fields:

(a) $\mathbf{u} = \dfrac{k}{r}\,\mathbf{e}_\theta,$     where $k$ is a constant     (a vortex of strength $2\pi k$);

(b) $\mathbf{u} = \dfrac{m}{r}\,\mathbf{e}_r,$     where $m$ is a constant     (a source of strength $2\pi m$).

---

The following procedure summarises the method for finding the stream function and the streamlines associated with it.

### Procedure 2.1

To find the stream function and the associated streamlines, when the velocity field $\mathbf{u}$ has been determined either as $\mathbf{u} = u_1\,\mathbf{i} + u_2\,\mathbf{j}$ or as $\mathbf{u} = u_r\,\mathbf{e}_r + u_\theta\,\mathbf{e}_\theta$, proceed as follows.

(a) Solve the differential equations defining the stream function,

$$u_1 = \frac{\partial \psi}{\partial y} \qquad \text{and} \qquad u_2 = -\frac{\partial \psi}{\partial x} \tag{2.1}$$

or

$$u_r = \frac{1}{r}\frac{\partial \psi}{\partial \theta} \qquad \text{and} \qquad u_\theta = -\frac{\partial \psi}{\partial r}, \tag{2.2}$$

to obtain $\psi(x, y)$ or $\psi(r, \theta)$.

(b) The streamlines are the contour lines of the stream function, $\psi$, and so are represented by the equation $\psi = \text{constant}$.

### Exercise 2.3

Find the stream functions for the following velocity fields:

(a) $\mathbf{u} = Kr\,\mathbf{e}_\theta,$     where $K$ is a constant;

(b) $\mathbf{u} = y\,\mathbf{i} - (x - 2t)\,\mathbf{j}.$

Sketch some of the streamlines for times $t = 0$ and $t = 1$ in part (b).

For the flow in part (a), the fluid rotates around the origin as if it were a rigid body.

---

In each of the examples and exercises, the expression for the stream function contains an arbitrary constant, $C$. Without any loss of generality, this constant is usually chosen to be zero — for example, the stream function for Example 2.3 is then $\psi(r, \theta) = U \sin \theta \left(r - a^2/r\right)$ — and the streamlines have the same defining equation as before. Since the velocity components are given as derivatives of $\psi$, the value chosen for the constant $C$ has no effect on the velocity vector field $\mathbf{u}$.

## 2.2  *Physical interpretation of the stream function*

The last subsection showed that one property of the stream function $\psi$ is that the contour lines, $\psi = $ constant, are the same as the streamlines of the flow. We now go on to demonstrate another physical property of the stream function, namely, that the change in $\psi$ between two points $P$ and $Q$ in the $(x, y)$-plane is equal to the volume flow rate across a surface of unit depth on *any* curve from $P$ to $Q$; see Figure 2.5, in which we consider a two-dimensional flow parallel to the $(x, y)$-plane. The surface $PQRT$ has unit depth parallel to the $z$-axis, so that $PT = QR = 1$. In Figure 2.6, this surface is seen from above, and in the following analysis the volume flow rate through a curve $PQ$ in the $(x, y)$-plane implies the volume flow rate through a surface $S$, perpendicular to the $(x, y)$-plane, through the curve $PQ$ and of unit depth.

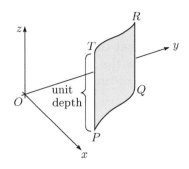

*Figure 2.5*

The volume flow rate (or flux) of fluid through the surface $S$ is given by

See *Unit 4* Subsection 2.1.

$$V = \int_S \mathbf{u} \cdot \mathbf{n}\, dA,$$

where $\mathbf{n}$ is the unit vector normal to the curve $PQ$ at an arbitrary point $B$, as shown in Figure 2.6. If the curve $PQ$ is parametrised in terms of the distance $s$ along it from $P$, then the area element can be taken as

$$\delta A = \delta s \times 1,$$

since the depth of the element is 1; see Figure 2.7. The surface integral for $V$ then becomes

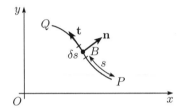

*Figure 2.6*

$$V = \int_P^Q \mathbf{u} \cdot \mathbf{n}\, ds.$$

We can find an expression for the unit normal, $\mathbf{n}$, in terms of $\mathbf{r}$, the position vector of $B$, and the unit vector $\mathbf{k}$. Since $s$ is a parameter representing distance along the curve from $P$, the unit tangent vector $\mathbf{t}$ to the curve $PQ$ at the point $B$ (see Figure 2.6) is

$$\mathbf{t} = \frac{d\mathbf{r}}{ds} = \frac{dx}{ds}\,\mathbf{i} + \frac{dy}{ds}\,\mathbf{j},$$

and the unit vector $\mathbf{n} = \mathbf{t} \times \mathbf{k}$ is normal to the curve and is given by

$$\mathbf{n} = \mathbf{t} \times \mathbf{k} = \left(\frac{dx}{ds}\,\mathbf{i} + \frac{dy}{ds}\,\mathbf{j}\right) \times \mathbf{k} = \frac{dy}{ds}\,\mathbf{i} - \frac{dx}{ds}\,\mathbf{j}.$$

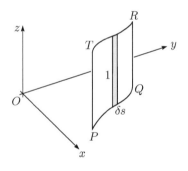

*Figure 2.7*

Putting $\mathbf{u} = (\partial\psi/\partial y)\,\mathbf{i} - (\partial\psi/\partial x)\,\mathbf{j}$ gives

$$
\begin{aligned}
V &= \int_P^Q \mathbf{u} \cdot \mathbf{n}\, ds \\
&= \int_P^Q \left(\frac{\partial\psi}{\partial y}\frac{dy}{ds} + \frac{\partial\psi}{\partial x}\frac{dx}{ds}\right) ds \\
&= \int_P^Q \frac{d\psi}{ds}\, ds \\
&= \psi(Q) - \psi(P).
\end{aligned}
$$

By the Chain Rule,
$$\frac{\partial\psi}{\partial y}\frac{dy}{ds} + \frac{\partial\psi}{\partial x}\frac{dx}{ds} = \frac{d\psi}{ds}.$$

If $V > 0$, the net flow is positive from left to right across any curve from $P$ to $Q$. If $V < 0$, the net flow is positive in the opposite direction.

Thus $V$ depends only on the values of $\psi$ at $P$ and $Q$, and not on the choice of curve $PQ$. This analysis has established the following result.

> The change in value of the stream function $\psi$ between any two points $P$, $Q$ in the fluid is the volume flow rate of fluid through any curve from $P$ to $Q$.

### Exercise 2.4

Show that the volume flow rate across a streamline is zero. (This result confirms the first 'important property' of Subsection 1.3 that, at any instant of time, there is no fluid crossing any streamline.)

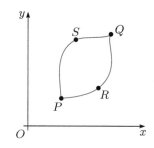

*Figure 2.8*

It follows from the highlighted result before Exercise 2.4 that the volume flow rates across any two curves joining $P$ to $Q$ are equal. This statement is equivalent to $\nabla \cdot \mathbf{u} = 0$, the continuity equation for a fluid of constant density. Consider the two paths $PRQ$ and $PSQ$, shown in Figure 2.8. The volume flow rate across $PRQ$ must equal the volume flow rate across $PSQ$, because $\nabla \cdot \mathbf{u} = 0$ implies that there can be no accumulation of fluid in the region enclosed by $PRQSP$. This provides an alternative form of expression for the continuity equation, which is derived now.

Figure 2.9 shows two streamlines, $AA'$ and $BB'$, in the flow of a constant-density fluid. Let $P$ and $Q$ be two points, on $AA'$ and $BB'$ respectively; then the volume flow rate crossing any curve joining $Q$ to $P$ is $\psi(P) - \psi(Q)$. Similarly, the volume flow rate crossing any curve joining $S$ (on $BB'$) to $R$ (on $AA'$) is $\psi(R) - \psi(S)$. Now, $P$ and $R$ lie on the same streamline $AA'$, so that $\psi(P) = \psi(R)$, and similarly $\psi(Q) = \psi(S)$. Hence the quantity $\psi(P) - \psi(Q)$ is equal to $\psi(R) - \psi(S)$. This establishes the following result.

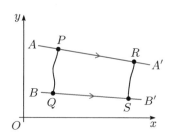

*Figure 2.9*

> The volume flow rate between two streamlines is constant, and is independent of where it is measured.

There is further discussion of the continuity equation in Section 4.

For more about the stream function, see the *Media Guide*.

## 2.3   Flow past boundaries

Exercise 2.4 showed that the volume flow rate across a streamline is zero, and this result reflects the fact that fluid does not flow through a streamline. Experience indicates that fluid cannot flow through solid boundaries; for instance, water does not flow through the sides of a bath. In this subsection, we show that the streamline equation, $\psi = \text{constant}$, provides one method of modelling solid boundaries.

All fluid flows occur in the presence of boundaries; these are often in the form of solid boundaries, but boundaries between two fluids, such as the surface of water open to the atmosphere, are also important. For a solid boundary, there is no flow through the boundary surface $S$, and so the normal velocity component of the fluid and that of the boundary (which may be moving) are equal. Figure 2.10 shows two flows past solid boundaries:

(a) a flow outside a solid boundary in the shape of an aerofoil (i.e. the cross-section of an aircraft wing);

(b) the flow in a channel of varying cross-section.

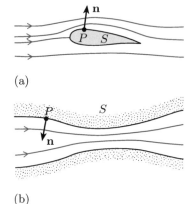

(a)

(b)

*Figure 2.10*

If, at some point $P$ on a solid boundary, the normal unit vector drawn *into* the fluid is $\mathbf{n}$, then we can express the 'no-flow-through' condition at the boundary as

$$\mathbf{u} \cdot \mathbf{n} = \mathbf{b} \cdot \mathbf{n},$$

where $\mathbf{u}$ is the fluid velocity at $P$ and $\mathbf{b}$ is the boundary velocity at $P$. If the boundary $S$ is at rest, then the normal velocity component of the fluid is zero on the boundary. This is usually called the *normal boundary condition*, and is valid for all real fluids.

### Normal boundary condition

For the flow of a fluid past a solid boundary at rest, $u_n = \mathbf{u} \cdot \mathbf{n} = 0$ at each point of the boundary, where $u_n$ is the fluid velocity component normal to the boundary.

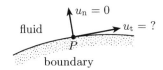

*Figure 2.11*

A second boundary condition may be required, to describe the value of the tangential velocity component on a solid boundary (see Figure 2.11).

If, in the model, the fluid is assumed to be inviscid, that is, if the viscous forces in the fluid are ignored, then there can be a relative tangential velocity between the fluid and the boundary. Hence the tangential velocity component of the fluid, $u_t$, and that of the boundary are not related, so no condition at the boundary is imposed on $u_t$ in this case.

If, however, the effects of viscosity are included in the model, then friction effects are present, and there is then no slippage between the boundary and the fluid, so that the tangential velocity component of the fluid *relative* to the boundary is zero. (These conditions apply only when the continuum hypothesis is valid, i.e. *always* in this course.)

This is known as the *no-slip condition* for the flow of viscous fluid past a boundary.

*Figure 2.12*

To illustrate these boundary conditions, consider the motion of a boat through otherwise still water, and a fluid particle at a point $P$ near the boat (see Figure 2.12). In the inviscid model, the particle is only pushed aside as the boat moves through the water; it is not dragged along with the boat. The layer of water 'next' to the boat slips past the boat in this case. When viscosity is included in the model, the particle is both pushed aside and pulled forwards by the boat. The layer of water 'next' to the boat is dragged along with the boat.

If the normal boundary condition is violated, then either the fluid flows into the 'solid' boundary (a permeable membrane or porous boundary), or the fluid flows away from the solid boundary leaving pockets of vapour. This latter phenomenon can occur with high speed propeller and turbine blades and is called *cavitation*. It usually occurs when the boundary is moved very rapidly and the adjacent fluid cannot keep up.

You will see an example of a porous boundary in *Unit 8*.

### Example 2.4

Find the boundary condition for an inviscid fluid moving in the presence of each of the following boundaries, $S$.

(a)  $S$ is the $x$-axis (at rest).

(b)  $S$ is parallel to the $x$-axis and is moving with velocity $U\,\mathbf{i} + V\,\mathbf{j}$.

(In each case, consider the fluid to be above the boundary.)

Recall that the flow is two-dimensional. Hence to say that $S$ is the $x$-axis means that $S$ is the $(x, z)$-plane.

29

### Solution

(a) The normal boundary condition

$$\mathbf{u} \cdot \mathbf{n} = 0 \qquad \text{on } S$$

becomes

$$\mathbf{u} \cdot \mathbf{j} = 0 \qquad \text{on } S,$$

since $\mathbf{n} = \mathbf{j}$ (see Figure 2.13). In terms of Cartesian components,

$$\mathbf{u} = u_1 \mathbf{i} + u_2 \mathbf{j}$$

and so

$$\mathbf{u} \cdot \mathbf{j} = u_2 = 0 \qquad \text{on } y = 0.$$

(b) For the moving boundary,

$$\mathbf{u} \cdot \mathbf{n} = (U \mathbf{i} + V \mathbf{j}) \cdot \mathbf{n} \qquad \text{on } S,$$

and again $\mathbf{n} = \mathbf{j}$ (see Figure 2.14). We have

$$\mathbf{u} \cdot \mathbf{j} = u_2 = V \qquad \text{on } S.$$

The fluid is inviscid, so there is no tangential boundary condition on $\mathbf{u}$ in either case.  ▪

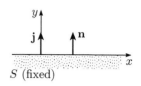

*Figure 2.13*

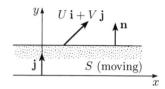

*Figure 2.14*

### Exercise 2.5

For each of the following models, find the boundary conditions for the flow of a fluid past a circular cylinder, of radius $a$, which is at rest with its axis along the $z$-axis.

(a) The fluid is assumed to be inviscid.

(b) The fluid is viscous.

*Hint:* Use plane polar coordinates.

---

In this unit and in *Unit 6*, we consider an inviscid model of a fluid, so it is only the normal boundary condition that can be applied. For the flow past a solid body at rest, using the inviscid model, the normal velocity component of the fluid is zero on the boundary of the body. Thus at any point of the boundary surface, the fluid velocity is parallel to the tangent to the boundary. This can be restated as follows.

A solid boundary is always a streamline in ideal flow.

As introduced in *Unit 1* Subsection 1.3, ideal flow neglects fluid viscosity.

Conversely, any streamline may be taken to represent a solid boundary. In the following example, we take a given stream function and determine fluid flows past a boundary which one of the streamlines could represent. There are, of course, many possibilities, since any streamline can be considered to be the boundary of a solid body.

### Example 2.5

Find the flow past a boundary represented by the stream function

$$\psi(r, \theta) = U \sin \theta \left( r - \frac{a^2}{r} \right).$$

This stream function was obtained in Example 2.3.

## Solution

We shall find some of the streamlines and suggest which of these might model the boundaries of a real flow. Consider first the streamline $\psi = 0$. This requires

either      $\sin \theta = 0$      or      $r^2 - a^2 = 0$;

that is,

$\theta = 0$ or $\pi$      or      $r = a$   (since $r \geq 0$ only).

The streamline $\psi = 0$ therefore consists of three parts (see Figure 2.15):
(i)   the circle $r = a$ for all $\theta$;
(ii)  the positive $x$-axis, for which $\theta = 0$;
(iii) the negative $x$-axis, for which $\theta = \pi$.

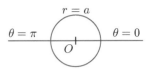

*Figure 2.15*   The streamline $\psi = 0$, which divides at the points $r = a$, $\theta = 0$ or $\pi$, where the velocity is zero.

Consider next the streamline $\psi = Ua$. Then

$$Ua = U \sin \theta \left( r - \frac{a^2}{r} \right)   \quad \text{or} \quad   a = r \sin \theta \left( 1 - \frac{a^2}{r^2} \right),$$

which can be written in terms of Cartesian coordinates as

$$\frac{a}{y} = 1 - \frac{a^2}{x^2 + y^2}. \tag{2.5}$$

Recall that $r \sin \theta = y$.

Now separate $x$ and $y$. Equation (2.5) may be re-expressed as

$$\frac{y/a}{y/a - 1} - \left( \frac{y}{a} \right)^2 = \left( \frac{x}{a} \right)^2   \quad (y \neq a).$$

This is done by first making $(x^2 + y^2)/a^2$ the subject of the equation, as you can check.

Choosing values for $y/a$ leads to the corresponding values for $x/a$, as shown in Table 2.1. This streamline is shown as the curve $ABC$ in Figure 2.16. The streamline $\psi = -Ua$ is the reflection of $ABC$ in the $(x/a)$-axis, since its equation is

$$-\frac{a}{y} = 1 - \frac{a^2}{x^2 + y^2}.$$

This streamline is shown as $A'B'C'$ in Figure 2.16.

Choosing $x/a$ and finding $y/a$ is more cumbersome, except when $x = 0$.

*Table 2.1*

| $y/a$ | $x/a$ |
|-------|-------|
| 1.04 | $\pm 4.99$ |
| 1.15 | $\pm 2.52$ |
| 1.30 | $\pm 1.63$ |
| 1.62 | 0 |

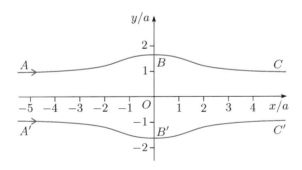

*Figure 2.16*   The streamlines $\psi = \pm Ua$

We should expect the streamlines $\psi = \pm 2Ua$ to be similar in form to the curves $ABC$ and $A'B'C'$, but to be approximately twice as far from the $(x/a)$-axis. These streamlines, which may be plotted in a similar way, are shown in Figure 2.17, overleaf.

The expectation of 'twice as far' is based on the fact that $\psi \simeq Uy$ for large $r$, so that (except close to $O$) doubling $\psi$ will double $y$.

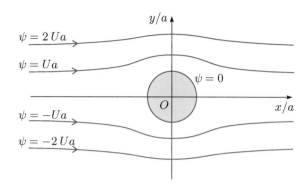

*Figure 2.17*

One possible flow modelled by this stream function is a uniform flow parallel to the $x$-axis, past the circular boundary $r = a$. For this flow, we ignore all streamlines inside the circle $r = a$ (see Figure 2.17).

Here 'uniform' refers to the flow far from the circular boundary.

Alternatively, we could take the streamlines $\psi = \pm Ua$ and the circular part of $\psi = 0$ to be solid boundaries, with a flow between the symmetrical pair of boundaries and past the circle $r = a$ (see Figure 2.18).   ■

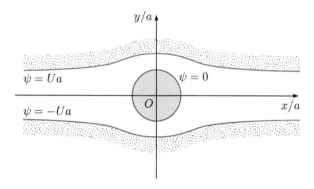

*Figure 2.18*

### Exercise 2.6

Given the stream function $\psi = 2xy$, sketch the streamlines for $\psi = 0, 2, 4, 10$. Suggest a possible boundary for this flow.

## End-of-section exercise

### Exercise 2.7

(a) Find the stream function $\psi(x, y)$ for the velocity field $\mathbf{u} = -2y\,\mathbf{i} - 2x\,\mathbf{j}$. (Express $\psi$ in a form in which any arbitrary constant is taken as zero.)

(b) Sketch the streamlines for $\psi = 0, 2, 4, 10$.

(c) Suggest a possible boundary for this flow.

# 3 Modelling by combining stream functions

For two-dimensional flows, the stream function $\psi$ introduced in Section 2 provides a representation of the fluid velocity, and the lines of constant $\psi$ are streamlines. The method of analysis was somewhat mathematical; given a velocity field we could find the stream function, and we found the stream functions for certain basic flows such as a source and a vortex. In order to move towards the modelling of real fluid flows, we try to recognise a real flow as a combination of these simpler basic flows. In this section, we concentrate on finding the stream functions for some of these combinations. By drawing the streamlines, it may then be possible to recognise one particular streamline as a boundary in the flow.

Recall that $\psi$ is a scalar field.

This idea was introduced in Subsection 2.3.

Of course, not all flows can be modelled in this way, because recognising a possible combination of basic flows (probably from one of the flow visualisation techniques) may not be easy.

We shall investigate a few examples of combinations of simple flow patterns which lead to results of practical interest. Again, we are building from a knowledge of the stream functions of the simple flows, and proposing possible applications for the stream functions of the combinations. However, this approach will provide an insight into how we could tackle problems of modelling real fluid flows.

Table 3.1 summarises the stream functions for some of the basic flows.

*Table 3.1*

| Type of flow | Velocity field $\mathbf{u}$ | Stream function $\psi$ | Reference |
|---|---|---|---|
| Uniform flow parallel to the $x$-axis | $U\,\mathbf{i}$ | $Uy$ (Cartesian); $Ur\sin\theta$ (polar) | Put $\alpha = 0$ in Example 2.1; Example 2.3 with $a = 0$ |
| Uniform flow at an angle $\alpha$ to the $x$-axis | $U\cos\alpha\,\mathbf{i} + U\sin\alpha\,\mathbf{j}$ | $-Ux\sin\alpha + Uy\cos\alpha$ | Example 2.1 |
| Source of strength $2\pi m$ at the origin | $\dfrac{m}{r}\,\mathbf{e}_r \quad (m > 0)$ | $m\theta$ | Exercise 2.2(b); with $m < 0$, this is a sink of strength $\lvert m \rvert$ |
| Vortex of strength $2\pi k$ at the origin | $\dfrac{k}{r}\,\mathbf{e}_\theta$ | $-k\ln r$ | Exercise 2.2(a) |
| Rigid body rotation | $Kr\,\mathbf{e}_\theta$ | $-\tfrac{1}{2}Kr^2$ | Exercise 2.3(a) |

## 3.1 The Principle of Superposition

The technique of modelling complicated flows by combining simple basic flows was developed in the nineteenth century by W. Rankine (1820–72). The method relies on an addition property of vector fields:

Rankine, a Scottish engineer, was a pioneer in the field of theoretical thermodynamics.

> for each point at which two vector fields exist, the resultant vector field is the vector sum of the two constituent fields.

Suppose that $\psi_1$ and $\psi_2$ are the stream functions associated with any two velocity vector fields, $\mathbf{u}_1$ and $\mathbf{u}_2$ respectively. We can use the result of Example 2.2(b) on page 24 to relate the velocity vectors and the stream functions; we have

$$\mathbf{u}_1 = \boldsymbol{\nabla}\psi_1 \times \mathbf{k} \qquad \text{and} \qquad \mathbf{u}_2 = \boldsymbol{\nabla}\psi_2 \times \mathbf{k}.$$

The resultant velocity vector field $\mathbf{u}$ is the sum of $\mathbf{u}_1$ and $\mathbf{u}_2$, so that

$$\mathbf{u} = \mathbf{u}_1 + \mathbf{u}_2 = (\boldsymbol{\nabla}\psi_1 \times \mathbf{k}) + (\boldsymbol{\nabla}\psi_2 \times \mathbf{k})$$
$$= (\boldsymbol{\nabla}\psi_1 + \boldsymbol{\nabla}\psi_2) \times \mathbf{k}$$
$$= \boldsymbol{\nabla}(\psi_1 + \psi_2) \times \mathbf{k}.$$

Thus the stream function for the flow field with velocity $\mathbf{u}_1 + \mathbf{u}_2$ is the sum $\psi_1 + \psi_2$. The velocity fields $\mathbf{u}_1$ and $\mathbf{u}_2$ are *superposed* to give the velocity field $\mathbf{u}_1 + \mathbf{u}_2$. This can be summarised as follows.

### The Principle of Superposition

If the velocity fields $\mathbf{u}_1$ and $\mathbf{u}_2$ have respective stream functions $\psi_1$ and $\psi_2$, then the velocity field $\mathbf{u}_1 + \mathbf{u}_2$ has stream function $\psi_1 + \psi_2$.

### Exercise 3.1

Show that $\mathbf{u} = \mathbf{u}_1 + \mathbf{u}_2$ satisfies the continuity equation, where $\mathbf{u}_1$ and $\mathbf{u}_2$ are velocity fields of constant-density fluid flows.

The Principle of Superposition can be used to find the stream functions for combinations of sources, sinks and uniform flows. The next example shows this idea applied to a flow pattern that consists of a source and sink pair.

The *Media Guide* session at the end of this section features an interactive exercise applying the Principle of Superposition.

### Example 3.1

Find the stream function and streamlines for the flow due to a source of strength $2\pi m$ at $A\,(-a, 0)$ and a sink of the same strength at $B\,(a, 0)$.

### Solution

Let $\theta_1$ be the polar angle as measured from $B$ as origin, and let $\theta_2$ be the polar angle as measured from $A$ as origin (see Figure 3.1). Then the stream function of the sink at $B$ is $\psi_1 = -m\theta_1$, and the stream function of the source at $A$ is $\psi_2 = m\theta_2$. By the Principle of Superposition, the overall flow, due to the combination of source and sink, has stream function

$$\psi = \psi_1 + \psi_2 = m(\theta_2 - \theta_1).$$

Now let $P$ be any point, other than $A$ or $B$, with coordinates $(x, y)$. From the definitions of $\theta_1$ and $\theta_2$, their values at $P$ will be given by

$$\tan\theta_1 = \frac{y}{x - a} \quad \text{and} \quad \tan\theta_2 = \frac{y}{x + a} \quad \text{(see Figure 3.1).}$$

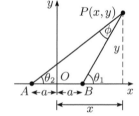

*Figure 3.1*

Using a standard trigonometric formula, it follows that

$$\tan(\theta_2 - \theta_1) = \frac{\tan\theta_2 - \tan\theta_1}{1 + \tan\theta_2\tan\theta_1}$$
$$= \frac{y/(x + a) - y/(x - a)}{1 + y^2/(x^2 - a^2)} = -\frac{2ay}{x^2 + y^2 - a^2}.$$

The stream function of the combined flow is therefore

$$\psi = m(\theta_2 - \theta_1) = m\arctan\left(-\frac{2ay}{x^2 + y^2 - a^2}\right).$$

The equation for streamlines is $\psi = \text{constant}$, that is, $\theta_2 - \theta_1 = \text{constant}$. Now $\theta_1 - \theta_2$ is equal to the angle $\phi$ subtended at $P$ by the line segment $AB$ (see Figure 3.1), and the locus of all such points as $P$ varies (while $\phi$ is held constant) is a circular arc through $A$ and $B$. Hence the streamlines are arcs of circles, as shown in Figure 3.2. By symmetry, each circle centre

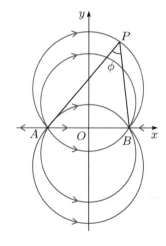

*Figure 3.2*

is on the $y$-axis. However, the special cases $\phi = 0$ and $\phi = \pi$ give the $x$-axis as a further streamline.

An alternative to this geometrical argument is as follows. If $\psi = \text{constant}$ then, from the Cartesian expression for the stream function,

$$x^2 + y^2 - a^2 = 2Cy, \qquad \text{or} \qquad x^2 + (y-C)^2 = a^2 + C^2,$$

where $C$ is a constant. This is the equation of a circle with centre at $(0, C)$, passing through $(\pm a, 0)$.  ∎

The constant value of $\psi$ here is $m \arctan(-a/C)$.

### Exercise 3.2

Find the stream function and equation of streamlines (in Cartesian coordinates) caused by placing two sources, each of strength $2\pi m$, at the points $A\ (-a, 0)$ and $B\ (a, 0)$. (There is no need to sketch the streamlines.)

### The doublet

Now consider a limiting case of the source and sink combination analysed in Example 3.1. Suppose that the source and sink are moved towards each other along the $x$-axis, by reducing $a$, while at the same time the strength $2\pi m$ of each is increased. If this is done in such a way that the product $ma$ (a constant multiple of strength × distance apart) is kept constant then, in the limit as $a \to 0$, a new basic flow called a **doublet** is created.

Another name for a doublet is a *dipole*.

The corresponding effect on the streamline pattern in Figure 3.2 is to yield the streamline pattern for a doublet (see Figure 3.3), consisting of all circles with centre on the $y$-axis that are tangent to the $x$-axis, plus the $x$-axis itself.

The line $AB$ joining the source and the sink is called the *axis* of the doublet. This is taken to be positive in the direction from sink to source, i.e. from $B$ to $A$. The *strength* of the doublet is defined to be $4\pi am$, which is the product of the strength $2\pi m$ of the source or sink and of the distance $2a$ between them before the limit is taken. The direction can be incorporated with the strength to define a *vector strength* $-4\pi am\,\mathbf{i}$.

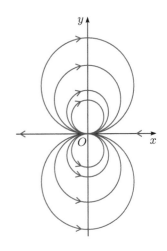

*Figure 3.3*   Streamline pattern for a doublet at the origin

To find an expression for the stream function of a doublet, we evaluate the limit of the stream function found in Example 3.1 for a source and sink combination, as $a \to 0$ and $m \to \infty$ while the product $am$ remains fixed.

The result from Example 3.1 was

$$\psi = m \arctan\left(-\frac{2ay}{x^2 + y^2 - a^2}\right),$$

which in plane polar coordinates is

$$\psi = m \arctan\left(-\frac{2ar\sin\theta}{r^2 - a^2}\right).$$

Now, for small $\alpha$, we have $\tan\alpha \simeq \alpha$. Hence, for small enough values of $a$,

$$\arctan\left(-\frac{2ar\sin\theta}{r^2 - a^2}\right) \simeq -\frac{2ar\sin\theta}{r^2 - a^2}.$$

It follows that

$$\psi \simeq -\frac{2amr\sin\theta}{r^2 - a^2} = -\frac{\lambda r\sin\theta}{r^2 - a^2}, \qquad \text{where } \lambda = 2am.$$

From above, in terms of $\lambda$, the doublet has strength $2\pi\lambda$ and vector strength $-2\pi\lambda\,\mathbf{i}$.

Now taking the limit as $a \to 0$ gives

$$\lim_{\substack{a \to 0 \\ m \to \infty \\ am \text{ constant}}} \left( -\frac{\lambda r \sin \theta}{r^2 - a^2} \right) = -\frac{\lambda r \sin \theta}{r^2} = -\frac{\lambda \sin \theta}{r}.$$

Thus the stream function for a doublet of vector strength $-2\pi\lambda \, \mathbf{i}$ is given by

$$\psi(r, \theta) = -\frac{\lambda \sin \theta}{r}.$$

Since both $A$ and $B$ tend to the origin in the limit, the streamlines are now circles through the origin with centres on the $y$-axis, as shown in Figure 3.3. The streamline pattern is symmetric about the $x$-axis.

This is also a good approximation to the stream function for the original source/sink pair when $r \gg a$, that is, far from the origin.

### Exercise 3.3

Find the velocity field of the flow caused by a doublet of vector strength $-2\pi\lambda \, \mathbf{i}$ at the origin.

## 3.2   Combining sources, doublets and uniform flows

The doublet provides another of the basic flows which can be used, in combination with sources, sinks and uniform flows, to model real fluid flows. In this subsection, we consider the combination of

(i) a source and a uniform flow, and

(ii) a doublet and a uniform flow.

Consider first a source and a steady uniform flow. Because both basic flows are steady, the streamlines are the same as the pathlines. So we can sketch the streamlines 'intuitively' by imagining the effect of fluid particles approaching the source along parallel straight lines and fluid particles leaving the origin $O$ along the radial lines. We should expect the uniform flow lines far from the source to be little changed due to the presence of the source. But fluid particles emanating from the source at $O$ into the oncoming uniform flow will be pushed back, as shown in Figure 3.4. At some point on the $x$-axis, $S$ say, the two separate velocities (due to the uniform flow and the source) will cancel, and the velocity of the fluid will be zero. A point in the fluid where the fluid velocity is zero is called a **stagnation point**.

The following example shows how the position of a stagnation point can be found using the stream function for a flow.

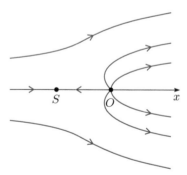

*Figure 3.4*

### Example 3.2

Find the position of the stagnation point for the combination of a source of strength $2\pi m$ at the origin and a uniform flow $U \, \mathbf{i}$.

### Solution

The stream function for this combination of a source at the origin and uniform flow is given by

$$\psi = m\theta + Uy$$
$$= m\theta + Ur\sin\theta.$$

At a stagnation point, the velocity components are both zero. In polar coordinates, from Equations (2.2), we have

$$u_r = \frac{1}{r}\frac{\partial\psi}{\partial\theta} = \frac{1}{r}(m + Ur\cos\theta) = 0 \qquad (3.1)$$

and

$$u_\theta = -\frac{\partial\psi}{\partial r} = -U\sin\theta = 0. \qquad (3.2)$$

Solving Equation (3.2) for $\theta$ gives $\theta = 0$ or $\theta = \pi$. From Equation (3.1), if $\theta = 0$, then $r = -m/U$, and if $\theta = \pi$, then $r = m/U$. Since $r$ cannot be negative (by definition), the solution $\theta = 0$ can be discounted as physically unrealistic, so that there is only one stagnation point, given by

$$\theta = \pi, \quad r = \frac{m}{U},$$

or by $(-m/U, 0)$ in Cartesian coordinates. ∎

This is consistent with the intuitive guess shown in Figure 3.4.

### Exercise 3.4

Find the positions of the stagnation points for the combination of a doublet of vector strength $-2\pi\lambda\,\mathbf{i}$ and a uniform flow $U\,\mathbf{i}$. Show that the stagnation points lie on the circle $r = \sqrt{\lambda/U}$, and that this circle is part of the streamline $\psi = 0$.

We now consider again the flow in Example 3.2. The solution to this example shows that there is a stagnation point at $r = m/U$, $\theta = \pi$; at this point, the fluid velocity is zero. The next example uses the value of the stream function at this point to help sketch the streamline pattern for a source in a uniform flow.

### Example 3.3

The stream function for a combination of a source of strength $2\pi m$ at the origin and a uniform flow with velocity $U\,\mathbf{i}$ is $\psi = m\theta + Uy$. By sketching the streamline pattern, show that this combination may be used as a model for the flow past a blunt body.

It is often convenient to use a combination of Cartesian and polar coordinates in this type of problem.

### Solution

First find the equation of the streamline that passes through the stagnation point, $S$. At this point (from Example 3.2), $\theta = \pi$ and $y = 0$, so that

$$\psi = m\pi \qquad \text{at } S.$$

Hence $S$ lies on the streamline

$$m\theta + Uy = m\pi \qquad \text{or} \qquad y = \frac{m}{U}(\pi - \theta). \qquad (3.3)$$

Since this equation is satisfied by $\theta = \pi$, $y = 0$, the negative $x$-axis ($NSO$ in Figure 3.5, on the next page) is part of this streamline.

Now we seek the rest of the streamline given by Equation (3.3). As $\theta$ decreases from $\pi$, $y$ increases and reaches the value $m\pi/(2U)$ when $\theta = \frac{1}{2}\pi$.

Then $y$ continues to increase as $\theta$ decreases. For positive values of $\theta$ close to zero, $y$ is close to the value $m\pi/U$. This reflects the fact that, far downstream, the uniform flow dominates the effect of the source, and the streamlines are (approximately) parallel to the $x$-axis. Put more technically, the line $y = m\pi/U$ is an asymptote for the streamline given by Equation (3.3). The part of the streamline for $0 < \theta \leq \pi$ is shown as $SRT$ in Figure 3.5. Since the uniform flow and source are symmetric about the $x$-axis, the streamlines in the region $y < 0$ are reflections in the $x$-axis of the streamlines in the region $y > 0$. Thus the curve $SR'T'$, i.e. the reflection of $SRT$ in the $x$-axis, is also part of the streamline through $S$.

Note that the streamline $\psi = m\pi$ has branches which meet at $S$.

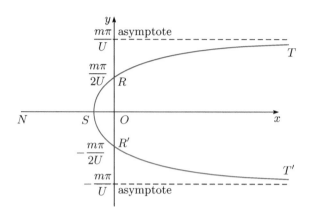

Figure 3.5   The streamline through $S$

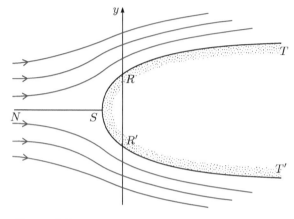

Figure 3.6

To draw some of the other streamlines, we could choose values for $\psi$, $\psi_n$ say, and then sketch the curves $m\theta + Uy = \psi_n$. However, we shall adopt a more intuitive approach. The curve $TRSR'T'$ can form a bounding streamline, and since fluid cannot cross a streamline, we could consider the fluid outside this boundary as flowing past a solid body. The flow is steady, so the pathlines and the streamlines coincide. Thus to sketch the streamline pattern outside $TRSR'T'$, we imagine the paths of fluid particles starting off along parallel lines for large negative $x$ and approaching the boundary. These particles will be deflected past the boundary and travel along the lines shown in Figure 3.6.

The bounding streamline can be taken as a solid boundary, and this combination of a source and a uniform flow can then be taken as a model for the flow of an incompressible fluid past a blunt body.

We have described the body as blunt, but have not shown that it is smooth, rather than pointed or kinked, at the stagnation point, $S$. This requires that the tangent to the curve $TRSR'T'$ should be vertical at $S$. The details of showing this are omitted.

In this example, we have sketched the streamline pattern outside the bounding streamline $TRSR'T'$, and the flow lines in the vicinity of the source do not appear, although the source is an essential part of the model. The source is a modelling device for obtaining the shape of the blunt solid boundary. ∎

One approach is to show that the curve $TRSR'T'$ always lies between the vertical line through $S$ and the circle through $S$ with centre $O$. Since both this line and the circle have a vertical tangent at $S$, the result follows.

### Exercise 3.5

For the flow in Example 3.3, by drawing the paths of fluid particles that emerge from the origin (i.e. from the source), sketch the streamline pattern inside the bounding streamline $TRSR'T'$.

The blunt body shown in Figure 3.6 is known as a *half body*, since it has a nose but no tail. The combination of the uniform flow and source provides the stream function and hence the velocity field for the flow past such a body. This provides a useful model for the flow at the upstream end of symmetrical bodies with a large length-to-width ratio, such as bridge supports. Alternatively, the streamline pattern in the region $y \geq 0$ could represent the flow of water in a river with a rise in the river bed, or the flow of wind over a hillside.

At the downstream end of the body, the streamlines and the solid boundary are almost parallel to the $x$-axis, so this combination cannot model the flow past a closed body, such as the one shown in Figure 3.7.

### Exercise 3.6

What basic flow can be added to the source and uniform flow, to model the flow past a closed body such as the one shown in Figure 3.7?

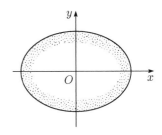

*Figure 3.7*

Next you are asked to look at flow past a special closed shape, the circle.

### Exercise 3.7

By sketching some streamlines, show that the combination of a doublet of vector strength $-2\pi\lambda\,\mathbf{i}$ at the origin and a uniform flow $U\,\mathbf{i}$ can be used to model the flow past a circle of radius $\sqrt{\lambda/U}$. (Sketch the streamlines outside this circle only.)

The streamline through the stagnation points is given in the solution to Exercise 3.4.

Figure 3.8 shows the streamline pattern for the combination of a doublet (of vector strength $-2\pi\lambda\,\mathbf{i}$) and a uniform flow, outside the streamline $\psi = 0$. This streamline is a circle of radius $\sqrt{\lambda/U}$ and can be taken to represent a solid boundary. The combination can then be used to model the flow of a fluid past a circular cylinder. The similarity between the streamline pattern in Figure 3.8, obtained from the doublet/uniform flow combination, and the streamline pattern for the flow of air past a cylinder, shown in Figure 3.9, is rather striking. It is behind the cylinder, in the wake, that the model breaks down.

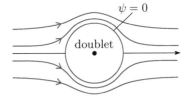

*Figure 3.8*

In this section, we started with some of the basic flows and suggested flows that combinations of them could represent. In practice, fluid mechanics is concerned with the 'inverse problem'; that is, for a flow past a given boundary, find the stream function. Investigating the flow of air past an aircraft wing or the flow of water past a hydrofoil are examples of such a problem.

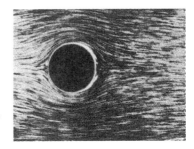

*Figure 3.9*

We can model problems of this type by combining sources and sinks with a uniform flow. The streamline pattern for a source in a uniform flow can model the ideal flow past a blunt object. If we introduce a sink on the $x$-axis, the effect is to pull the streamlines back in, and a combination of a source at $A$ $(-a, 0)$, a sink at $B$ $(a, 0)$ and a uniform flow, models the flow past a closed body (see Figure 3.10). This is a similar streamline pattern to that shown in Figure 3.8, but the solid boundary, $\psi = 0$, is now not a circle but is more elliptical in shape. (The shape created in this way is known as a *Rankine oval*.) Adding further sources and sinks (indicated by $+$ and $-$ respectively in Figure 3.11, overleaf) can produce a flatter boundary, with the shape of the cross-section of an aircraft wing.

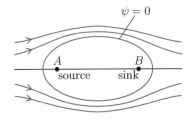

*Figure 3.10*   Rankine oval

The stream function for the flow can be written down in terms of those for the sources and sinks and that for the uniform flow, and from this stream function we can deduce the streamline pattern and the velocity field. This will show the features of the flow near a solid boundary. Furthermore, as you will see in Section 5, a knowledge of the velocity field allows us to predict the pressure distribution and hence the net force on a solid boundary, due to the flow of a fluid past it.

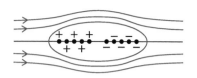

*Figure 3.11*

To conclude this section, you are invited to visually explore the flow effects that can be produced with various different basic flows.

---

**Carry out the activities for this section in the Media Guide.**

---

## *End-of-section exercise*

### Exercise 3.8

Four sources, of equal strength $2\pi m$, are placed with one at each of the points $(1,1)$, $(1,-1)$, $(-1,1)$ and $(-1,-1)$.

(a) Write down the stream function for this combination of sources, in Cartesian coordinates.

(b) Show that the origin is a stagnation point.

(c) Show that the $x$- and $y$-axes are streamlines.

(d) Use your intuition to sketch the streamline pattern, and show that this combination could model the flow produced by a source at $(1,1)$ in a corner (see Figure 3.12).

*Figure 3.12*

# 4 Description of fluid motions

In describing fluid motions we have used the terms 'steady', 'uniform' and 'incompressible'. Subsection 4.1 specifies more precisely what is meant by these terms, and gives examples of their use.

In order to prepare for the derivation of *Euler's equation of motion*, in Section 5, it is necessary to specify flow properties (such as velocity and density) as functions of position and time, and to distinguish two different types of time derivative of such functions. These matters are addressed in Subsection 4.2.

We also look more closely at the continuity equation, in Subsection 4.3, and derive two special cases of it.

The continuity equation was derived in *Unit 4* Subsection 3.3.

# 4.1  Steady and uniform flows

The flow of a real fluid is usually very complicated, and a complete solution of the equations for the associated model is seldom possible. In order to make progress, we are forced to modify the original model by making further simplifying assumptions about

(i)  the properties of the fluid, and

(ii) the type of flow.

*Unit 1* discussed two simplifying assumptions about fluid properties, which allow the successful modelling of many flow situations. These were to ignore the compressibility and the viscosity of the fluid. Throughout Block 2 (*Units 5–8*), it is usually assumed that the fluids under discussion are liquids, and as such are taken to be incompressible; in most cases, this means that the density is constant. This model is discussed further in Subsection 4.3.

Gases may also be modelled as incompressible under certain conditions, but liquids are much less compressible than gases.

In *Units 5* and *6*, we assume that the viscosity is negligible; you will see the limitations of the inviscid model in *Unit 7*, and in *Unit 8* we revise the model to take viscosity into account. Viscous effects are important for all flows in the vicinity of solid boundaries, and also for liquids whose coefficient of viscosity is high (for example, lubricating oil, which is a hundred times more viscous than water at 20°C).

The incompressible and inviscid assumptions concern properties of the fluid. Assumptions about the type of flow are usually expressed as conditions on the time and spatial (partial) derivatives of the flow variables (for example, velocity and density). In *Unit 1*, we described flows in which conditions at every point are independent of time, $t$, as 'steady'. Mathematically, this means, for example, that $\partial \mathbf{u}/\partial t = \mathbf{0}$ and $\partial \rho/\partial t = 0$, where $\mathbf{u}$ is the velocity and $\rho$ is the density. We define a **steady flow** to be one for which the partial derivatives with respect to time of all flow and fluid properties are zero at each point in the region of flow. Flows in which changes with time do occur are called *non-steady* (or *unsteady*).

If, at a particular instant of time, the velocity vector field $\mathbf{u}$ does not change from point to point, the flow is said to be **uniform**. Thus uniform flows have the form $\mathbf{u} = $ constant vector or $\mathbf{u} = \mathbf{u}(t)$, and so, for a uniform flow,

$$\frac{\partial \mathbf{u}}{\partial x} = \frac{\partial \mathbf{u}}{\partial y} = \frac{\partial \mathbf{u}}{\partial z} = \mathbf{0}.$$

If changes in $\mathbf{u}$ with position do occur, then the flow is called *non-uniform*. Often the term 'uniform' is given a looser meaning than that above. For example, $\mathbf{u} = u_1(x)\,\mathbf{i}$ is *uniform in the y-direction* and $\mathbf{u} = u_1(y)\,\mathbf{i}$ is *uniform in the x-direction.*

For example, the shear flow of Exercise 2.1 is uniform in the $x$-direction.

Uniform flows can exist only for ideal fluids (with zero viscosity), but they can be a good model for fluids with low viscosities in regions far from boundaries. For example, the flow of a river is not uniform across its width — it is slower near the banks and the river-bed because of the effects of viscosity — but in the region at the middle of the river and well above its bed, the flow is approximately uniform. It may be possible to approximate the flow in a river as a uniform flow for the whole width and depth of the river. Figure 4.1 shows the velocity profile taken along a horizontal line across a river.

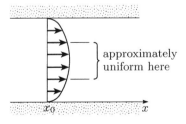

*Figure 4.1*  Velocity vectors at $x = x_0$ for flow in a river.

Table 4.1 summarises, with examples, each of the four possible combinations of steady, non-steady, uniform and non-uniform flows.

*Table 4.1*

| Flow type | Implication for $\mathbf{u}$ | Example |
|---|---|---|
| A: Steady, uniform | $\mathbf{u} = \mathbf{u}_0$, a constant, no time dependence, no spatial dependence | $\mathbf{u} = U \cos \alpha \, \mathbf{i} + U \sin \alpha \, \mathbf{j}$ (uniform stream at angle $\alpha$) |
| B: Steady, non-uniform | $\mathbf{u} = \mathbf{u}(x, y, z)$, no time dependence | $\mathbf{u} = Uy \, \mathbf{i}$ (shear flow) |
| C: Non-steady, uniform | $\mathbf{u} = \mathbf{u}(t)$, no spatial dependence | A uniformly accelerating flow (most uncommon) |
| D: Non-steady, non-uniform | $\mathbf{u} = \mathbf{u}(x, y, z, t)$ | The flow past an aerofoil |

Figure 4.2 shows the flow from left to right past a stalled aerofoil. Flow types A, B and D can be used to model the flow in the regions indicated.

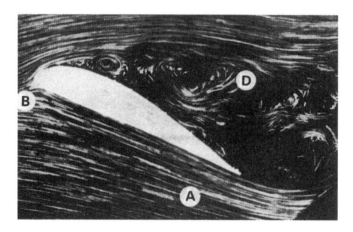

*Figure 4.2*

### Exercise 4.1

Which of the flow types in Table 4.1 (A, B, C or D) is the most appropriate candidate to model each of the following flows?

(a) Flow in a long horizontal pipe of constant cross-section.

(b) The flow from a dripping tap.

(c) The flow down a long inclined channel.

(d) The flow in a hurricane.

(e) The flow from a rotary fan.

## 4.2   Rate of change following the motion

In *Unit 1*, when developing the continuum model, a fluid particle was defined as the limit of a fluid element as the size of the element tends to zero. In order to describe the motion of a fluid particle, a frame of reference is defined so that the position of the particle at any time can be specified, as $(x, y, z, t)$ for example. This specification then provides a means of forming mathematical relationships between the position, velocity and acceleration of a particle at any time.

This approach should be familiar to you from solid particle mechanics.

In solid mechanics, each particle has a position vector $\mathbf{r}(t)$, whose first two time derivatives give the velocity and acceleration of the particle. In fluid mechanics, the fluid particles can move relative to each other (unlike the particles of a rigid body), and this factor makes the position vector approach rather unwieldy. Instead, flows are described by specifying the mathematical form of the flow parameters as functions of the space variables $x$, $y$, $z$ and time, $t$. (From here on, the Cartesian coordinate system is used for reference purposes.) In other words, the whole flow can be described, throughout space and time, by specifying the appropriate scalar and vector fields, for example, $\rho(x,y,z,t)$ and $\mathbf{u}(x,y,z,t)$.

In Cartesian coordinates,
$\mathbf{r}(t) = x(t)\,\mathbf{i} + y(t)\,\mathbf{j} + z(t)\,\mathbf{k}$.

These functions are scalar and vector fields.

Imagine a stream running steadily from a hot spring. The hot water cools as it travels downstream. Let $\Theta(x,y,z,t)$ be the scalar field which gives the temperature at any point and time in the flow. The partial derivative $\partial\Theta/\partial t$ has the following physical interpretation. Suppose that thermometer $A$ is held in the water at a fixed point $P$. The rate of change of temperature with time, as observed from thermometer $A$, will be given by $\partial\Theta/\partial t$, since $x$, $y$ and $z$ are constant at $P$. This is the *local rate of change* of temperature, the rate of change at the fixed point $P$.

At different times, the point $(x,y,z)$ is occupied by different fluid particles.

Now consider thermometer $B$, moving downstream with the flow; the temperature measured by this thermometer changes with time, but it also changes with position. However, the position of thermometer $B$ itself depends on time, so in effect this temperature is dependent on only one variable, the time $t$, with each of $x$, $y$ and $z$ being a function of $t$. The rate of change now is that obtained *following the motion* of thermometer $B$. The rate of change of temperature with time observed by the two thermometers will differ, in general.

Suppose, in particular, that the temperature of the stream does not vary at any fixed point, and depends only on the distance $x$ downstream from the spring. Then $\Theta = \Theta(x)$, so $\partial\Theta/\partial t = 0$ and *locally* the temperature does not change. However, for thermometer $B$, with path $x = x(t)$, there will be a rate of temperature change

$$\frac{d\Theta}{dt} = \frac{d\Theta}{dx}\frac{dx}{dt},$$

depending on the spatial derivative $\Theta'(x)$ and the speed $dx/dt$ of thermometer $B$. This rate of change is due to the motion of the thermometer, and is known as the *convective rate of change*. This application of the simplest form of the Chain Rule is now generalised.

The Chain Rule for functions of two variables, used earlier in this unit, extends following the same pattern to functions of four variables. Consider a scalar field which is a function of four variables, $f(x,y,z,t)$. If each of these variables, $x$, $y$, $z$ and $t$, is a function of one parameter, $s$ say, then $f$ can also be considered as a function of the single variable $s$, i.e. $f(s)$.

This is the version of the Chain Rule introduced in MST209 *Unit 12*.

(Here we adopt a customary abuse of notation, using the same symbol $f$ to stand both for the function of four variables and for a function of one variable. However, it should be clear from the context which version of $f$ is intended at each stage.)

The Chain Rule in this case is

$$\frac{df}{ds} = \frac{dx}{ds}\frac{\partial f}{\partial x} + \frac{dy}{ds}\frac{\partial f}{\partial y} + \frac{dz}{ds}\frac{\partial f}{\partial z} + \frac{dt}{ds}\frac{\partial f}{\partial t}. \tag{4.1}$$

Thus in Equation (4.1), $f$ stands for $f(s)$ on the left-hand side and for $f(x,y,z,t)$ on the right-hand side. We also write $x$ for $x(s)$, $y$ for $y(s)$, etc.

Now suppose that the position vector is a function of time, $\mathbf{r}(t) = x(t)\,\mathbf{i} + y(t)\,\mathbf{j} + z(t)\,\mathbf{k}$. The corresponding velocity is

$$\mathbf{v} = \frac{d\mathbf{r}}{dt} = \frac{dx}{dt}\mathbf{i} + \frac{dy}{dt}\mathbf{j} + \frac{dz}{dt}\mathbf{k}. \tag{4.2}$$

Replacing the parameter $s$ by $t$ throughout Equation (4.1) gives

$$\frac{df}{dt} = \frac{dx}{dt}\frac{\partial f}{\partial x} + \frac{dy}{dt}\frac{\partial f}{\partial y} + \frac{dz}{dt}\frac{\partial f}{\partial z} + \frac{\partial f}{\partial t}. \qquad (4.3)$$

The expression for the last term follows from the fact that $dt/dt = 1$.

The rate of change $df/dt$ here is equal to the sum of the local rate of change of $f(x, y, z, t)$, which is $\partial f/\partial t$, and the rate of change of $f(x, y, z, t)$ due to the motion, which is given by the other terms on the right-hand side of Equation (4.3).

### Exercise 4.2

Consider the stream described above that runs from a hot spring. Suppose that the stream is straight and of uniform width. Using a coordinate system that has origin $O$ at the source of the stream, at its centre, let $x$ be the distance downstream from the source, and $y$ be measured across the stream, as shown in Figure 4.3. If $O$ is on the water surface, then $z$ denotes depth below the surface. The temperature $\Theta$ of the water is modelled by the function

$$\Theta = 50\,(1 + 0.05\cos(0.1t))\,e^{-0.01x}(1 - 0.02y^2)(1 - 0.04z) \qquad \text{(in } {}^{\circ}\text{C)}.$$

(a)  For a thermometer held fixed at the point $(5, 0.2, 0.1)$, what is the rate of change of temperature?

(b)  For a thermometer moving across the stream, on the path given by $\mathbf{r}(t) = 5\,\mathbf{i} + 2t\,\mathbf{j} + 0.1\,\mathbf{k}$, what is the rate of change of temperature at the point $(5, 0.2, 0.1)$?

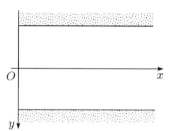

*Figure 4.3*

The right-hand side of Equation (4.3) can be written in operator form as

$$\left( \frac{\partial}{\partial t} + \frac{dx}{dt}\frac{\partial}{\partial x} + \frac{dy}{dt}\frac{\partial}{\partial y} + \frac{dz}{dt}\frac{\partial}{\partial z} \right) f.$$

Using the operator $\nabla$ and Equation (4.2), this is

$$\left( \frac{\partial}{\partial t} + \mathbf{v} \cdot \nabla \right) f.$$

The vector differential operator $\nabla$ and scalar differential operator $\mathbf{a} \cdot \nabla$ were introduced in *Unit 4* Section 5.

Rather than applying this for any given motion, we restrict attention now to the motion of fluid particles, that is, motion along pathlines. In this case, the vector $\mathbf{v}$ above is replaced by the fluid velocity vector, $\mathbf{u}$. So, for **differentiation following the motion** of fluid particles, we have

$$\frac{df}{dt} = \left( \frac{\partial}{\partial t} + \mathbf{u} \cdot \nabla \right) f. \qquad (4.4)$$

Note here that
$$u_1 = \frac{dx}{dt}, \quad u_2 = \frac{dy}{dt}, \quad u_3 = \frac{dz}{dt}.$$

The operator $\partial/\partial t + \mathbf{u} \cdot \nabla$ is referred to as the **total derivative** operator, and is sometimes written as $D/Dt$. This notation will not be used in this course, since it will be clear from the context whether $d/dt$ refers to differentiating a function of one variable, or differentiating a function of several variables each of which depends on the same single variable. In Equation (4.4), the two terms on the right-hand side have the following interpretation:

This is also called the *material derivative* operator.

$\dfrac{\partial f}{\partial t}$ is the *local* rate of change;

$(\mathbf{u} \cdot \nabla)\, f$ is the *convective* rate of change, following the motion.

The total derivative is therefore the sum of the local and convective rates of change. It can be applied to any scalar field, such as pressure, density or chemical concentration.

For more explanation of the rates of change discussed here, see the *Media Guide*.

## Exercise 4.3

Suppose that a fluid particle is in a one-dimensional motion for which $x = t^2$, and that the density of the fluid is $\rho(x, t) = x^2 t + \cos t$. Evaluate $d\rho/dt$, by

(a) using differentiation following the motion, then substituting for $x$ in terms of $t$;

(b) substituting for $x$ in the expression for $\rho$, then differentiating with respect to $t$.

## Exercise 4.4

Simplify Equation (4.4) for the total derivative of the scalar field $f(x, y, z)$ in a flow with velocity field $\mathbf{u}$, in each of the following cases:

(a)  $\mathbf{u} = u_1(x, y, z)\,\mathbf{i}$,      $f(x, y, z) = y + z$;

(b) steady flow.

---

The total derivative of a scalar field was introduced above. The extension to taking the total derivative of a vector field is fairly straightforward, at least in Cartesian coordinates, because the total derivative is a linear operator, and the unit vectors $\mathbf{i}$, $\mathbf{j}$ and $\mathbf{k}$ are all constant.

Consider a vector field

$$\mathbf{F}(x, y, z, t) = F_1(x, y, z, t)\,\mathbf{i} + F_2(x, y, z, t)\,\mathbf{j} + F_3(x, y, z, t)\,\mathbf{k},$$

in which each of $x$, $y$ and $z$ is a function of $t$, and apply the Chain Rule to each component of $\mathbf{F}$:

$$\frac{dF_i}{dt} = \left(\frac{\partial}{\partial t} + \mathbf{u} \cdot \boldsymbol{\nabla}\right) F_i, \qquad \text{where } i = 1, 2, 3.$$

Now combine the components in vectorial form, to obtain

$$\begin{aligned}
\frac{d\mathbf{F}}{dt} &= \frac{dF_1}{dt}\,\mathbf{i} + \frac{dF_2}{dt}\,\mathbf{j} + \frac{dF_3}{dt}\,\mathbf{k} \\
&= \left(\frac{\partial}{\partial t} + \mathbf{u} \cdot \boldsymbol{\nabla}\right) F_1\,\mathbf{i} + \left(\frac{\partial}{\partial t} + \mathbf{u} \cdot \boldsymbol{\nabla}\right) F_2\,\mathbf{j} + \left(\frac{\partial}{\partial t} + \mathbf{u} \cdot \boldsymbol{\nabla}\right) F_3\,\mathbf{k} \\
&= \frac{\partial F_1}{\partial t}\,\mathbf{i} + \frac{\partial F_2}{\partial t}\,\mathbf{j} + \frac{\partial F_3}{\partial t}\,\mathbf{k} + (\mathbf{u} \cdot \boldsymbol{\nabla}) F_1\,\mathbf{i} + (\mathbf{u} \cdot \boldsymbol{\nabla}) F_2\,\mathbf{j} + (\mathbf{u} \cdot \boldsymbol{\nabla}) F_3\,\mathbf{k} \\
&= \frac{\partial \mathbf{F}}{\partial t} + (\mathbf{u} \cdot \boldsymbol{\nabla})\,\mathbf{F} \\
&= \left(\frac{\partial}{\partial t} + \mathbf{u} \cdot \boldsymbol{\nabla}\right) \mathbf{F}.
\end{aligned}$$

Any vector field can be expressed in terms of three (scalar) Cartesian component fields, to each of which the total derivative can be applied. Note that
$$(\mathbf{u} \cdot \boldsymbol{\nabla})(F_1\,\mathbf{i}) = (\mathbf{u} \cdot \boldsymbol{\nabla}) F_1\,\mathbf{i},$$
since $\mathbf{i}$ is a constant vector, and similarly for $F_2\,\mathbf{j}$, $F_3\,\mathbf{k}$.

The velocity vector field $\mathbf{u}$ is the one whose total derivative is used most often, and $d\mathbf{u}/dt$ is the *acceleration* of a fluid particle. Hence, the **acceleration of a fluid particle** is given by

Note that if $\phi$ is a scalar field, then $(\mathbf{u} \cdot \boldsymbol{\nabla})\phi = \mathbf{u} \cdot (\boldsymbol{\nabla}\phi)$, but for a vector field $\mathbf{F}$ always write $(\mathbf{u} \cdot \boldsymbol{\nabla})\,\mathbf{F}$, since $\mathbf{u} \cdot (\boldsymbol{\nabla}\mathbf{F})$ has no meaning.

$$\mathbf{a} = \frac{d\mathbf{u}}{dt} = \left(\frac{\partial}{\partial t} + \mathbf{u} \cdot \boldsymbol{\nabla}\right) \mathbf{u}. \tag{4.5}$$

### Exercise 4.5

Consider a river with a section of rapids in which the flow can be modelled as one-dimensional with velocity field $\mathbf{u} = u_1\,\mathbf{i}$, where

$$u_1(x) = U\left(1 + e^{-x^2}\right) \qquad (-5 < x < 5)$$

and $x$ is distance along the river, $x = 0$ being at the centre of the rapids.

(a) Sketch $u_1$ against $x$, and find both $\partial \mathbf{u}/\partial t$ and $d\mathbf{u}/dt$. Evaluate $du_1/dt$ at $x = \pm 1,\ \pm 0.5,\ \pm 0.25,\ 0$.

(b) Relate the derivatives $\partial \mathbf{u}/\partial t$ and $d\mathbf{u}/dt$ to physical quantities, as estimated by a fixed observer on the bank who watches

  (i) a trail of sticks flowing past the centre of the rapids;

  (ii) a single stick flowing through the rapids.

---

Exercise 4.5 demonstrates that, even in steady flow, fluid particles can have an acceleration (due to the convective term).

The operator $\mathbf{u} \cdot \nabla$ was introduced from consideration of Cartesian coordinates. However, this operator is independent of the coordinate system chosen, and if another system is used, then $\mathbf{u}$ and $\nabla$ are expressed in that coordinate system. For example, using cylindrical polar coordinates, we have

$$\mathbf{u} = u_r\,\mathbf{e}_r + u_\theta\,\mathbf{e}_\theta + u_z\,\mathbf{e}_z \qquad \text{and} \qquad \nabla = \mathbf{e}_r\frac{\partial}{\partial r} + \mathbf{e}_\theta\frac{1}{r}\frac{\partial}{\partial \theta} + \mathbf{e}_z\frac{\partial}{\partial z},$$

so that the convective rate of change is given by

$$\mathbf{u} \cdot \nabla = u_r\frac{\partial}{\partial r} + \frac{u_\theta}{r}\frac{\partial}{\partial \theta} + u_z\frac{\partial}{\partial z}. \tag{4.6}$$

The spherical polar coordinate expression may be obtained similarly. The next exercise illustrates the use of cylindrical polar coordinates.

This is the cylindrical polar version of **grad**, as in *Unit 4* Subsection 1.3.

### Exercise 4.6

Find the acceleration of a fluid particle moving in a rotating flow, with velocity field given by

$$\mathbf{u} = \frac{K(t)}{r}\,\mathbf{e}_\theta \qquad (r \neq 0),$$

where $K$ is a function of one variable and $r$, $\theta$, $z$ are cylindrical polar coordinates. (Note that the unit vector $\mathbf{e}_\theta$ is not constant.)

Recall that
$$\mathbf{e}_r = \cos\theta\,\mathbf{i} + \sin\theta\,\mathbf{j},$$
$$\mathbf{e}_\theta = -\sin\theta\,\mathbf{i} + \cos\theta\,\mathbf{j},$$
so that
$$\frac{\partial \mathbf{e}_\theta}{\partial \theta} = -\mathbf{e}_r.$$

## 4.3 A model for inviscid incompressible flows

In *Unit 1*, it was said that a fluid is *incompressible* if the volume of a given mass of the fluid cannot be reduced by applying a compressional force. For example, any fluid for which the density $\rho$ is given by $\rho = \rho_0$ (constant) is incompressible. The mathematical definition of incompressibility is as follows: a fluid is **incompressible** if the rate of change of density *following the motion* is zero, that is, if

$$\frac{d\rho}{dt} = \frac{\partial \rho}{\partial t} + (\mathbf{u} \cdot \nabla)\rho = 0.$$

In general, liquids can be modelled as incompressible at constant temperature.

This definition expresses the fact that as a fluid particle proceeds along a pathline, the density at each point it occupies is the same, i.e. each pathline is a line of constant density.

This definition is useful to find the form of the continuity equation for an incompressible fluid. The continuity equation is

$$\frac{\partial \rho}{\partial t} + \boldsymbol{\nabla} \cdot (\rho \mathbf{u}) = 0; \tag{4.7}$$

*Unit 4* Subsection 3.3

expanding the second term gives

$$\frac{\partial \rho}{\partial t} + (\mathbf{u} \cdot \boldsymbol{\nabla}) \rho + \rho \boldsymbol{\nabla} \cdot \mathbf{u} = 0.$$

See Equation (5.2) of *Unit 4*.

In terms of the derivative following the motion, this becomes

$$\frac{d\rho}{dt} + \rho \boldsymbol{\nabla} \cdot \mathbf{u} = 0.$$

Now if the fluid is incompressible, then $d\rho/dt = 0$, and so we arrive at the following result.

For a fluid of constant density, this was the outcome of *Unit 4*, Exercise 3.8(a).

The continuity equation for an incompressible fluid is $\boldsymbol{\nabla} \cdot \mathbf{u} = 0$.

Clearly, the reverse of this result is also true: if the continuity equation is satisfied and $\boldsymbol{\nabla} \cdot \mathbf{u} = 0$, then the fluid is incompressible.

Note that this equation is expressed in terms of the velocity vector field, suggesting that we may talk about *incompressible flows* as well as incompressible fluids. In other words, an incompressible flow is a flow in which the fluid behaves as if it were incompressible.

## Example 4.1

Show that the flow due to a two-dimensional source of strength $2\pi m$ is incompressible, except at the source point itself.

### Solution

The velocity vector field for such a source, with the origin chosen to be at the source point, is

$$\mathbf{u} = \frac{m}{r} \, \mathbf{e}_r \qquad (r \neq 0),$$

in cylindrical polar coordinates. We have

$$\boldsymbol{\nabla} \cdot \mathbf{u} = \frac{1}{r} \frac{\partial}{\partial r} (r u_r) + \frac{1}{r} \frac{\partial}{\partial \theta} (u_\theta) + \frac{\partial}{\partial z} (u_z).$$

The expression for div in cylindrical polar coordinates was given in *Unit 4* Subsection 3.1. See also the back of the *Handbook*.

Thus, in this case,

$$\boldsymbol{\nabla} \cdot \mathbf{u} = \frac{1}{r} \frac{\partial}{\partial r} \left( r \frac{m}{r} \right) = 0 \qquad (r \neq 0).$$

This flow is incompressible everywhere except at $r = 0$. ∎

## Exercise 4.7

Which of the following vector fields could be the velocity field for an incompressible flow?

(a) $\mathbf{u} = x\,\mathbf{i} + y\,\mathbf{j} - 2z\,\mathbf{k}$

(b) $\mathbf{u} = x\,\mathbf{i} + 2y\,\mathbf{j} + 0\,\mathbf{k}$

(c) $\mathbf{u} = \dfrac{K}{r^2}\,\mathbf{e}_\theta,$ where $K$ is constant (cylindrical polar coordinates)

---

If the density is $\rho = \rho_0$ (constant) then, for all velocity fields $\mathbf{u}$,

$$\frac{d\rho}{dt} = \frac{\partial \rho}{\partial t} + u_1 \frac{\partial \rho}{\partial x} + u_2 \frac{\partial \rho}{\partial y} + u_3 \frac{\partial \rho}{\partial z} = 0,$$

since all partial derivatives of $\rho$ are zero everywhere, and so the fluid is incompressible. But there are other possibilities for $\rho$ and $\mathbf{u}$ which satisfy the incompressible version of the continuity equation, $\boldsymbol{\nabla} \cdot \mathbf{u} = 0$, as the next example shows.

### Example 4.2

Show that the flow for which $\rho = \rho(y)$ and $\mathbf{u} = u(y)\,\mathbf{i}$ satisfies the continuity equation (4.7) and is an incompressible flow.

### Solution

We have

$$\frac{\partial \rho}{\partial t} + \boldsymbol{\nabla} \cdot (\rho \mathbf{u}) = 0 + \frac{\partial}{\partial x}\left(\rho(y)\,u(y)\right) = 0,$$

so the continuity equation is satisfied. Also

$$\boldsymbol{\nabla} \cdot \mathbf{u} = \frac{\partial}{\partial x}\left(u(y)\right) = 0,$$

showing that the flow is incompressible.  ■

The flow in Example 4.2 is an example of a *stratified flow*. (Density stratification occurs, for example, in river estuaries due to salinity changes, and in the atmosphere due to temperature changes, layers of autumn mist being a case in point.) Each fluid particle at a given height has the same density, and because there is no $y$-component of velocity, each particle stays at a constant height. This is an incompressible flow in stratified layers, as illustrated in Figure 4.4.

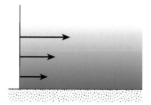

*Figure 4.4*   Stratified flow in which velocity increases with height, and density decreases with height

### Applicability of the incompressible model

The incompressible fluid model is applicable, in particular, to any (real) fluid whose density may be modelled as constant at all points and at all times. For most liquids, this condition is satisfied provided that the temperature is constant. There is a small density variation with temperature for most liquids; for example, water decreases in density by about 4% as the temperature increases from 0°C to 100°C. The density variation of a liquid with pressure is comparatively small; for example, for water an increase of 1 atmosphere causes an increase in density of less than 0.005%.

However, even for gases, certain types of flow past a body at moderate speed can be modelled well as incompressible flows. In such flows, the pressure and density variations are relatively small. For example, density variations in air are less than 1% for flow speeds of up to about $50\,\mathrm{m\,s^{-1}}$.

Recall that $50\,\mathrm{m\,s^{-1}} = 180\,\mathrm{kph} \simeq 112\,\mathrm{mph}.$

The speed of sound in a fluid is a measure of how much the fluid density can change with pressure, since sound waves are transmitted in the fluid by density changes due to pressure, the more compressible fluids taking longer to transmit the pulses forming the wave.

At 20°C, the speed of sound for air is 343 m s$^{-1}$; for pure water, it is 1482 m s$^{-1}$. Water is denser and much less compressible than air.

The incompressible model breaks down for compressible fluids moving at high speeds (that is, speeds comparable to or greater than the speed of sound for the fluid). Compressible flows can be significantly different in kind from incompressible flows. For example, small pressure disturbances are propagated through a compressible fluid as wave motions, travelling at the speed of sound for that fluid. This contrasts with the incompressible fluid model, in which small disturbances are transmitted instantaneously to the whole region occupied by the fluid. The incompressible model implies that the speed of sound in the fluid is infinite.

A good estimate of the speed of sound in a gas is given by $\sqrt{\gamma p_0 / \rho_0}$, where $p_0$, $\rho_0$ are the background pressure and density, and $\gamma$ is a constant for the gas ($\gamma \simeq 1.4$ for air). This formula is derived in MS324 Block I *Chapter 1.*

## *Alternative forms of the continuity equation*

To conclude this section, we now turn attention to the form of the continuity equation for two special types of steady incompressible flow. As you know, the mathematical expression of this equation is $\nabla \cdot \mathbf{u} = 0$. We now find forms of the equation which do not involve differentiation.

In Subsection 2.2, you saw that there is no flow across a streamline. Imagine now the family of all streamlines which pass through a simple closed curve (see Figure 4.5); such a set of streamlines is called a **streamtube**. Since we are considering steady flow, each streamline is a pathline, and so we may consider the streamtube to be a model of a fixed boundary for the flow.

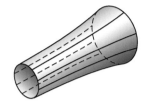

*Figure 4.5*  A streamtube

Consider the special case of a constant-density fluid and a streamtube which is such that across any plane normal section of it, the fluid velocity is constant and normal to the section (see Figure 4.6). Let the speed at sections 1 and 2 be $u_1$ and $u_2$, respectively. Then, since the flow is steady, the law of conservation of mass says that the mass of fluid crossing section 1 per unit time equals that at section 2; that is,

$$\rho \, u_1 A_1 = \rho \, u_2 A_2,$$

where $A_1$, $A_2$ are the areas of sections 1 and 2, and $\rho$ is the constant density. Hence the volume flow rates are equal, and

$$u_1 A_1 = u_2 A_2. \tag{4.8}$$

This form of the continuity equation does not involve differentiation, and can be used to model the steady flow of low-viscosity liquids (e.g. water) in pipes where the flow is approximately constant across a cross-section.

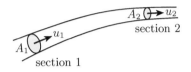

*Figure 4.6*

It can be shown that Equation (4.8) is a consequence of the form $\nabla \cdot \mathbf{u} = 0$ of the continuity equation, by applying Gauss' (Divergence) Theorem, from *Unit 4*, over the streamtube in Figure 4.6.

### *Exercise 4.8*

A straight circular pipe carrying water has a cross-section which converges from an area of 0.3 m$^2$ to 0.15 m$^2$. If the speed of the water at the larger section is 1.8 m s$^{-1}$, estimate the speed at the smaller section.

The next special case is that of unidirectional flow, in which $\mathbf{u}$ depends only on the space coordinate in the direction of flow (for example, $\mathbf{u} = u(x)\,\mathbf{i}$). In this case, any streamtube of unit thickness into the page, imagined from the real flow, will have rectangular normal sections (see Figure 4.7).

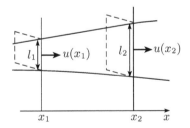

*Figure 4.7*

### *Exercise 4.9*

(a) If the distance between the streamlines is $l_1$ at $x_1$ and $l_2$ at $x_2$ (see Figure 4.7), to what does Equation (4.8) reduce in this case?

(b) Figure 4.8 shows a section of a stationary river bore. Explain how to model this flow by means of a streamtube, and use your answer to part (a) to calculate the speed $u$.

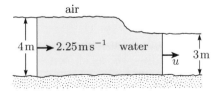

*Figure 4.8*

49

As you may have realised, the derivation of Equation (4.8) involved an approximation, in that if the streamtube expands or contracts, the fluid velocity across a plane section cannot be exactly normal to it at all points. In fact Equation (4.8) is exact if $u_1$ and $u_2$ are taken to be velocity components normal to the sections, but these will be close to the corresponding speeds if the rate of streamtube expansion or contraction at the sections is small. Similar remarks apply to the result of Exercise 4.9(a); the flow illustrated in Figure 4.7 must have some vertical component for the streamlines to diverge, but this is assumed small enough to ignore.

## End-of-section exercises

### Exercise 4.10

Classify the flows given by the following velocity fields as steady or non-steady, and as uniform or non-uniform.

(a) $\mathbf{u} = 3\mathbf{i} + 10\mathbf{j}$

(b) $\mathbf{u} = (3x + 4y)\mathbf{i} + 10\mathbf{j}$

(c) $\mathbf{u} = \dfrac{2t}{r}\mathbf{e}_\theta \qquad (r \neq 0)$

(d) $\mathbf{u} = 3\mathbf{e}_r + \dfrac{2}{r}\mathbf{e}_\theta \qquad (r \neq 0)$

(e) $\mathbf{u} = (3t + 1)\mathbf{i} + 4\mathbf{j}$

### Exercise 4.11

Find the acceleration following the motion for each of the velocity fields below.

(a) $\mathbf{u} = Uy\,\mathbf{i}, \qquad$ where $U$ is constant

(b) $\mathbf{u} = U(t)y\,\mathbf{i}$

(c) $\mathbf{u} = U\left(1 + \dfrac{a^2}{r^2}\right)\sin\theta\,\mathbf{e}_\theta, \qquad$ where $U$ is constant (polar coordinates)

### Exercise 4.12

Which of the following velocity fields could represent incompressible flows?

(a) $\mathbf{u} = U\cos\alpha\,\mathbf{i} + U\sin\alpha\,\mathbf{j} \qquad (U, \alpha \text{ constants})$

(b) $\mathbf{u} = -\dfrac{Ky}{x^2 + y^2}\mathbf{i} + \dfrac{Kx}{x^2 + y^2}\mathbf{j} + 2xy\,\mathbf{k} \qquad (K \text{ constant})$

(c) $\mathbf{u} = U\cos\theta\left(1 - \dfrac{a^2}{r^2}\right)\mathbf{e}_r - U\sin\theta\left(1 + \dfrac{a^2}{r^2}\right)\mathbf{e}_\theta \qquad (U, a \text{ constants})$

(d) $\mathbf{u} = \dfrac{K}{r}\mathbf{e}_\theta \qquad (r \neq 0, K \text{ constant})$

### Exercise 4.13

Consider the steady flow of a constant-density fluid through a pipe of radius $a$ (constant) which splits into two pipes, each of radius $\frac{1}{2}a$, as shown in Figure 4.9, all motion being horizontal. Express the speeds at section 2 in the narrower pipes in terms of the speed $u_1$ at section 1, mentioning any assumptions that you make about the nature of the flow.

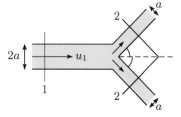

*Figure 4.9*

# 5  Euler's equation

Section 4 provided a mathematical framework in which the properties of a fluid in motion can be described as functions of position and time. The continuity equation provides a relationship between density and velocity changes, and takes on the simple form $\nabla \cdot \mathbf{u} = 0$ for an incompressible fluid. Any vector field satisfying this equation can be used to model such a fluid in motion.

Many problems in fluid mechanics involve the flow of a fluid past a solid boundary, and it is often important to determine the force produced on a solid body by the fluid flowing past it. A simple example was described in *Unit 1*, where we investigated the force on a lock gate due to the water in a canal. In this case the fluid was at rest. In Section 3 of this unit, we found the stream function, and the streamline pattern, for the flow of a constant-density fluid past a cylinder. From this stream function the velocity of the fluid at any point can be found. The effect on the cylinder of the fluid flowing past it can be described by the net force on the cylinder due to the fluid. Other examples where the force is important are the aerodynamic forces on an aircraft (the lift and drag), the drag force on a motor car and the force on a bend in a pipe caused by fluid flowing within it. All of these arise from a momentum change of the fluid.

See Exercises 3.4 and 3.7.

In this section, an equation of motion is developed which relates the change in momentum to the forces acting in a fluid. We continue with the inviscid model, so that forces due to viscosity will not be included in the equation of motion.

## 5.1  Derivation of Euler's equation

The linear momentum conservation equation, sometimes called the equation of motion, is an application of Newton's Second Law to a region moving with the fluid and containing a fixed mass of fluid. To obtain an equation of motion that is valid at each point in the fluid, the region is shrunk to a point, as was done in the derivation of the continuity equation in *Unit 4*. We can do this because, in the continuum model, every region enclosing a point, however small, contains some fluid. We equate the rate of change of linear momentum of the region to the net force on the region.

The mass is fixed because the moving region always contains the same set of fluid particles.

### Rate of change of linear momentum

Consider a region $B$ of fluid. Divide this region into $N$ fluid volume elements, so that the $i$th volume element has volume $\delta V_i$ and contains the point $P_i$, for $i = 1, 2, \ldots, N$ (see Figure 5.1).

*Figure 5.1*

The linear momentum of the $i$th element, $\delta \mathbf{p}_i$, is given approximately by the product of the fluid velocity at $P_i$ and the mass $\delta M_i$ of the element, that is,

$$\delta \mathbf{p}_i \simeq \mathbf{u}(P_i)\, \delta M_i.$$

The total linear momentum of the fluid within region $B$ is the sum

Linear momentum was defined in MST209 *Unit 19*. It is customary to denote the momentum vector by $\mathbf{p}$. This is unconnected with the (scalar) pressure $p$, introduced later in the argument.

$$\mathbf{p} = \sum_{i=1}^{N} \delta \mathbf{p}_i \simeq \sum_{i=1}^{N} \mathbf{u}(P_i)\, \delta M_i.$$

The rate of change of linear momentum (following the motion) is

$$\frac{d\mathbf{p}}{dt} \simeq \frac{d}{dt}\left(\sum_{i=1}^{N} \mathbf{u}(P_i)\,\delta M_i\right) \simeq \sum_{i=1}^{N} \frac{d\mathbf{u}}{dt}(P_i)\,\delta M_i.$$

In this differentiation, each $\delta M_i$ is constant because the volume element always contains the same fluid as it moves with the fluid.

Writing the mass in terms of the volume for each element, we have

$$\frac{d\mathbf{p}}{dt} \simeq \sum_{i=1}^{N} \frac{d\mathbf{u}}{dt}(P_i)\,\rho(P_i)\,\delta V_i.$$

Here we put $\delta M_i \simeq \rho(P_i)\,\delta V_i$, where $\rho$ is the density of the fluid.

Taking smaller and smaller elements, the changes in $\rho$ and $d\mathbf{u}/dt$ throughout each element are reduced, and the sum on the right-hand side becomes a closer approximation to the rate of change of linear momentum of the fluid in region $B$. In the limit as each element shrinks to a point, the summation becomes a volume integral, and so the rate of change of linear momentum of $B$ is

$$\frac{d\mathbf{p}}{dt} = \int_{B} \rho\,\frac{d\mathbf{u}}{dt}\,dV. \tag{5.1}$$

## Two types of force

Next, we find an expression for the net force on $B$. The forces acting on a fluid element may be of two types:

(i)  surface forces due to the action of the rest of the fluid on the fluid element under consideration;

(ii) body forces which are forces whose origin is external to the fluid, like gravitational and electromagnetic forces.

The different types of force acting on a fluid element were introduced in *Unit 1* Subsection 3.4.

In the discussion of surface forces in *Unit 1*, you saw that surface forces are in general of two kinds — forces normal to the boundary surface of the fluid element, which are called pressure forces, and forces acting in the tangent plane to the surface, which are called viscous forces and are due to the viscosity of the fluid. These viscous forces do not occur in the inviscid model. In this unit, we assume that all the surface forces are normal to the surface of the fluid element. *Unit 8* will introduce viscous forces into the model.

## Surface forces

Consider the surface $S$ of the region $B$ as being split into $N$ small surface elements, so that the $i$th surface element has area $\delta A_i$ and contains the point $Q_i$, for $i = 1, 2, \ldots, N$ (see Figure 5.2). The surface force acting on the $i$th surface element, exerted by the surrounding fluid, is given by

$$\delta\mathbf{F}_i \simeq -p(Q_i)\,\mathbf{n}(Q_i)\,\delta A_i,$$

Pressure and the surface force due to pressure were discussed in *Unit 1* Subsection 3.2.

where the pressure $p$ is a time-dependent scalar field and $\mathbf{n}$ is the outward unit normal vector, shown in Figure 5.2. The negative sign expresses the fact that the rest of the fluid exerts an inward pressure at each point $Q_i$ on the surface $S$. In all applications, the pressure $p$ is positive or zero.

The net surface force acting on the surface $S$ is

$$\mathbf{F}_S = \sum_{i=1}^{N} \delta\mathbf{F}_i \simeq \sum_{i=1}^{N} \left(-p(Q_i)\,\mathbf{n}(Q_i)\,\delta A_i\right).$$

*Figure 5.2*

Taking smaller and smaller surface elements, the limit of the sum as each element shrinks to a point is the surface integral

$$\mathbf{F}_S = \int_{S} (-p\,\mathbf{n})\,dA. \tag{5.2}$$

We next convert this surface integral to a volume integral (since the body forces on region $B$ will also be given by a volume integral). Let $\mathbf{e}$ be an arbitrary constant unit vector. Then

$$\int_B \mathrm{div}(-p\,\mathbf{e})\,dV = \int_S (-p\,\mathbf{e}) \cdot \mathbf{n}\,dA \qquad \text{(by Gauss' Theorem)}$$

See *Unit 4* Subsection 3.2.

$$= \mathbf{e} \cdot \int_S (-p\,\mathbf{n})\,dA \qquad \text{(since } \mathbf{e} \text{ is constant).}$$

Also,

$$\int_B \mathrm{div}(-p\,\mathbf{e})\,dV = \int_B (\mathbf{e} \cdot \mathbf{grad}(-p) + (-p)\,\mathrm{div}\,\mathbf{e})\,dV$$

$$= \mathbf{e} \cdot \int_B \mathbf{grad}(-p)\,dV \qquad \text{(since } \mathbf{e} \text{ is constant).}$$

See Equation (5.2) of *Unit 4*, with div for $\nabla\cdot$ and **grad** for $\nabla$.

The last two results feature the same left-hand side, so the two right-hand sides must equal each other, that is,

$$\mathbf{e} \cdot \int_S (-p\,\mathbf{n})\,dA = \mathbf{e} \cdot \int_B \mathbf{grad}(-p)\,dV.$$

Since $\mathbf{e}$ is arbitrary, this means that

$$\int_S (-p\,\mathbf{n})\,dA = \int_B \mathbf{grad}(-p)\,dV,$$

so that, from Equation (5.2),

$$\mathbf{F}_S = \int_B \mathbf{grad}(-p)\,dV = \int_B (-\nabla p)\,dV. \tag{5.3}$$

The same argument works with any scalar field $\phi$ in place of $-p$, giving a corollary to Gauss' Theorem:

$$\int_S \phi\,\mathbf{n}\,dA = \int_B \mathbf{grad}\,\phi\,dV.$$

## Body forces

Consider now the body forces. These are forces which act at every point in a fluid element, and it is convenient to model such forces by vector fields per unit mass. For example, the force of gravity on a body of mass $m$ is $-mg\,\mathbf{k}$; we could model the acceleration due to gravity by the vector field $\mathbf{F}_{\mathrm{grav}} = -g\,\mathbf{k}$, and then the force on the body becomes $m\,\mathbf{F}_{\mathrm{grav}}$. If the total body force per unit mass is denoted by $\mathbf{F}$, then the force acting on the fluid element at $P_i$ (see Figure 5.1) is

$$\delta\mathbf{F}_i \simeq \mathbf{F}(P_i)\,\rho(P_i)\,\delta V_i \qquad (i = 1, 2, \ldots, N).$$

The net body force acting on the fluid in the region $B$ is therefore given by the volume integral

$$\mathbf{F}_B = \int_B \rho\,\mathbf{F}\,dV. \tag{5.4}$$

$\mathbf{F}$ is the vector sum of all possible body forces per unit mass. If $\mathbf{F}_{\mathrm{grav}}$ and $\mathbf{F}_{\mathrm{mag}}$ represent the body forces per unit mass of gravity and a magnetic field, then

$$\mathbf{F} = \mathbf{F}_{\mathrm{grav}} + \mathbf{F}_{\mathrm{mag}}.$$

## Total force and Newton's Second Law

The total force $\mathbf{F}_R$ acting on the region $B$ is the sum of the net surface and body forces. Using Equations (5.3) and (5.4), we have

$$\mathbf{F}_R = \mathbf{F}_S + \mathbf{F}_B = \int_B (-\nabla p)\,dV + \int_B \rho\,\mathbf{F}\,dV = \int_B (-\nabla p + \rho\,\mathbf{F})\,dV.$$

Equating this total force on the region $B$ to the rate of change of linear momentum, in Equation (5.1), gives

$$\int_B \rho\,\frac{d\mathbf{u}}{dt}\,dV = \int_B (-\nabla p + \rho\,\mathbf{F})\,dV$$

or, writing this as one volume integral,

$$\int_B \left( \rho\,\frac{d\mathbf{u}}{dt} + \nabla p - \rho\,\mathbf{F} \right) dV = \mathbf{0}.$$

This is the same as applying Newton's Second Law in solid mechanics. In MST209 *Unit 19* this was expressed as

$$\mathbf{F}^{\mathrm{ext}} = \dot{\mathbf{P}}.$$

The equivalent here is

$$\frac{d\mathbf{p}}{dt} = \mathbf{F}_R.$$

Since this equation is derived for an arbitrary region of fluid $B$, the usual assumption of smoothness of the integrand enables us to write

$$\rho \frac{d\mathbf{u}}{dt} = -\nabla p + \rho \mathbf{F}. \tag{5.5}$$

This is known as **Euler's equation**, and is satisfied at every point in an inviscid fluid.

### Exercise 5.1

Show that, for a fluid at rest where the only body force is due to gravity, Euler's equation reduces to the basic equation of fluid statics,

$$\frac{dp}{dz} = -\rho g, \qquad \text{where } p = p(z).$$

Euler's equation and the continuity equation together provide a description for a fluid in motion. The acceleration term on the left-hand side of Euler's equation can be written in terms of the local rate of change of $\mathbf{u}$ at a fixed point and the convective rate of change. We then have

$$\rho \frac{\partial \mathbf{u}}{\partial t} + \rho \left( \mathbf{u} \cdot \nabla \right) \mathbf{u} = -\nabla p + \rho \mathbf{F}. \tag{5.6}$$

Here $\partial \mathbf{u}/\partial t$ is the local time rate of change of $\mathbf{u}$; in steady flows, this is zero. The term $(\mathbf{u} \cdot \nabla) \mathbf{u}$ is non-linear in the velocity and is the convective acceleration. As you saw in Exercise 4.5, this convective acceleration can be non-zero even in steady flows.

Euler's equation (5.5) or (5.6) relates the pressure, $p$, and the total body force per unit mass, $\mathbf{F}$, to the velocity vector field, $\mathbf{u}$. This equation is fundamental to much of the rest of the course. If viscosity is neglected (as here), then Euler's equation must be satisfied at each point in a fluid and at all times.

Dividing Equation (5.6) by $\rho$ gives

$$\frac{\partial \mathbf{u}}{\partial t} + (\mathbf{u} \cdot \nabla) \mathbf{u} = -\frac{1}{\rho} \nabla p + \mathbf{F}. \tag{5.7}$$

The acceleration following the motion, seen on the left-hand side, is equal to the total force per unit mass seen on the right-hand side.

The forces causing the acceleration consist of the body forces, such as weight (due to gravity), together with the surface force caused by pressure. A uniform pressure by itself does not cause acceleration since, on any element, the pressure on one face is matched by an equal pressure on an opposite face, and so no motion occurs. It is natural to expect the *gradient* of the pressure, i.e. the spatial rate of change of $p$, to be the accelerating surface force.

Essentially, Euler's equation gives a means of finding the pressure, $p$, when the body forces per unit mass, $\mathbf{F}$, and the velocity field, $\mathbf{u}$, are known. The possibly daunting form of Euler's equation suggests that further modelling assumptions need to be made in order to make progress with its solution.

The idea of 'dropping the integral sign' because $B$ is an arbitrary region was discussed in the derivation of the continuity equation in *Unit 4*.

Equation (5.5) is also called *Euler's momentum equation*. *Unit 1* referred to Euler's *equations* (plural); it may be regarded as one vector equation or three scalar equations.

This equation was derived in *Unit 1* Subsection 4.1.

See Equation (4.5).

The velocity field $\mathbf{u}$ must satisfy the continuity equation. In general, Euler's equation is also needed to determine $\mathbf{u}$ in full.

### Exercise 5.2

Find the form of Euler's equation for the irrotational steady flow of a fluid of constant density $\rho_0$ in a conservative force field with scalar potential $\Omega$.

*Hint:* To simplify $(\mathbf{u} \cdot \boldsymbol{\nabla})\,\mathbf{u}$, use the identity

$$(\mathbf{u} \cdot \boldsymbol{\nabla})\,\mathbf{u} = \boldsymbol{\nabla}(\tfrac{1}{2}u^2) - \mathbf{u} \times (\boldsymbol{\nabla} \times \mathbf{u}), \qquad \text{where } u = |\mathbf{u}|.$$

If $\mathbf{F}$ is conservative, then there is a scalar potential field $\Omega$ such that $\mathbf{F} = \boldsymbol{\nabla}\Omega$ (see MST209 *Unit 24*, but with $\Omega$ in place of $-U$).

For the vector identity given here, see *Unit 4*, Exercise 5.5.

The formula obtained in Exercise 5.2 provides some hope for progress. Euler's equation cannot, in general, be integrated. However, for a conservative force field, Euler's equation can be expressed as

$$\frac{\partial \mathbf{u}}{\partial t} - \mathbf{u} \times (\boldsymbol{\nabla} \times \mathbf{u}) = -\frac{1}{\rho}\boldsymbol{\nabla}p + \boldsymbol{\nabla}\Omega - \boldsymbol{\nabla}(\tfrac{1}{2}u^2), \tag{5.8}$$

and now both sides can be integrated along the streamlines to give a form of energy equation. This equation and its application to some flow problems form the subject of *Unit 6*.

## 5.2  Applications of Euler's equation

In one sense, much of the rest of the course uses the continuity equation and Euler's equation to solve problems in fluid mechanics. However, viscosity has been neglected, and this can drastically affect the behaviour of a fluid in the region near a body and, by convection, downstream of it. Viscosity will be included in the model in *Unit 8*.

The strategy for solving fluid flow problems that is developed in this unit depends on first finding the velocity field $\mathbf{u}$. One way of doing so is to model the flow field and boundaries by the superposition of several basic flow types, e.g. uniform flow, source, doublet, vortex, using perhaps the streamlines or experience to suggest suitable basic flow types whose parameters can be adjusted to fit the particular flow circumstances. This may involve use of the stream function to compare the model's streamlines with the flow-visualised streamlines. From the velocity field, Euler's equation is used to determine the pressure.

Use of the stream function takes the continuity equation into account.

### Example 5.1

A particular flow of a constant-density fluid is given by the velocity field

$$\mathbf{u} = 2yt\,\mathbf{i} - 2x\,\mathbf{j},$$

and the body force per unit mass is

$$\mathbf{F} = 2y\,\mathbf{i}.$$

Find an expression for the pressure at a general point $(x, y)$.

### Solution

Euler's equation, in the form (5.7), is

$$\frac{\partial \mathbf{u}}{\partial t} + (\mathbf{u} \cdot \boldsymbol{\nabla})\mathbf{u} = -\frac{1}{\rho}\boldsymbol{\nabla}p + \mathbf{F}.$$

With $\mathbf{u} = 2yt\,\mathbf{i} - 2x\,\mathbf{j}$ and $\mathbf{F} = 2y\,\mathbf{i}$, this becomes

$$2y\,\mathbf{i} + \left(2yt\frac{\partial}{\partial x} - 2x\frac{\partial}{\partial y}\right)(2yt\,\mathbf{i} - 2x\,\mathbf{j}) = -\frac{1}{\rho}\boldsymbol{\nabla}p + 2y\,\mathbf{i},$$

which reduces to

$$-4xt\,\mathbf{i} - 4yt\,\mathbf{j} = -\frac{1}{\rho}\boldsymbol{\nabla}p. \tag{5.9}$$

The $x$-component of this equation gives

$$\frac{\partial p}{\partial x} = 4x\rho t$$

which, since $\rho$ is a constant, integrates to give

$$p(x, y, t) = 2x^2 \rho t + f(y, t), \tag{5.10}$$

where $f$ is an arbitrary function of two variables. The $y$-component of Equation (5.9) then gives

$$\frac{\partial p}{\partial y} = 4y\rho t = \frac{\partial f}{\partial y},$$

which integrates to give

$$f(y, t) = 2y^2 \rho t + g(t),$$

where $g$ is an arbitrary function. Hence, from Equation (5.10), the pressure at $(x, y)$ and time $t$ is

$$p(x, y, t) = 2(x^2 + y^2)\rho t + g(t). \quad \blacksquare$$

### Exercise 5.3

The stream function for a source of strength $2\pi m$ at $(0, b)$, outside a wall along the $x$-axis (see Figure 5.3), is

$$\psi = m\left(\arctan\left(\frac{y - b}{x}\right) + \arctan\left(\frac{y + b}{x}\right)\right).$$

Find the velocity at the wall, and deduce the pressure at any point of the wall. Assume that the fluid is inviscid and of constant density, that the flow is two-dimensional and irrotational, that body forces can be neglected, and that the pressure is $p_0$ at $x = \pm\infty$.

*Hint:* Use the result of Exercise 5.2 and the remark after that exercise about integrating along a streamline.

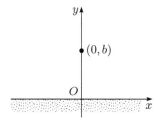

*Figure 5.3*

# End-of-section exercise

### Exercise 5.4

A two-dimensional flow of a constant-density, inviscid fluid is given by the velocity field

$$\mathbf{u} = -2x\,\mathbf{i} + (2y + 5t)\,\mathbf{j},$$

and the body force per unit mass is

$$\mathbf{F} = 5\,\mathbf{j}.$$

Find $\nabla p$, using Euler's equation in the form (5.6). Then integrate to find $p$.

# Outcomes

After studying this unit, you should be able to:

- define and explain the terms pathline, streamline and stream function;
- derive the pathlines in Cartesian and polar form from a velocity field;
- derive the streamlines in Cartesian and polar form from a velocity field;
- define and explain the terms source, sink, vortex and doublet;
- derive the stream function from a velocity field;
- explain how streamlines may be found from the stream function;
- explain how the stream function may be interpreted physically;
- explain why stream functions may be added to create further flows;
- model different flows from a combination of uniform flows, sources, sinks and doublets;
- explain what is meant by the local rate of change of a scalar or vector field;
- explain what is meant by differentiation following the motion of a scalar or vector field;
- use the continuity equation to determine whether an inviscid flow is incompressible;
- understand how Euler's equation is derived, and what it represents;
- use Euler's equation to find the pressure distribution from a velocity field.

# Acknowledgements

Grateful acknowledgement is made to the following for permission to reproduce photographs in this text:

Figures 1.1 and 4.2: The Blackie Publishing Group, Scotland;

Figure 3.9: Milne-Thomson, L.M. (1968) *Theoretical Hydrodynamics*, Macmillan.

Every effort has been made to contact copyright holders. If any have been inadvertently overlooked the publishers will be pleased to make the necessary arrangements at the first opportunity.

# Solutions to the exercises

## Section 1

### Solution 1.1

From Equation (1.3), we have $d\mathbf{r}/dt = \mathbf{u} = U\,\mathbf{i}$, or
$$\frac{dx}{dt} = U, \qquad \frac{dy}{dt} = 0.$$
Integrating these equations gives
$$x = Ut + C, \qquad y = D,$$
where $C$ and $D$ are arbitrary constants.

The pathline through $(x_0, y_0)$ at time $t = 0$ is given by
$$x = Ut + x_0, \qquad y = y_0.$$
So each pathline is a line parallel to the $x$-axis, the particle being at $(Ut + x_0, y_0)$ at time $t$. Since $U > 0$, each fluid particle moves steadily to the right.

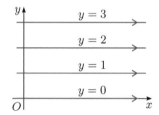

### Solution 1.2

**(a)** From Equations (1.3) and (1.4), we have
$$\frac{dr}{dt} = 0, \qquad r\frac{d\theta}{dt} = \frac{k}{r} \quad \text{or} \quad \frac{d\theta}{dt} = \frac{k}{r^2}.$$
Integrating gives $r = C$, an arbitrary constant, and
$$\theta = \frac{kt}{C^2} + D \qquad (\text{since } r = C),$$
where $D$ is an arbitrary constant.

These pathlines are circles with centre at the origin; particles move steadily around these circles, the speed being slower further away from the origin, because $u_\theta = k/r$ decreases as $r$ increases. Since $\dot\theta > 0$, the fluid moves in an anticlockwise direction.

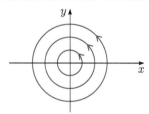

**(b)** From Equations (1.3) and (1.4), we have
$$\frac{dx}{dt} = x(3t + 1), \qquad \frac{dy}{dt} = 2y \quad (x > 0,\ y > 0),$$
or
$$\frac{1}{x}\frac{dx}{dt} = 3t + 1, \qquad \frac{1}{y}\frac{dy}{dt} = 2.$$
Integrating these gives (since $x > 0$, $y > 0$)
$$\ln x = \tfrac{3}{2}t^2 + t + C, \qquad \ln y = 2t + D,$$
where $C$ and $D$ are arbitrary constants. Taking exponentials of both sides in each case,
$$x = A\exp\left(\tfrac{3}{2}t^2 + t\right), \qquad \text{where } A = e^C,$$
$$y = B\exp(2t), \qquad \text{where } B = e^D.$$

From the second equation, $t = \tfrac{1}{2}\ln(y/B)$, giving
$$x = A\exp\left[\tfrac{3}{8}\left(\ln\left(\tfrac{y}{B}\right)\right)^2 + \tfrac{1}{2}\ln\left(\tfrac{y}{B}\right)\right].$$

### Solution 1.3

From Equation (1.5), we have
$$\frac{dy}{dx} = \frac{u_2}{u_1} = \frac{U\sin\alpha}{U\cos\alpha} = \tan\alpha.$$
Integrating gives
$$y = (\tan\alpha)\,x + C,$$
where $C$ is an arbitrary constant.

If $(x_0, y_0)$ lies on a streamline, then
$$y_0 = (\tan\alpha)\,x_0 + C,$$
so that, on subtraction,
$$y - y_0 = (x - x_0)\tan\alpha.$$
(If $\alpha = \pm\tfrac{1}{2}\pi$, then $\mathbf{u} = \pm U\,\mathbf{j}$ and the streamlines are given by $x = x_0$.)

The streamlines are (at all times) the parallel lines inclined at angle $\alpha$ to the $x$-axis. The figure below shows directions on the streamlines for the case $U > 0$.

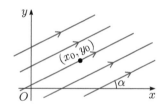

### Solution 1.4

**(a)** Since $u_r = 0$, the streamlines are given by $r = \text{constant}$. Thus the streamlines are circles with centre at the origin. (Note that, because this flow is steady, the streamlines are identical to the pathlines, as found in Solution 1.2(a).)

**(b)** From Equation (1.5),
$$\frac{dy}{dx} = \frac{2y}{x(3t + 1)} \quad (x \neq 0) \quad \text{or} \quad \frac{1}{y}\frac{dy}{dx} = \frac{2}{x(3t + 1)}.$$
With $t$ constant $(\neq -\tfrac{1}{3})$, we integrate with respect to $x$ to obtain (since $x > 0$, $y > 0$)
$$\ln y = \frac{2}{3t + 1}\ln x + C,$$
where $C$ is an arbitrary constant, so that
$$y = Ax^{2/(3t+1)} \quad (t \neq -\tfrac{1}{3}), \qquad \text{where } A = e^C.$$
If $(x_0, y_0) = (1, 1)$ then
$$1 = A \times 1^{2/(3t+1)} = A, \qquad \text{since } 1^{2/(3t+1)} = 1.$$
Thus $A = 1$ for the streamline through $(1,1)$ at any time $t$.

The streamlines $y = x^2$, $y = x$, $y = x^{1/2}$ (for $t = 0$, $t = \tfrac{1}{3}$, $t = 1$, respectively) are shown in the following figure. (Note that the equations differ from those of the pathlines, given in Solution 1.2(b).)

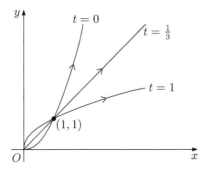

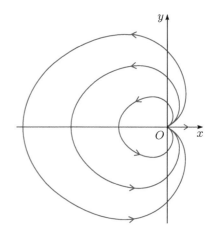

## Solution 1.5

From Equations (1.3) and (1.4), the pathlines are given by

$$\frac{dx}{dt} = a\cos(\omega t), \qquad \frac{dy}{dt} = a\sin(\omega t).$$

Integrating gives

$$x = \frac{a}{\omega}\sin(\omega t) + C, \qquad y = -\frac{a}{\omega}\cos(\omega t) + D,$$

where $C$ and $D$ are arbitrary constants.
When $t = 0$, $(x, y) = (0, 0)$, so that

$$C = 0 \quad \text{and} \quad D = \frac{a}{\omega}.$$

The required pathline is

$$x = \frac{a}{\omega}\sin(\omega t), \qquad y = \frac{a}{\omega}\left(1 - \cos(\omega t)\right),$$

which, on eliminating $t$, gives

$$x^2 + \left(y - \frac{a}{\omega}\right)^2 = \frac{a^2}{\omega^2}.$$

This is a circle with radius $a/\omega$ and centre $(0, a/\omega)$.
From Equation (1.5), the streamlines are given by

$$\frac{dy}{dx} = \frac{a\sin(\omega t)}{a\cos(\omega t)} = \tan(\omega t),$$

which, on integrating, gives

$$y = x\tan(\omega t) + E,$$

where $E$ is an arbitrary constant. When $t = 0$, $(x, y) = (0, 0)$, so that $E = 0$. The required streamline is $y = 0$.

## Solution 1.6

Since this is a steady flow, the streamlines and the pathlines are the same. We shall determine their equations from the differential equation (1.6) for the streamlines:

$$\frac{1}{r}\frac{dr}{d\theta} = \frac{u_r}{u_\theta} = \frac{r\cos(\frac{1}{2}\theta)}{r\sin(\frac{1}{2}\theta)}.$$

Integrating with respect to $\theta$, we obtain

$$\ln r = 2\ln\left|\sin\tfrac{1}{2}\theta\right| + C \qquad (\theta \neq 0),$$

where $C$ is an arbitrary constant. Taking exponentials of both sides gives

$$r = A\sin^2\left(\tfrac{1}{2}\theta\right), \quad \text{where } A = e^C.$$

(These streamlines, shown in the following figure, are heart-shaped curves known as *cardioids*. Note that $\theta = 0$, the positive $x$-axis, which was excluded above, is also a streamline.)

# Section 2

## Solution 2.1

From Equations (2.1), we have

$$u_1 = ay = \frac{\partial\psi}{\partial y}, \qquad u_2 = 0 = -\frac{\partial\psi}{\partial x}.$$

Integrating the first equation with respect to $y$ gives

$$\psi(x, y) = \tfrac{1}{2}ay^2 + f(x),$$

where $f$ is an arbitrary function. Hence

$$\frac{\partial\psi}{\partial x} = f'(x) = 0,$$

so $f(x) = C$, where $C$ is a constant, giving

$$\psi(x, y) = \tfrac{1}{2}ay^2 + C.$$

The figure below shows the contour lines $\psi = $ constant, which are the lines $y = $ constant. (Since $a > 0$, the flow is from left to right for $y > 0$ and from right to left for $y < 0$. There is no flow along $y = 0$.)

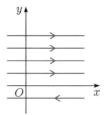

## Solution 2.2

**(a)** From Equations (2.2), we have

$$u_r = 0 = \frac{1}{r}\frac{\partial\psi}{\partial\theta}, \qquad u_\theta = \frac{k}{r} = -\frac{\partial\psi}{\partial r}.$$

Integrating the second equation with respect to $r$ gives

$$\psi(r, \theta) = -k\ln r + f(\theta),$$

where $f$ is an arbitrary function. Hence

$$\frac{\partial\psi}{\partial\theta} = f'(\theta) = 0,$$

so $f(\theta) = C$, where $C$ is a constant, giving

$$\psi(r, \theta) = -k\ln r + C.$$

**(b)** From Equations (2.2), we have

$$u_r = \frac{m}{r} = \frac{1}{r}\frac{\partial\psi}{\partial\theta}, \qquad u_\theta = 0 = -\frac{\partial\psi}{\partial r}.$$

Integrating the first equation with respect to $\theta$ gives

$$\psi(r,\theta) = m\theta + f(r),$$

where $f$ is an arbitrary function. Hence

$$\frac{\partial \psi}{\partial r} = f'(r) = 0,$$

so $f(r) = C$, where $C$ is a constant, giving

$$\psi(r,\theta) = m\theta + C.$$

## Solution 2.3

**(a)** From Equations (2.2), we have

$$u_r = 0 = \frac{1}{r}\frac{\partial \psi}{\partial \theta}, \qquad u_\theta = Kr = -\frac{\partial \psi}{\partial r}.$$

Integrating the second equation with respect to $r$ gives

$$\psi(r,\theta) = -\tfrac{1}{2}Kr^2 + f(\theta),$$

where $f$ is an arbitrary function. Hence

$$\frac{\partial \psi}{\partial \theta} = f'(\theta) = 0,$$

so $f(\theta) = C$, where $C$ is a constant, giving

$$\psi(r,\theta) = -\tfrac{1}{2}Kr^2 + C.$$

**(b)** From Equations (2.1), we have

$$u_1 = y = \frac{\partial \psi}{\partial y}, \qquad u_2 = -(x - 2t) = -\frac{\partial \psi}{\partial x}.$$

Integrating the second equation with respect to $x$ gives

$$\psi(x,y) = \tfrac{1}{2}x^2 - 2tx + f(y),$$

where $f$ is an arbitrary function. (Note that $t$ is kept fixed throughout; hence we write $f(y)$ rather than $f(y,t)$ here.) Now

$$\frac{\partial \psi}{\partial y} = f'(y) = y,$$

so that $f(y) = \tfrac{1}{2}y^2 + C$, where $C$ is a constant. Thus

$$\psi(x,y) = \tfrac{1}{2}(x^2 + y^2) - 2tx + C \qquad \text{(with } t \text{ constant)}.$$

If $t = 0$, then $\psi(x,y) = \tfrac{1}{2}(x^2 + y^2) + C$, and the streamlines $\psi = \text{constant}$ are circles with centre at the origin. Since $u_1 = y$ (or since $u_2 = -x$), the flow is in the clockwise direction.

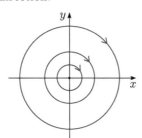

If $t = 1$, then $\psi(x,y) = \tfrac{1}{2}(x^2 + y^2) - 2x + C$, and the streamlines are circles with centre $(2,0)$. Again, the flow is clockwise.

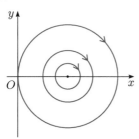

## Solution 2.4

Let $P$ and $Q$ be two points on a streamline, and let $PQ$ be the segment of the streamline between $P$ and $Q$. Then $\psi(P) = \psi(Q)$, since $\psi$ is constant along a streamline. Therefore $V$, the volume flow rate across $PQ$, is given by

$$V = \int_P^Q \frac{d\psi}{ds}\, ds = \psi(Q) - \psi(P) = 0.$$

## Solution 2.5

**(a)** The unit vector normal to the surface is $\mathbf{n} = \mathbf{e}_r$. Hence the normal boundary condition is

$$\mathbf{u}\cdot\mathbf{n} = u_r = 0 \qquad \text{on } r = a.$$

**(b)** In addition to the normal boundary condition from part (a), the tangential component of $\mathbf{u}$ must be zero on the cylinder; that is,

$$\mathbf{u}\cdot\mathbf{e}_\theta = u_\theta = 0 \qquad \text{on } r = a.$$

## Solution 2.6

When $\psi = 0$, the streamline is $xy = 0$, which describes the $x$- and $y$-axes. If $\psi = 2$, then $y = 1/x$; if $\psi = 4$, then $y = 2/x$; if $\psi = 10$, then $y = 5/x$. These streamlines are shown below.

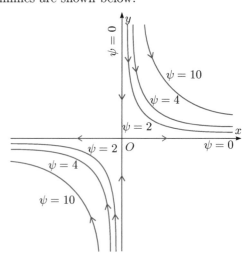

The velocity vector field is

$$\mathbf{u} = \frac{\partial \psi}{\partial y}\mathbf{i} - \frac{\partial \psi}{\partial x}\mathbf{j} = 2x\,\mathbf{i} - 2y\,\mathbf{j},$$

which gives the directions of flow, as shown.

One possible flow would be past a right-angled corner in the first quadrant, which is modelled by choosing as boundaries the streamlines

$$x = 0,\; y \geq 0 \qquad \text{and} \qquad y = 0,\; x \geq 0.$$

## Solution 2.7

**(a)** From Equations (2.1), we have

$$u_1 = -2y = \frac{\partial \psi}{\partial y}, \qquad u_2 = -2x = -\frac{\partial \psi}{\partial x}.$$

Integrating the second equation with respect to $x$ gives

$$\psi(x,y) = x^2 + f(y),$$

where $f$ is an arbitrary function. Hence

$$\frac{\partial \psi}{\partial y} = f'(y) = -2y,$$

so that
$$f(y) = -y^2 + C, \qquad \text{where } C \text{ is a constant.}$$
Thus
$$\psi(x, y) = x^2 - y^2 \qquad (\text{taking } C = 0).$$

**(b)** When $\psi = 0$, the streamline is $x^2 - y^2 = 0$, which describes the pair of straight lines $x = y$, $x = -y$. If $\psi = 2$, then $x^2 - y^2 = 2$; if $\psi = 4$, then $x^2 - y^2 = 4$; if $\psi = 10$, then $x^2 - y^2 = 10$. These are hyperbolas, as shown below.

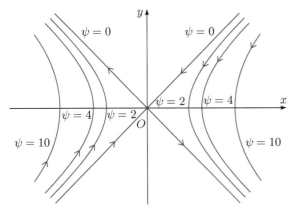

**(c)** One possible flow would be in the region for which $x > |y|$, with boundary $x = y$ and $x = -y$ $(x > 0)$.

# Section 3

## Solution 3.1

The continuity equation here is $\nabla \cdot \mathbf{u} = 0$. Now $\mathbf{u}_1$ and $\mathbf{u}_2$ must each satisfy this equation, so
$$\nabla \cdot \mathbf{u}_1 = 0 \qquad \text{and} \qquad \nabla \cdot \mathbf{u}_2 = 0.$$
Hence,
$$\nabla \cdot (\mathbf{u}_1 + \mathbf{u}_2) = \nabla \cdot \mathbf{u}_1 + \nabla \cdot \mathbf{u}_2 = 0,$$
showing that $\mathbf{u}_1 + \mathbf{u}_2$ satisfies the continuity equation.

## Solution 3.2

The method required is very similar to that of Example 3.1. By the Principle of Superposition, the overall flow, due to the combination of two sources, has stream function
$$\psi = m(\theta_1 + \theta_2),$$
where $\theta_1$, $\theta_2$ are defined in Example 3.1. As before,
$$\tan \theta_1 = \frac{y}{x - a}, \qquad \tan \theta_2 = \frac{y}{x + a},$$
so that
$$\tan(\theta_1 + \theta_2) = \frac{\tan \theta_1 + \tan \theta_2}{1 - \tan \theta_1 \tan \theta_2}$$
$$= \frac{y/(x - a) + y/(x + a)}{1 - y^2/(x^2 - a^2)} = \frac{2xy}{x^2 - y^2 - a^2}.$$
The stream function of the combined flow is therefore
$$\psi(x, y) = m \arctan \left( \frac{2xy}{x^2 - y^2 - a^2} \right).$$
The equation for streamlines is $\psi = \text{constant}$, that is,
$$\frac{2xy}{x^2 - y^2 - a^2} = \text{constant} \quad \text{or} \quad x^2 - y^2 - a^2 = 2Cxy,$$

where $C$ is constant. The two axes, $x = 0$ and $y = 0$, are also streamlines.

(Apart from the two axes, these streamlines are rectangular hyperbolas ('rectangular' meaning that the two asymptotes are at right angles) passing through $(\pm a, 0)$. The angle of these asymptotes depends on the choice of $C$. Some streamlines are sketched below.)

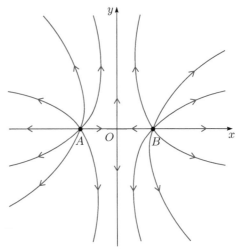

## Solution 3.3

The stream function for the doublet is
$$\psi(r, \theta) = -\frac{\lambda \sin \theta}{r}.$$
From Equations (2.2), the corresponding velocity components are
$$u_r = \frac{1}{r} \frac{\partial \psi}{\partial \theta} = -\frac{\lambda \cos \theta}{r^2}, \qquad u_\theta = -\frac{\partial \psi}{\partial r} = -\frac{\lambda \sin \theta}{r^2}.$$
Hence the velocity field is given by
$$\mathbf{u} = -\frac{\lambda}{r^2} (\cos \theta \, \mathbf{e}_r + \sin \theta \, \mathbf{e}_\theta).$$
(The speed of the flow is $|\mathbf{u}| = \lambda/r^2$.)

## Solution 3.4

The stream function for the combination of a doublet of vector strength $-2\pi\lambda \, \mathbf{i}$ and uniform flow $U \, \mathbf{i}$ is
$$\psi(r, \theta) = Ur \sin \theta - \frac{\lambda \sin \theta}{r}.$$
From Equations (2.2), the velocity $\mathbf{u} = u_r \, \mathbf{e}_r + u_\theta \, \mathbf{e}_\theta$ is given by
$$u_r = \frac{1}{r} \frac{\partial \psi}{\partial \theta} = U \cos \theta - \frac{\lambda \cos \theta}{r^2}, \tag{S.1}$$
$$u_\theta = -\frac{\partial \psi}{\partial r} = -U \sin \theta - \frac{\lambda \sin \theta}{r^2}. \tag{S.2}$$
At a stagnation point, $u_r = u_\theta = 0$, so from Equation (S.1), $\theta = \pm\pi/2$ or $r = \sqrt{\lambda/U}$; and from Equation (S.2), $\theta = 0$ or $\pi$, or $r = \sqrt{-\lambda/U}$ (which is not a real number and therefore is not an admissible value for $r$). Hence the stagnation points have polar coordinates $r = \sqrt{\lambda/U}$, $\theta = 0$ and $r = \sqrt{\lambda/U}$, $\theta = \pi$. These both lie on the circle $r = \sqrt{\lambda/U}$ (at the points where the circle crosses the $x$-axis).

The streamline
$$\psi(r, \theta) = Ur \sin \theta - \frac{\lambda \sin \theta}{r} = 0$$
is composed of two parts:
$$\theta = 0 \text{ and } \theta = \pi, \qquad \text{which make up the } x\text{-axis,}$$

and
$$r = \sqrt{\lambda/U},$$
which is the circle on which the stagnation points lie.

## Solution 3.5

The streamline pattern is below.

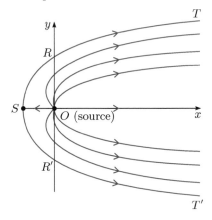

A particle emerging into the region $x < 0$ will be turned back by the uniform stream, and will remain within the boundary $TRSR'T'$. (Alternatively, we may regard the particle as being turned back owing to the presence of the boundary.) Particles emerging into the region $x > 0$ will be swept along by the uniform stream.

## Solution 3.6

A sink or a doublet (with vector strength $-2\pi\lambda\,\mathbf{i}$), placed on the positive $x$-axis, will have this effect.

## Solution 3.7

The stream function is $\psi(r,\theta) = Ur\sin\theta - \lambda\sin\theta/r$. From Solution 3.4, part of the streamline $\psi = 0$ is the circle $r = \sqrt{\lambda/U}$, so we can take this circle as a boundary. A particle from upstream with $y > 0$ will be deflected upwards by the doublet as it approaches the circle $r = \sqrt{\lambda/U}$, and then will be drawn back to the line of its original path again by the doublet. (Thinking of the doublet as a source and sink combination aids intuition here.) Since the flow is symmetric about the $x$-axis, the resulting pattern is as shown below. (Here $S_1$ and $S_2$ are the two stagnation points of the flow, as found in Solution 3.4.)

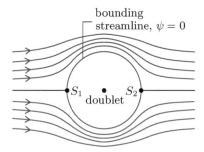

bounding streamline, $\psi = 0$

## Solution 3.8

(a) Let $\theta_1$, $\theta_2$, $\theta_3$ and $\theta_4$ be defined as in the figure below.

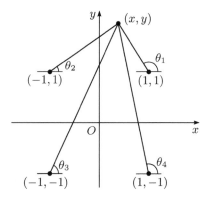

The stream function is then
$$\psi = m(\theta_1 + \theta_2 + \theta_3 + \theta_4)$$
$$= m\left( \arctan\left(\frac{y-1}{x-1}\right) + \arctan\left(\frac{y-1}{x+1}\right) \right.$$
$$\left. + \arctan\left(\frac{y+1}{x+1}\right) + \arctan\left(\frac{y+1}{x-1}\right) \right).$$

(b) Noting that (from a standard derivative and the Composite Rule)
$$\frac{\partial}{\partial x}\left( \arctan\left(\frac{y}{x}\right) \right) = \frac{1}{1+(y/x)^2} \frac{\partial}{\partial x}\left(\frac{y}{x}\right)$$
$$= \frac{1}{1+(y/x)^2}\left(\frac{-y}{x^2}\right) = -\frac{y}{x^2+y^2}$$
and
$$\frac{\partial}{\partial y}\left( \arctan\left(\frac{y}{x}\right) \right) = \frac{1}{1+(y/x)^2} \frac{\partial}{\partial y}\left(\frac{y}{x}\right)$$
$$= \frac{1}{1+(y/x)^2}\left(\frac{1}{x}\right) = \frac{x}{x^2+y^2},$$
the partial derivatives of $\psi$ are
$$\frac{\partial\psi}{\partial x} = m\left( \frac{-(y-1)}{(x-1)^2+(y-1)^2} - \frac{y-1}{(x+1)^2+(y-1)^2} \right.$$
$$\left. - \frac{y+1}{(x+1)^2+(y+1)^2} - \frac{y+1}{(x-1)^2+(y+1)^2} \right),$$
$$\frac{\partial\psi}{\partial y} = m\left( \frac{x-1}{(x-1)^2+(y-1)^2} + \frac{x+1}{(x+1)^2+(y-1)^2} \right.$$
$$\left. + \frac{x+1}{(x+1)^2+(y+1)^2} + \frac{x-1}{(x-1)^2+(y+1)^2} \right)$$
If $x = y = 0$, then
$$u_1 = \frac{\partial\psi}{\partial y} = 0 \qquad \text{and} \qquad u_2 = -\frac{\partial\psi}{\partial x} = 0,$$
so the origin is a stagnation point.

(c) If $x = 0$, then
$$\psi = m\left( \arctan\left(-(y-1)\right) + \arctan(y-1) \right.$$
$$\left. + \arctan(y+1) + \arctan\left(-(y+1)\right) \right) = 0,$$
since $\tan(-\theta) = -\tan\theta$. Thus $\psi = 0$ for all $y$. Similarly, if $y = 0$, then $\psi = 0$ for all $x$. Hence the $x$- and $y$-axes are parts of the streamline $\psi = 0$ (in fact, there are no other parts).

(d) The streamline pattern is as follows.

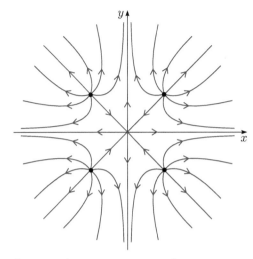

Since the $x$- and $y$-axes are streamlines, we can take the non-negative $x$- and $y$-axes as boundaries. The streamlines in the region $x > 0$, $y > 0$ then model the flow due to a source in a corner.

# Section 4

## Solution 4.1

(a) The flow (if not turbulent) can be taken as steady. In the inner region of the pipe (away from the wall) the flow is more or less uniform: type A. Close to the wall, the velocity varies with distance from the wall: type B.

(b) The drops from the tap do not form a continuum, so overall none of the classifications is relevant, but each drop can be considered to be a flow of type D.

(c) The fluid will accelerate down the inclined channel, and so the flow is steady but non-uniform: type B.

(d) Ignoring wind gusts and sideways movement of the hurricane, the flow could be modelled as steady but non-uniform: type B. If sideways movement is included, then type D is appropriate.

(e) A rotary fan produces almost steady flow, and it can be modelled as such: type B.

## Solution 4.2

(a) The rate of temperature change for a fixed thermometer is the local rate of change of temperature, which is
$$\frac{\partial \Theta}{\partial t} = -0.25\sin(0.1t)\,e^{-0.01x}(1 - 0.02y^2)(1 - 0.04z).$$
Evaluated at the point $(5, 0.2, 0.1)$, this gives
$$\frac{\partial \Theta}{\partial t} \simeq -0.24\sin(0.1t).$$

(b) In this case $\mathbf{v} = 2\mathbf{j}$, and so, from Equation (4.2), $dx/dt = 0$, $dy/dt = 2$, and $dz/dt = 0$. Hence Equation (4.3) gives
$$\frac{d\Theta}{dt} = 2\frac{\partial \Theta}{\partial y} + \frac{\partial \Theta}{\partial t}.$$

The expression for $\partial \Theta/\partial t$ is as in part (a). Also
$$\frac{\partial \Theta}{\partial y} = 50(1 + 0.05\cos(0.1t))\,e^{-0.01x}(-0.04y)(1 - 0.04z).$$
Evaluated at the point $(5, 0.2, 0.1)$, we have
$$\frac{d\Theta}{dt} \simeq -0.24\sin(0.1t) - 0.76(1 + 0.05\cos(0.1t)).$$
This thermometer reaches $(5, 0.2, 0.1)$ at time $t = 0.1$, for which $d\Theta/dt \simeq -0.80$. (At this time, the fixed thermometer gives $\partial \Theta/\partial t \simeq -0.0024$.)

## Solution 4.3

(a) The total derivative is
$$\begin{aligned}\frac{d\rho}{dt} &= \frac{\partial \rho}{\partial t} + u_1\frac{\partial \rho}{\partial x}\\ &= x^2 - \sin t + \frac{dx}{dt}(2xt).\end{aligned}$$
Putting $x = t^2$, this becomes
$$\frac{d\rho}{dt} = t^4 - \sin t + 2t\,(2t^2 \times t) = 5t^4 - \sin t.$$

(b) Putting $x = t^2$ gives
$$\rho = (t^2)^2 t + \cos t = t^5 + \cos t.$$
The (ordinary) derivative of this is
$$\frac{d\rho}{dt} = 5t^4 - \sin t,$$
which, as expected, is the same as in part (a).

## Solution 4.4

(a) Since $\partial f/\partial t = 0$, $\partial f/\partial x = 0$ and $u_2 = u_3 = 0$, Equation (4.4) becomes
$$\frac{df}{dt} = 0.$$

(b) For steady flow, the time partial derivative $\partial f/\partial t$ is zero. Hence Equation (4.4) becomes
$$\frac{df}{dt} = (\mathbf{u} \cdot \boldsymbol{\nabla})f = u_1\frac{\partial f}{\partial x} + u_2\frac{\partial f}{\partial y} + u_3\frac{\partial f}{\partial z}.$$

## Solution 4.5

(a) The graph of $u_1$ against $x$ is shown in the figure that follows. (From a speed of approximately $U$ at $x = -5$, the river speeds up to $2U$ at $x = 0$, and then slows down almost to $U$ at $x = 5$.)

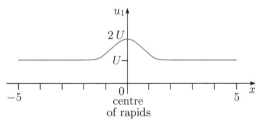

The local (time) rate of change of $\mathbf{u}$ is
$$\frac{\partial \mathbf{u}}{\partial t} = \frac{\partial u_1}{\partial t}\mathbf{i} = \mathbf{0}$$
everywhere, since $u_1$ depends on $x$ only.

The total rate of change of $\mathbf{u}$ is

$$\frac{d\mathbf{u}}{dt} = \frac{du_1}{dt}\mathbf{i} = \left(\frac{\partial u_1}{\partial t} + (\mathbf{u}\cdot\boldsymbol{\nabla})u_1\right)\mathbf{i}$$

$$= \left(0 + u_1\frac{\partial}{\partial x}(u_1)\right)\mathbf{i}$$

$$= U\left(1 + e^{-x^2}\right)U\left(-2xe^{-x^2}\right)\mathbf{i}$$

$$= -2U^2x\,e^{-x^2}\left(1 + e^{-x^2}\right)\mathbf{i}.$$

(So $du_1/dt$ is an odd function, being positive when $x$ is negative, and vice versa.)

The values of $du_1/dt$ are as follows.

| $x$ | $-1$ | $-0.5$ | $-0.25$ | 0 | 0.25 | 0.5 | 1 |
|---|---|---|---|---|---|---|---|
| $du_1/dt$ $(\div U^2)$ | 1.006 | 1.385 | 0.911 | 0 | $-0.911$ | $-1.385$ | $-1.006$ |

**(b) (i)** A stationary observer on the bank, watching a trail of sticks pass through the centre of the rapids, would note that each stick had the same velocity at the point $x = 0$ (i.e. $\partial u_1/\partial t = 0$), and so there is no local acceleration of water at that point of the river.

**(ii)** The observer on the bank would see the stick accelerate into the rapids (as shown by the table in part (a), the maximum speed being attained when $x = 0$, at which point $du_1/dt = 0$), and decelerate out.

## Solution 4.6

Using Equation (4.5), the total derivative is

$$\frac{d\mathbf{u}}{dt} = \frac{\partial\mathbf{u}}{\partial t} + (\mathbf{u}\cdot\boldsymbol{\nabla})\,\mathbf{u}.$$

Since $\partial\mathbf{e}_\theta/\partial t = 0$, we have

$$\frac{\partial\mathbf{u}}{\partial t} = \frac{\partial}{\partial t}\left(\frac{K(t)}{r}\right)\mathbf{e}_\theta = \frac{1}{r}\frac{dK(t)}{dt}\mathbf{e}_\theta = \frac{K'(t)}{r}\mathbf{e}_\theta.$$

Also, from Equation (4.6), $(\mathbf{u}\cdot\boldsymbol{\nabla})\mathbf{u}$ is equal to

$$\left(\frac{K(t)}{r}\mathbf{e}_\theta\cdot\left(\mathbf{e}_r\frac{\partial}{\partial r} + \mathbf{e}_\theta\frac{1}{r}\frac{\partial}{\partial\theta} + \mathbf{e}_z\frac{\partial}{\partial z}\right)\right)\left(\frac{K(t)}{r}\mathbf{e}_\theta\right)$$

$$= \frac{K(t)}{r^2}\frac{\partial}{\partial\theta}\left(\frac{K(t)}{r}\mathbf{e}_\theta\right)$$

$$= -\frac{(K(t))^2}{r^3}\mathbf{e}_r, \qquad \text{since } \frac{\partial\mathbf{e}_\theta}{\partial\theta} = -\mathbf{e}_r.$$

Hence we obtain

$$\frac{d\mathbf{u}}{dt} = \frac{K'(t)}{r}\mathbf{e}_\theta - \frac{(K(t))^2}{r^3}\mathbf{e}_r.$$

(Note that, although the velocity $\mathbf{u}$ has only one non-zero component, the acceleration has both a radial and a transverse component.)

## Solution 4.7

In each case, we check whether $\boldsymbol{\nabla}\cdot\mathbf{u}$ is zero.

**(a)** $\boldsymbol{\nabla}\cdot\mathbf{u} = \dfrac{\partial}{\partial x}(x) + \dfrac{\partial}{\partial y}(y) + \dfrac{\partial}{\partial z}(-2z) = 0,$

so this could be an incompressible flow.

**(b)** $\boldsymbol{\nabla}\cdot\mathbf{u} = \dfrac{\partial}{\partial x}(x) + \dfrac{\partial}{\partial y}(2y) + \dfrac{\partial}{\partial z}(0) = 3,$

so this cannot be an incompressible flow.

**(c)** $\boldsymbol{\nabla}\cdot\mathbf{u} = \dfrac{1}{r}\dfrac{\partial}{\partial r}(ru_r) + \dfrac{1}{r}\dfrac{\partial}{\partial\theta}(u_\theta) + \dfrac{\partial}{\partial z}(u_z)$

$$= \frac{1}{r}\frac{\partial}{\partial\theta}\left(\frac{K}{r^2}\right) = 0, \qquad \text{since } \mathbf{u} = \frac{K}{r^2}\mathbf{e}_\theta,$$

so this could be an incompressible flow.

## Solution 4.8

Using Equation (4.8), we have

$$0.3 \times 1.8 = 0.15 \times u,$$

where $u$ is the speed at the smaller section. Hence $u = 3.6\,\mathrm{m\,s^{-1}}$.

(This calculation confirms intuition: a contraction leads to a higher speed. *Unit 6* will show that it also implies a *lower* pressure.)

## Solution 4.9

**(a)** Equation (4.8), $u_1A_1 = u_2A_2$, becomes

$$u(x_1)(l_1 \times 1) = u(x_2)(l_2 \times 1), \qquad \text{or}$$

$$l_1u(x_1) = l_2u(x_2).$$

(This means that the speed is greater when the streamlines are closer.)

**(b)** Model the air/water boundary and the river bed by streamlines, and assume that the speed of flow at any vertical section is independent of the depth of the river. Then, from part (a), we have

$$4 \times 2.25 = 3 \times u, \qquad \text{so} \qquad u = \tfrac{9}{3} = 3\,\mathrm{m\,s^{-1}}.$$

## Solution 4.10

**(a)** Steady, uniform

**(b)** Steady, non-uniform

**(c)** Non-steady, non-uniform

**(d)** Steady, non-uniform

**(e)** Non-steady, uniform

## Solution 4.11

In each case, the acceleration following the motion is given by

$$\frac{d\mathbf{u}}{dt} = \frac{\partial\mathbf{u}}{\partial t} + (\mathbf{u}\cdot\boldsymbol{\nabla})\,\mathbf{u}.$$

**(a)** If $\mathbf{u} = Uy\,\mathbf{i}$, then

$$\frac{d\mathbf{u}}{dt} = (Uy\,\mathbf{i}\cdot\boldsymbol{\nabla})(Uy\,\mathbf{i}) = Uy\frac{\partial}{\partial x}(Uy)\,\mathbf{i} = \mathbf{0}.$$

**(b)** If $\mathbf{u} = U(t)y\,\mathbf{i}$, then

$$\frac{d\mathbf{u}}{dt} = \frac{\partial}{\partial t}(U(t)y\,\mathbf{i}) + (U(t)y\,\mathbf{i}\cdot\boldsymbol{\nabla})(U(t)y\,\mathbf{i})$$

$$= U'(t)y\,\mathbf{i} + U(t)y\frac{\partial}{\partial x}(U(t)y)\,\mathbf{i}$$

$$= U'(t)y\,\mathbf{i}.$$

**(c)** If $\mathbf{u} = U(1 + a^2/r^2)\sin\theta\,\mathbf{e}_\theta = u_\theta\,\mathbf{e}_\theta$ then, from Equation (4.6), we have

$$\frac{d\mathbf{u}}{dt} = \left(\frac{u_\theta}{r}\frac{\partial}{\partial\theta}\right)(u_\theta\,\mathbf{e}_\theta)$$

$$= U\left(1 + \frac{a^2}{r^2}\right)\frac{\sin\theta}{r}\,U\left(1 + \frac{a^2}{r^2}\right)\left(\cos\theta\,\mathbf{e}_\theta + \sin\theta\,\frac{\partial\mathbf{e}_\theta}{\partial\theta}\right)$$

$$= U^2\left(1 + \frac{a^2}{r^2}\right)^2\frac{\sin\theta}{r}\,(\cos\theta\,\mathbf{e}_\theta - \sin\theta\,\mathbf{e}_r)\,.$$

## Solution 4.12

If $\boldsymbol{\nabla}\cdot\mathbf{u} = 0$ then the flow is incompressible.

**(a)** Here we have

$$\boldsymbol{\nabla}\cdot\mathbf{u} = \frac{\partial}{\partial x}(U\cos\alpha) + \frac{\partial}{\partial y}(U\sin\alpha)$$

$$= 0, \qquad \text{since } U \text{ and } \alpha \text{ are constants.}$$

This is a possible incompressible flow.

**(b)** Here we have

$$\boldsymbol{\nabla}\cdot\mathbf{u} = \frac{\partial}{\partial x}\left(-\frac{Ky}{x^2+y^2}\right) + \frac{\partial}{\partial y}\left(\frac{Kx}{x^2+y^2}\right) + \frac{\partial}{\partial z}(2xy)$$

$$= -\frac{-Ky(2x)}{(x^2+y^2)^2} + \frac{-Kx(2y)}{(x^2+y^2)^2} + 0 = 0.$$

This is a possible incompressible flow.

**(c)** Here we have

$$\boldsymbol{\nabla}\cdot\mathbf{u} = \frac{1}{r}\frac{\partial}{\partial r}(ru_r) + \frac{1}{r}\frac{\partial}{\partial\theta}(u_\theta)$$

$$= \frac{1}{r}\frac{\partial}{\partial r}\left(rU\cos\theta\left(1 - \frac{a^2}{r^2}\right)\right)$$

$$+ \frac{1}{r}\frac{\partial}{\partial\theta}\left(-U\sin\theta\left(1 + \frac{a^2}{r^2}\right)\right)$$

$$= \frac{1}{r}\left(U\cos\theta + U\cos\theta\,\frac{a^2}{r^2}\right)$$

$$+ \frac{1}{r}(-U\cos\theta)\left(1 + \frac{a^2}{r^2}\right) = 0.$$

This is a possible incompressible flow.

**(d)** Here we have

$$\boldsymbol{\nabla}\cdot\mathbf{u} = \frac{1}{r}\frac{\partial}{\partial\theta}\left(\frac{K}{r}\right) = 0 \qquad (r\neq 0).$$

This is a possible incompressible flow.

## Solution 4.13

By symmetry (since the flow is horizontal) the speeds at each section 2 will be the same, $u_2$ say. By the continuity equation (4.8), we have

$$u_1 A_1 = 2(u_2 A_2) \qquad \text{so} \qquad u_2 = \frac{u_1 A_1}{2A_2}.$$

But $A_1 = \pi a^2$, $A_2 = \frac{1}{4}\pi a^2$; hence $A_1/A_2 = 4$, and

$$u_2 = 2u_1.$$

# Section 5

## Solution 5.1

In this case, $\mathbf{u} = \mathbf{0}$ and $\mathbf{F} = -g\,\mathbf{k}$, so that Euler's equation (5.5), $\rho\,d\mathbf{u}/dt = -\boldsymbol{\nabla}p + \rho\mathbf{F}$, becomes

$$\mathbf{0} = -\boldsymbol{\nabla}p - \rho g\,\mathbf{k}.$$

Therefore

$$\frac{\partial p}{\partial x} = 0, \qquad \frac{\partial p}{\partial y} = 0, \qquad \frac{\partial p}{\partial z} = -\rho g.$$

From the first two equations, $p = p(z)$ and so $\partial p/\partial z = dp/dz$, giving the required result.

## Solution 5.2

Euler's equation (5.6) is

$$\rho\frac{\partial\mathbf{u}}{\partial t} + \rho\,(\mathbf{u}\cdot\boldsymbol{\nabla})\,\mathbf{u} = -\boldsymbol{\nabla}p + \rho\mathbf{F}.$$

Using the hint, we have

$$\rho\frac{\partial\mathbf{u}}{\partial t} + \rho\boldsymbol{\nabla}(\tfrac{1}{2}u^2) - \rho\mathbf{u}\times(\boldsymbol{\nabla}\times\mathbf{u})$$

$$= -\boldsymbol{\nabla}p + \rho\mathbf{F}. \qquad\qquad\text{(S.3)}$$

Steady flow implies $\partial\mathbf{u}/\partial t = \mathbf{0}$.

Irrotational flow implies $\boldsymbol{\nabla}\times\mathbf{u} = \mathbf{0}$.

Conservative force field implies the existence of a scalar field $\Omega$ for which $\mathbf{F} = \boldsymbol{\nabla}\Omega$.

Constant density implies $\rho = \rho_0$.

Thus Equation (S.3) becomes

$$\rho_0\boldsymbol{\nabla}(\tfrac{1}{2}u^2) = -\boldsymbol{\nabla}p + \rho_0\boldsymbol{\nabla}\Omega,$$

which may be written as

$$\boldsymbol{\nabla}\left(\tfrac{1}{2}u^2 + \frac{p}{\rho_0} - \Omega\right) = \mathbf{0}.$$

## Solution 5.3

The given stream function is

$$\psi = m\left(\arctan\left(\frac{y-b}{x}\right) + \arctan\left(\frac{y+b}{x}\right)\right).$$

The velocity at the wall $y = 0$ must have $y$-component zero, so $\mathbf{u}(x,0) = u_1(x,0)\,\mathbf{i}$. Now by Equations (2.1),

$$u_1 = \frac{\partial\psi}{\partial y} = m\left(\frac{x}{x^2+(y-b)^2} + \frac{x}{x^2+(y+b)^2}\right),$$

so that

$$u_1(x,0) = \frac{2mx}{x^2+b^2}.$$

Since the flow is steady and irrotational with $\mathbf{F} = \mathbf{0}$, we have, from Solution 5.2,

$$\boldsymbol{\nabla}\left(\tfrac{1}{2}u^2 + \frac{p}{\rho}\right) = \mathbf{0}.$$

Integrating along the boundary wall (a streamline),

$$\tfrac{1}{2}u_1^2 + \frac{p}{\rho} = \text{constant} \qquad \text{on } y = 0.$$

When $x = \pm\infty$, we have $p = p_0$ and $u_1 = 0$; hence

$$\tfrac{1}{2}\rho u_1^2 + p = p_0 \qquad \text{on } y = 0.$$

Thus the pressure distribution on the wall is

$$p(x,0) = p_0 - \tfrac{1}{2}\rho u_1^2(x,0) = p_0 - \frac{2\rho m^2 x^2}{(x^2+b^2)^2}.$$

## Solution 5.4

Equation (5.6) gives

$$\rho \frac{\partial \mathbf{u}}{\partial t} + \rho (\mathbf{u} \cdot \nabla) \mathbf{u} = -\nabla p + \rho \mathbf{F}.$$

Now $\mathbf{F} = 5\,\mathbf{j} = \partial \mathbf{u}/\partial t$, and so

$$\nabla p = \rho \left( \mathbf{F} - \frac{\partial \mathbf{u}}{\partial t} - (\mathbf{u} \cdot \nabla)\mathbf{u} \right)$$

$$= -\rho \left( -2x \frac{\partial}{\partial x} + (2y + 5t) \frac{\partial}{\partial y} \right)(-2x\,\mathbf{i} + (2y + 5t)\,\mathbf{j})$$

$$= -\rho \left( 4x\,\mathbf{i} + 2(2y + 5t)\,\mathbf{j} \right).$$

In terms of components, we have

$$\frac{\partial p}{\partial x} = -4\rho x, \qquad \frac{\partial p}{\partial y} = -2\rho (2y + 5t).$$

Integrating the first equation gives

$$p(x, y, t) = -2\rho x^2 + f(y, t),$$

where $f$ is an arbitrary function of two variables.
Hence

$$\frac{\partial p}{\partial y} = \frac{\partial f}{\partial y} = -2\rho (2y + 5t),$$

from which

$$f(y, t) = -2\rho y (y + 5t) + g(t),$$

where $g$ is an arbitrary function. Therefore

$$p(x, y, t) = -2\rho x^2 - 2\rho y (y + 5t) + g(t).$$

# UNIT 6   *Bernoulli's equation*

## Study guide

This unit explains how an integral form of Euler's equation (from *Unit 5* Subsection 5.1) can be used to predict the behaviour of some fluid flows. There are many references back to *Unit 5*, and some also to *Unit 4*.

The unit is shorter than most other units in the course. In part this is to leave adequate study time for non-textual activities, as described in the *Media Guide*. However, note that *Units 7* and *8* will both require study times closer to the average.

There is no audio activity associated with this unit.

## Introduction

This unit is about a general integral of Euler's equation called *Bernoulli's equation*, which provides a simple relationship between the pressure, speed and body forces in the flow of an inviscid, constant-density fluid.

Section 1 derives different forms of Bernoulli's equation, depending on whether the flow considered is steady or unsteady, rotational or irrotational. The solving of some simple problems shows how use of the continuity equation and Bernoulli's equation can provide a method of solution for flow problems.

Section 2 investigates three applications of Bernoulli's equation.

Section 3 deals with flows in open channels. These can be used as models for flows in rivers, canals, irrigation ditches, and so on.

# 1 Bernoulli's equation

Euler's equation, which describes the flow of an inviscid fluid, was formulated in *Unit 5*. The inviscid assumption is less restrictive than it may seem. Many fluids have low coefficients of viscosity, and for flows of such fluids, viscous forces are significant only very close to solid boundaries. *Unit 5* stated that Euler's equation could be thought of as an equation for the pressure distribution, once the velocity field is known. Given a velocity vector field **u**, Euler's equation provides an expression for **grad** $p$, where $p$ is the pressure. In principle, this can be integrated to give a formula for $p$. However, it is laborious to have to go through these steps for every problem, and this section derives more general integrals of Euler's equation that relate pressure, speed (effectively kinetic energy) and potential energy. The form of the resulting equation depends on the initial assumptions that are made, and each equation is a special form of a general result called *Bernoulli's equation*.

## 1.1 Bernoulli's equation for steady flows

We start with Euler's equation, in the form

$$\frac{\partial \mathbf{u}}{\partial t} + \boldsymbol{\nabla}\left(\tfrac{1}{2}u^2\right) - \mathbf{u} \times (\boldsymbol{\nabla} \times \mathbf{u}) = \mathbf{F} - \frac{1}{\rho}\boldsymbol{\nabla}p, \qquad (1.1)$$

See Equation (5.7) and the identity in Exercise 5.2 of *Unit 5*. Note that $u = |\mathbf{u}|$.

in which the velocity **u** and pressure $p$ are, in general, not constant and can vary with position and time, as can the density, $\rho$, and the body force per unit mass, **F**. This equation applies to the flow of both compressible and incompressible fluids, but its formulation ignores the effects of viscosity.

As it stands, Equation (1.1) is awkward to apply, because it is very general, but by investigating a restricted class of fluid flows it is possible to derive an equation that is easier to use. What has to be done is to strike a balance between imposing too many simplifying assumptions, which will result in very specialised applications, and not imposing sufficient conditions to lead to a manageable equation.

For example, a complete absence of motion in the fluid would give $\mathbf{u} = \mathbf{0}$, and then Equation (1.1) becomes

$$\mathbf{0} = \mathbf{F} - \frac{1}{\rho}\boldsymbol{\nabla}p,$$

This equation was derived, for the case with $\mathbf{F} = -g\,\mathbf{k}$, in *Unit 1* Subsection 4.1.

which is a form of the basic equation of fluid statics. However, the aim is to model fluids in motion. An important stage in the modelling process is to make simplifying assumptions in such a way that the important features of the problem are retained. Consider the effect of the following four assumptions on the flow of a fluid.

*Assumption 1* The fluid is inviscid.

The consequences of this assumption have been discussed before (in *Units 1* and *5*). For this analysis, it means that Euler's equation will be the starting point.

*Assumption 2* The fluid is of constant density.

*Unit 1* introduced a mathematical model of an incompressible fluid, namely, taking the density $\rho$ to be constant. With this assumption, the discussion restricts the analysis to the flow of liquids and to gas flows at relatively low speeds.

Throughout this unit the density $\rho$ is always taken as constant. Application of the incompressible model to gas flows was considered in *Unit 5* Subsection 4.3.

*Assumption 3*    The flow is steady.

The mathematical consequence of this assumption is that all partial derivatives with respect to time are zero; in particular, $\partial \mathbf{u}/\partial t = \mathbf{0}$.

*Assumption 4*    The body force per unit mass is conservative.

If the vector field $\mathbf{F}$ is conservative, then $\mathbf{curl}\,\mathbf{F} = \mathbf{0}$, and $\mathbf{F}$ can be represented by the gradient of a scalar field, that is, $\mathbf{F} = \boldsymbol{\nabla}\Omega$, where the scalar field $\Omega$ is called the *body force potential*.

You met the idea of a conservative vector field in *Unit 4* Subsection 4.3.

These assumptions may appear rather restrictive. However, there are many engineering applications for which they provide a good model. The flow of water through pipes and channels, and over weirs, are examples of such problems; these are discussed in Sections 2 and 3. In all these cases, water can be modelled as an inviscid, constant-density fluid in steady flow, and the only body force acting is gravity, which is conservative, so that the assumptions above prove reasonable in modelling such flows.

With these four assumptions, we shall show that the flow variables $u$ (speed), $p$ (pressure) and $\Omega$ (body force potential) are related by the equation

$$\frac{p}{\rho} + \tfrac{1}{2}u^2 - \Omega = \text{constant along a streamline.}$$

This is called *Bernoulli's equation*, after the Swiss mathematician Daniel Bernoulli (1700–82), who first formulated it.

The first assumption provides the starting point; for an inviscid fluid, Euler's equation applies:

$$\frac{\partial \mathbf{u}}{\partial t} + \boldsymbol{\nabla}\left(\tfrac{1}{2}u^2\right) - \mathbf{u} \times (\boldsymbol{\nabla} \times \mathbf{u}) = \mathbf{F} - \frac{1}{\rho}\boldsymbol{\nabla}p. \tag{1.1}$$

We now invoke Assumptions 2, 3 and 4, in order to simplify this equation.

Since the density $\rho$ of the fluid is taken to be constant, we can write the last term in Equation (1.1) as

Assumption 2

$$-\frac{1}{\rho}\boldsymbol{\nabla}p = -\boldsymbol{\nabla}\left(\frac{p}{\rho}\right).$$

Since the flow is steady, we have

Assumption 3

$$\frac{\partial \mathbf{u}}{\partial t} = \mathbf{0}.$$

Since the body force vector field is conservative, we can write $\mathbf{F} = \boldsymbol{\nabla}\Omega$.

Assumption 4

Collecting together the terms involving $\boldsymbol{\nabla}$, Equation (1.1) can now be expressed as

$$\boldsymbol{\nabla}\left(\frac{p}{\rho} + \tfrac{1}{2}u^2 - \Omega\right) = \mathbf{u} \times (\boldsymbol{\nabla} \times \mathbf{u}). \tag{1.2}$$

This vector equation can be simplified further by considering what happens along an arbitrary streamline. Since the flow is steady, the streamlines do not change position or shape, and so it is reasonable to consider what happens along them.

In *Unit 5*, you saw that a streamline is a curve for which the tangent at any point on it is parallel to the velocity vector at that point.

The aim is to integrate Equation (1.2) along a streamline. Suppose that $s$ is a parameter for the streamline. Then $d\mathbf{r}/ds$ is a tangent vector to the streamline (see Figure 1.1, overleaf). Consider the scalar (dot) product of $d\mathbf{r}/ds$ with each side of Equation (1.2):

$$\frac{d\mathbf{r}}{ds} \cdot \boldsymbol{\nabla}\left(\frac{p}{\rho} + \tfrac{1}{2}u^2 - \Omega\right) = \frac{d\mathbf{r}}{ds} \cdot (\mathbf{u} \times (\boldsymbol{\nabla} \times \mathbf{u})). \tag{1.3}$$

(i)  For the right-hand side of Equation (1.3), by using the definitions of the scalar and vector products, it can be shown that

$$\frac{d\mathbf{r}}{ds} \cdot (\mathbf{u} \times (\boldsymbol{\nabla} \times \mathbf{u})) = 0,$$

as follows. The vector $\mathbf{d} = \mathbf{u} \times (\boldsymbol{\nabla} \times \mathbf{u})$ is perpendicular to both $\mathbf{u}$ and $\boldsymbol{\nabla} \times \mathbf{u}$, from the definition of the vector product. Since $d\mathbf{r}/ds$ is parallel to $\mathbf{u}$, by the definition of streamlines, and $\mathbf{d}$ is perpendicular to $\mathbf{u}$, it follows that $d\mathbf{r}/ds$ is perpendicular to $\mathbf{d}$. Hence $(d\mathbf{r}/ds) \cdot \mathbf{d} = 0$, because the scalar product of two perpendicular vectors is zero.

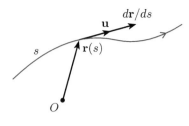

*Figure 1.1*

See MST209 *Unit 4.*

(ii)  Let $b(x, y, z) = p/\rho + \frac{1}{2}u^2 - \Omega$. Then the left-hand side of Equation (1.3) is

$$\frac{d\mathbf{r}}{ds} \cdot \boldsymbol{\nabla} b.$$

Along the chosen streamline, we have $\mathbf{r} = \mathbf{r}(s)$, that is,

$$\mathbf{r} = x(s)\,\mathbf{i} + y(s)\,\mathbf{j} + z(s)\,\mathbf{k}.$$

Writing $d\mathbf{r}/ds$ and $\boldsymbol{\nabla} b$ in Cartesian coordinates gives

$$\frac{d\mathbf{r}}{ds} \cdot \boldsymbol{\nabla} b = \left( \frac{dx}{ds}\mathbf{i} + \frac{dy}{ds}\mathbf{j} + \frac{dz}{ds}\mathbf{k} \right) \cdot \left( \frac{\partial b}{\partial x}\mathbf{i} + \frac{\partial b}{\partial y}\mathbf{j} + \frac{\partial b}{\partial z}\mathbf{k} \right)$$

$$= \frac{dx}{ds}\frac{\partial b}{\partial x} + \frac{dy}{ds}\frac{\partial b}{\partial y} + \frac{dz}{ds}\frac{\partial b}{\partial z}.$$

Using the Chain Rule,

$$\frac{dx}{ds}\frac{\partial b}{\partial x} + \frac{dy}{ds}\frac{\partial b}{\partial y} + \frac{dz}{ds}\frac{\partial b}{\partial z} = \frac{db}{ds},$$

so that

$$\frac{d\mathbf{r}}{ds} \cdot \boldsymbol{\nabla} b = \frac{db}{ds}.$$

Hence Equation (1.3) can be simplified to

$$\frac{d}{ds}\left( \frac{p}{\rho} + \frac{1}{2}u^2 - \Omega \right) = 0,$$

where $d/ds$ means the derivative *along the streamline*. Integrate this equation with respect to $s$ to obtain **Bernoulli's equation,**

$$\frac{p}{\rho} + \frac{1}{2}u^2 - \Omega = \text{constant along a streamline,} \qquad (1.4)$$

for the steady flow of an inviscid fluid of constant density in a conservative force field. Since the streamline above is chosen quite arbitrarily, the expression $p/\rho + \frac{1}{2}u^2 - \Omega$ is constant along *any* streamline, although, of course, the constant may vary from streamline to streamline.

On a particular streamline, we have $p = p(s)$, $u = u(s)$ and $\Omega = \Omega(s)$, and Bernoulli's equation gives a relationship between $p$, $u$ and $\Omega$ along the streamline. Provided that the constant for a particular streamline is known (from the boundary conditions of a problem), Bernoulli's equation may be thought of as giving the pressure, $p$, in terms of the speed, $u$, and the potential, $\Omega$, at any point on the streamline.

## *Exercise 1.1*

Consider the steady flow of a constant-density, inviscid fluid in which the only body force is gravity. Taking $\mathbf{F} = -g\,\mathbf{k}$, find $\Omega$ and hence write down Bernoulli's equation for such a flow.

The solution to this exercise is the form of Bernoulli's equation that is used in much of this unit when *steady* flows are considered. In Subsection 1.3, a form of Bernoulli's equation for unsteady flows is developed. So far, we have the following.

### *Bernoulli's equation for steady flow under gravity*

For the steady flow of an inviscid fluid of constant density, where the only body force is gravity,

$$\frac{p}{\rho} + \tfrac{1}{2}u^2 + gz = \text{constant along a streamline.} \qquad (1.5)$$

However, as you will see shortly, the 'along a streamline' requirement can be relaxed when the flow is irrotational.

Bernoulli's equation looks rather like the energy equation per unit mass of a particle in Newtonian mechanics, except that now there is an additional term, $p/\rho$, due to pressure. The second term, $\tfrac{1}{2}u^2$, represents the kinetic energy per unit mass of the fluid, and the third term, $gz$, may be regarded as the gravitational potential energy per unit mass of the fluid. The pressure term, $p/\rho$, does not have an energy analogue in particle mechanics problems, although it can be thought of as representing an energy per unit mass, because Bernoulli's equation is dimensionally correct.

See MST209 *Unit 8*.

## *Exercise 1.2*

Show that $p/\rho$ has the dimensions of energy per unit mass.

Dimensional analysis was covered in MST209 *Unit 16*. Alternatively, see Section 5 of the *Revision Booklet*.

The term $p/\rho$ contributes to the internal energy of the fluid, a concept which is modelled in an area of applied mathematics and engineering called thermodynamics. Essentially, the internal energy of a fluid is associated with molecular motions, and the term $p/\rho$ is a part measure of the amount of internal energy which can be changed into kinetic or potential energy.

An alternative interpretation of the terms in Bernoulli's equation (1.5) can be given in terms of pressure. If each term in this equation is multiplied by the fluid density $\rho$, which is constant, then we have

$$p + \tfrac{1}{2}\rho u^2 + \rho g z = \text{constant along a streamline.} \qquad (1.6)$$

Now each term in this equation has the dimensions of pressure. The first term, $p$, is called the **static pressure**; this term is rather misleading because, in general, the fluid is moving. The static pressure, $p$, is the pressure existing in the fluid, and it is in terms of $p$ that the net force on a body immersed in the fluid can be expressed.

We shall refer to 'static pressure' simply as 'pressure'.

From the discussion of fluid statics in *Unit 1*, the term $\rho g z$ is recognisable as the extra pressure at the bottom of a column of fluid going from a height $z$ down to the datum level. This term is called the **potential pressure**, by analogy with the potential energy $mgz$ of a particle in mechanics. The term $\tfrac{1}{2}\rho u^2$ is called the **dynamic pressure**, because it is due to the motion of the fluid.

*Unit 5* introduced the notion of a stagnation point as a point in a fluid flow where the velocity is zero. For example, for the steady two-dimensional flow of a constant-density fluid past a vertical cylinder, there are two stagnation points in the flow, at $S$ and $T$ in Figure 1.2. The line $RSTV$, including a semi-circle on the cylinder boundary, is a streamline in the flow, and so along this curve Equation (1.6) gives

$$p + \tfrac{1}{2}\rho u^2 + \rho g z = \text{constant}.$$

Since every point along the streamline lies in the same plane $z = \text{constant}$, this equation simplifies to

$$p + \tfrac{1}{2}\rho u^2 = p_R + \tfrac{1}{2}\rho u_R^2,$$

where $p_R$ and $u_R$ are the values of $p$ and $u$ in the undisturbed uniform flow, $R$ being a point representative of the uniform flow.

Consequently, since $u$ at $S$ is zero, the pressure at $S$ is given by

$$p_S = p_R + \tfrac{1}{2}\rho u_R^2.$$

This quantity is called the **stagnation pressure**; it is the highest pressure encountered anywhere in the flow. (At any point $A$, say, other than $S$ or $T$, we have $u_A > 0$, so that $p_A = p_R + \tfrac{1}{2}\rho u_R^2 - \tfrac{1}{2}\rho u_A^2 = p_S - \tfrac{1}{2}\rho u_A^2 < p_S$.)

The stagnation pressure consists of two parts:

(i) $p_R$ is the pressure in the uniformly flowing fluid;

(ii) $\tfrac{1}{2}\rho u_R^2$ is the contribution from the dynamic pressure; it is a pressure arising from the fluid, previously travelling at speed $u_R$, having been brought to a halt.

See *Unit 5* Subsection 3.2, where the flow referred to here was modelled by the combination of a uniform stream and a doublet.

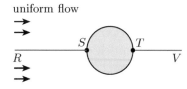

uniform flow

*Figure 1.2*

This pressure, $p_R + \tfrac{1}{2}\rho u_R^2$, occurs at both $S$ and $T$ in the inviscid model.

## 1.2  Using Bernoulli's equation: a simple example

Consider two points $A$ and $B$, lying on the same streamline in an inviscid, incompressible fluid in steady motion, where the only body force is gravity. Then, according to Bernoulli's equation (1.5),

$$\frac{p_A}{\rho} + \tfrac{1}{2}u_A^2 + g z_A = c \qquad \text{and} \qquad \frac{p_B}{\rho} + \tfrac{1}{2}u_B^2 + g z_B = c,$$

where $c$ is the same constant in each case, because $A$ and $B$ lie on the same streamline. Thus

$$\frac{p_A}{\rho} + \tfrac{1}{2}u_A^2 + g z_A = \frac{p_B}{\rho} + \tfrac{1}{2}u_B^2 + g z_B. \tag{1.7}$$

It does not matter whether the actual trajectory of the streamline is specified: knowing just that $A$ and $B$ are on the same streamline enables Equation (1.7) to be written down. If the pressure, speed and height (above some datum level) are known at the point $A$, then Equation (1.7) enables these parameters to be related at $B$. The following example illustrates how this equation can be used.

Throughout this unit, it is convenient to use subscripts to denote the values of variables at given points.

### Example 1.1

The photograph in Figure 1.3 shows water flowing vertically from a tap of circular cross-section. The shape of the water stream is like a funnel, and Table 1.1 gives values for the radius, $r$, of the circular cross-section of the funnel at different vertical distances, $h$, below a typical tap.

Use Bernoulli's equation and the continuity equation to predict the shape of the water surface, by finding how the radius $r$ of the stream depends on distance $h$ below the tap. Then use the data in Table 1.1 to check whether this model is valid.

*Figure 1.3*

## Solution

Suppose that water can be modelled as an inviscid fluid of constant density, and that the flow is steady. Since the only body force is gravity, which is a conservative force field, apply Bernoulli's equation along a streamline.

Because of rotational symmetry, the water/air surface is composed of streamlines, and their shape (see Figure 1.4) can be estimated. In fact, it is not necessary to be particular about which one to choose or even what its actual trajectory is, because the conditions around any horizontal circle on the surface of the tube do not change.

*Table 1.1*

| $h$ (mm) | $r$ (mm) |
|---|---|
| 0 | 10.0 |
| 20 | 6.5 |
| 40 | 5.6 |
| 60 | 5.2 |
| 80 | 4.9 |
| 100 | 4.7 |

The four main steps in this solution are indicated in the margin.

Step (a): Select a streamline, and choose two points $A$ and $B$ on the streamline.

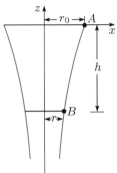

*Figure 1.4*                              *Figure 1.5*

So consider two points, $A$ and $B$ say, on one of these streamlines; let $A$ be at the level where the water leaves the tap and $B$ be at a depth $h$ below $A$ (see Figure 1.5). Measure $z$ upwards from the level of $A$, so that $z_B = -h$. Along the streamline $AB$ the pressure is atmospheric, so $p_A = p_B = p_0$. Suppose that the radius of the cross-section at $A$ is $r_0$, and that the speed of the water as it leaves the tap is $u_0$ (assumed constant across the section).

Applying Bernoulli's equation along the streamline $AB$ gives

$$\frac{p_A}{\rho} + \tfrac{1}{2}u_A^2 + gz_A = \frac{p_B}{\rho} + \tfrac{1}{2}u_B^2 + gz_B,$$

Step (b): Apply Bernoulli's equation.

where $u_A$ and $u_B$ are the water speeds at the horizontal levels of $A$ and $B$, and $z_A$, $z_B$ are the $z$-coordinates of $A$, $B$. Now $z_A = 0$ and $z_B = -h$, while $p_A = p_B = p_0$ and $u_A = u_0$. Hence we have

$$\frac{p_0}{\rho} + \tfrac{1}{2}u_0^2 = \frac{p_0}{\rho} + \tfrac{1}{2}u_B^2 - gh.$$

Solving this equation for $u_B$ gives

$$u_B = \sqrt{u_0^2 + 2gh}. \tag{1.8}$$

The problem statement asks for the shape of the water surface, i.e. for a relationship between $r$ and $h$. To obtain this relationship, use the continuity equation to relate $u_B$ and $r_B$, and then apply Equation (1.8) to eliminate $u_B$.

Step (c): Use the continuity equation, in the form

volume flow rate = constant.

Because the water has constant density, the quantity flowing through the cross-section at $A$ must be the same as that flowing through the cross-section at $B$. The horizontal cross-sections are bounded by circles, so assuming that the flow is uniform across each cross-section, we have

$$\pi r_0^2 u_0 = \pi r_B^2 u_B \qquad \text{or} \qquad u_B = \frac{r_0^2}{r_B^2}\, u_0.$$

This is a special case of Equation (4.8) in *Unit 5*. Here the area is $\pi r^2$.

Using Equation (1.8), and writing $r$ for $r_B$, we obtain

$$\frac{r_0^2}{r^2}\, u_0 = \sqrt{u_0^2 + 2gh}.$$

Step (d): Manipulate the equations of Steps (b) and (c).

Rearranging this equation to express $r$ as a function of $h$ gives

$$r = \frac{r_0}{(1 + 2gh/u_0^2)^{1/4}},\qquad(1.9)$$

which specifies the shape of the water surface.

In order to compare this prediction with the given data, it is helpful to use the alternative rearrangement

$$\frac{r_0^4}{r^4} = 1 + \frac{2g}{u_0^2}\,h,$$

which predicts that $(r_0/r)^4$ should be a linear function of $h$.

Plotting $(r_0/r)^4$ against $h$ for the given data, and then drawing the 'best fit' straight line, gives the graph in Figure 1.6.

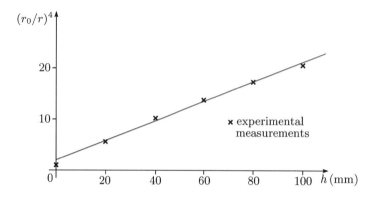

*Figure 1.6*

This graph appears to confirm the linearity between $(r_0/r)^4$ and $h$, which suggests that Bernoulli's equation does provide a fairly good model for the flow of water from a tap.  ■

Without further data, it is not possible to validate the measurable value for the slope of the line, which provides an estimate for $2g/u_0^2$ and hence for $u_0$.

This example is a familiar situation that you can observe at home. Turn on the water tap and check that the shape of the water funnel is rotationally symmetric and smooth. The model from Equation (1.9),

$$\frac{r}{r_0} = \frac{1}{\left(1 + 2gh/u_0^2\right)^{1/4}},$$

Check that the tap has a circular cross-section.

is good for quite a considerable length of water funnel. However, when modelling any physical situation, it is important to identify those regions for which the model may break down. Eventually, given a sufficient drop in height, the flow becomes unstable and breaks up into globules. The funnel has become sufficiently narrow for forces other than gravity and pressure to become important. In this region, Bernoulli's equation no longer applies. Also, at the top of the funnel, any effects around the circumference of the tap lip have been neglected, and again the model is not expected to be good here. Example 1.1 has shown that Bernoulli's equation provides a good representation for much of the water funnel.

The four steps indicated in the margin alongside the solution to Example 1.1 can be used to solve any problem in which Bernoulli's equation provides a good model.

The first step is to consider two points on the same streamline in the flow. Identifying the streamlines does *not* have to be done mathematically (as was the case in *Unit 5* Subsection 1.3). Often a streamline is chosen in the free surface, along which the pressure remains at a constant value, i.e. atmospheric pressure. This technique was used in Example 1.1. If the problem does not involve a free surface, then make use of the fact that rigid boundaries are composed of streamlines. For example, in the flow in a narrowing pipe, it is best to choose two points $A$ and $B$ on the pipe and to use the wall of the pipe as providing a streamline (see Figure 1.7). Often, in such a problem, a suitable model assumes the speed at every point on the cross-section at $A$ to be the same, and similarly at $B$.

*Figure 1.7*

Now use Bernoulli's equation and the continuity equation to attempt the following exercise. Do not worry at this stage if the solution seems difficult; Sections 2 and 3 contain several applications of Bernoulli's equation, and they all require the same procedure.

### Exercise 1.3

A pipe carrying water of density $1000 \, \text{kg m}^{-3}$ tapers from a cross-sectional area of $0.3 \, \text{m}^2$ at $A$ to $0.15 \, \text{m}^2$ at $B$. At $A$, the fluid speed is $1.8 \, \text{m s}^{-1}$ and the pressure is $1 \times 10^5 \, \text{Pa}$. The points $A$ and $B$ are on the same streamline, and $B$ is $5 \, \text{m}$ above the level of $A$ (see Figure 1.8).

(a) Use the continuity equation to find the speed of the water at $B$. (Assume that the speed is the same at any point on each of the cross-sections at $A$ and $B$.)

(b) Use Bernoulli's equation to find the pressure at $B$.

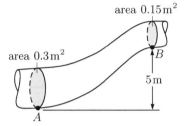

*Figure 1.8*

## 1.3  Bernoulli's equation for irrotational flows

In Subsection 1.1, Euler's equation was integrated along a streamline to obtain a form of Bernoulli's equation for steady flows. In the discussion, no assumption was made about the rotational nature of the fluid velocity. However, the example and exercise in Subsection 1.2 dealt with velocity fields which are irrotational. Alternative forms of Bernoulli's equation are possible for irrotational flows. (Of course, these alternative forms when applied to solve Example 1.1 and Exercise 1.3 will give the same solutions.)

*A fluid flow is rotational if $\textbf{curl u} \neq \textbf{0}$ and irrotational if $\textbf{curl u} = \textbf{0}$ (see Unit 4 Subsection 4.3).*

We start with three of the same assumptions as before about the type of fluid and the body force:

(a) the fluid is inviscid;

(b) the fluid has constant density, $\rho$ say;

(c) the body force is conservative, so $\mathbf{F} = \nabla \Omega$.

*However, we do not assume now that the flow is steady.*

Euler's equation for the flow of such a fluid is

$$\frac{\partial \mathbf{u}}{\partial t} + \nabla \left( \tfrac{1}{2} u^2 \right) - \mathbf{u} \times (\nabla \times \mathbf{u}) = \nabla \left( -\frac{p}{\rho} + \Omega \right).$$

If the flow is irrotational (a new assumption at this point), then $\textbf{curl u} = \textbf{0}$, and the gradient of a scalar field can represent $\mathbf{u}$, i.e. $\mathbf{u} = \textbf{grad}\, \phi$, where the scalar field $\phi$ is called the *velocity potential*.

*Unit 11 deals with the velocity potential in some detail. Here only the existence of the velocity potential is needed, not its possible forms.*

### Exercise 1.4

For the unsteady, irrotational flow of a fluid satisfying assumptions (a)–(c) above, show that Euler's equation becomes

$$\nabla \left( \frac{\partial \phi}{\partial t} + \tfrac{1}{2} u^2 + \frac{p}{\rho} - \Omega \right) = \mathbf{0}.$$

The aim now is to integrate the result of Exercise 1.4, to find a relationship between $p$, $u$, $\Omega$ and $\partial\phi/\partial t$. Consider *any* curve drawn in the fluid, and suppose that $s$ is a parameter for this curve. (Note that the curve chosen here is not necessarily a streamline.) Then $d\mathbf{r}/ds$ is a tangent vector to the curve. Take the scalar product of $d\mathbf{r}/ds$ with each side of the equation

Here $\mathbf{r} = \mathbf{r}(s)$ is the position vector of a point on the curve.

$$\nabla\left(\frac{p}{\rho} + \tfrac{1}{2}u^2 - \Omega + \frac{\partial\phi}{\partial t}\right) = \mathbf{0},$$

to obtain

$$\frac{d\mathbf{r}}{ds}\cdot\nabla\left(\frac{p}{\rho} + \tfrac{1}{2}u^2 - \Omega + \frac{\partial\phi}{\partial t}\right) = 0.$$

By the argument used in Subsection 1.1, this can be written as

$$\frac{d}{ds}\left(\frac{p}{\rho} + \tfrac{1}{2}u^2 - \Omega + \frac{\partial\phi}{\partial t}\right) = 0.$$

Here $d/ds$ is the derivative along the chosen curve.

Integrating this equation with respect to $s$, remembering that the curve was chosen arbitrarily, gives

$$\frac{p}{\rho} + \tfrac{1}{2}u^2 - \Omega + \frac{\partial\phi}{\partial t} = f(t) \quad \text{along any curve,} \tag{1.10}$$

The integration for each fixed time leads to the appearance of an arbitrary constant, but the value of this 'constant' may change with time, giving the arbitrary function $f(t)$.

where $f$ is an arbitrary function. This is *Bernoulli's equation* for the unsteady, irrotational flow of an inviscid fluid of constant density in a conservative force field. In this form of Bernoulli's equation, the combination of $p$, $u$, $\Omega$ and $\phi$ will, in general, depend on time, because each of the flow parameters may depend on time as the flow is unsteady. It is possible to choose the curve to be one of the streamlines, but these may change their shape as time passes, which is a disadvantage of such a choice. It is often more convenient to choose a fixed curve in the fluid. This unsteady form of Bernoulli's equation will be used in the discussion of water waves in *Unit 12*. The rest of this unit considers only steady flow.

## Exercise 1.5

Use Equation (1.10) to write down Bernoulli's equation for a steady, irrotational flow of an inviscid, constant-density fluid, where the only body force is gravity.

---

The solution to this exercise provides a form of Bernoulli's equation which is very similar to that derived in Subsection 1.1. If the flow is steady and *irrotational*, then (with $\Omega$ in place of $-gz$)

$$\frac{p}{\rho} + \tfrac{1}{2}u^2 - \Omega = \text{constant along } \textit{any} \text{ curve in the fluid,} \tag{1.11}$$

whereas for a rotational flow this holds only along a streamline. Of course, a streamline can be chosen even in the irrotational case, but application of Bernoulli's equation is not then restricted to streamlines as in the rotational case. The choice of curve will depend on what is most convenient to solve the problem at hand.

The form of Bernoulli's equation that is required depends in general on the *type of flow*, that is, whether the flow is steady or unsteady, rotational or irrotational. The three forms of Bernoulli's equation that have been derived in this section are summarised in the table below.

*Table 1.2*

| Type of flow | Bernoulli's equation, where $b = \dfrac{p}{\rho} + \frac{1}{2}u^2 - \Omega$ | Reference |
|---|---|---|
| steady, rotational | $b = $ constant along *a streamline* | Equation (1.4) |
| unsteady, irrotational | $b = -\dfrac{\partial \phi}{\partial t} + f(t)$ along *any curve* in the fluid | Equation (1.10) |
| steady, irrotational | $b = $ constant along *any curve* in the fluid | Equation (1.11) |

In each of these cases, the fluid is assumed to be inviscid and of constant density, and the body forces are assumed to be conservative. The values of $p$, $u$ and $\Omega$ may vary at different points along the curve.

In this course, the body force is always the force of gravity, and hence $\Omega = -gz$.

## Exercise 1.6

A liquid of constant density is in two-dimensional horizontal motion in which gravity is the only body force and the pressure distribution, $p(r, \theta)$, is unknown. (Here cylindrical polar coordinates are used, and the flow parameters are independent of $z$.) For each of the following velocity vector fields, $\mathbf{u} = u_r\,\mathbf{e}_r + u_\theta\,\mathbf{e}_\theta$, decide which form of Bernoulli's equation could be used to obtain the pressure distribution in terms of the speed of the liquid.

The formula for **curl** in cylindrical polar coordinates is in *Unit 4* Subsection 4.1, or at the back of the *Handbook*.

(a) $\mathbf{u} = \dfrac{k}{r}\,\mathbf{e}_\theta$     (b) $\mathbf{u} = \dfrac{A}{r}\,\mathbf{e}_r + B\,\mathbf{e}_\theta$     (c) $\mathbf{u} = \dfrac{mt^2}{r}\,\mathbf{e}_r$

Here $k$, $A$, $B$ and $m$ are non-zero constants, and $r \neq 0$.

The fluid flows described in the remainder of this unit are irrotational, so it is not necessary to find the streamlines in order to apply Bernoulli's equation. A relationship between $p$, $u$ and $\Omega$ along any convenient curve joining the two points of interest can be written down. However, it is often convenient to use the streamlines if these can be deduced easily.

Often, a streamline can provide some extra information; thus, in Example 1.1 (the 'tap problem') it is convenient to take a streamline in the water/air surface, because along such a streamline the pressure at all points is equal to atmospheric pressure, in which case the pressure term, $p/\rho$, does not enter into the solution explicitly. Similarly, for flows of water in an open channel (discussed in Section 3), the water/air surface provides streamlines along which the pressure is constant, so the simplified form of Bernoulli's equation that does not involve the pressure term explicitly can be used. Of course, if a flow is rotational (i.e. **curl u** $\neq$ **0**), then Bernoulli's equation *must* be applied along the streamlines.

In Example 1.1, four steps were identified in the process of solving the 'tap problem'. These four steps apply in solving most problems in which one form or other of Bernoulli's equation is to be used, and it is convenient to summarise the method as a procedure.

## Procedure 1.1

To solve problems involving the *steady* flow of an *inviscid* fluid of *constant density* in a *conservative* force field, proceed as follows.

(a) Choose two points $A$ and $B$ on a 'suitable' curve drawn in the fluid. If the flow is rotational (i.e. **curl u** $\neq$ **0**), then this curve must be a streamline; otherwise, any curve will do.

(b) By applying the form of Bernoulli's equation appropriate to the curve in Step (a) (see Table 1.2 on page 77), find a relationship between the pressure and speed of flow at $A$ and $B$.

(c) By using the continuity equation, find a second relationship between the speed of flow at $A$ and $B$.

In all the examples in this unit, the continuity equation takes the form

volume flow rate = constant.

(d) Manipulate the equations from Steps (b) and (c) to find the solution to the problem.

Use the steps in this procedure to solve the following exercise.

## Exercise 1.7

Water of density $1000\,\mathrm{kg\,m^{-3}}$ is flowing in an open rectangular channel of width $1\,\mathrm{m}$ at a depth of $1.2\,\mathrm{m}$ and speed $2.5\,\mathrm{m\,s^{-1}}$. It then flows smoothly down a chute into another open rectangular channel, of width $0.4\,\mathrm{m}$, where the depth is $0.6\,\mathrm{m}$ (see Figure 1.9). Both channel floors are horizontal.

Flows of this type will be studied in more detail in Section 3.

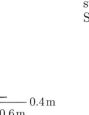

*Figure 1.9*

Assuming that water can be modelled as an inviscid fluid of constant density, and that the flow is steady and irrotational, find the difference in height of the water surfaces in the two channels. Deduce the height difference in the channel floors.

As well as providing a quantitative method for solving fluid flow problems, Bernoulli's equation can be used to explain certain phenomena qualitatively. The essential message that Bernoulli's equation carries, in a region where the body force potential does not vary greatly, is that

high speed implies low pressure, and low speed implies high pressure.

Each implication is reversible; for example, low pressure implies high speed.

This can be used to explain some of the experiments of the audio session in *Unit 1* Section 2. Although the equation was derived for a fluid of constant density, it is possible to show that the same equation holds for the flow of air with speeds much less than the speed of sound (about $340\,\mathrm{m\,s^{-1}}$). Certainly, the speed of the air in the audio session experiments is less than this.

See *Unit 5* Subsection 4.3.

Consider the experiment of blowing between two sheets of paper. As air flows between the sheets, the speed of air is increased and, according to Bernoulli's equation, this creates a lower pressure. The net effect for the two sheets is that the higher pressure on the outside of the sheets causes them to move together.

### Exercise 1.8

Consider the cotton reel experiment (Figure 1.10). Explain qualitatively, in terms of Bernoulli's equation, why when you blow *down* the cotton reel there is an *upward* force on the card. (Assume that the speed of the air is sufficiently less than the speed of sound, so that the air can be modelled as a constant-density fluid.)

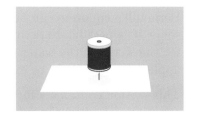

*Figure 1.10*

# End-of-section exercises

### Exercise 1.9

(a) In the derivation of the various forms of Bernoulli's equation in this section, two assumptions about the properties of the *fluid* are necessary in each case. What are they?

(b) What is the assumption about the body force?

(c) Depending on the assumptions made about the *flow*, different forms of Bernoulli's equation are derived. What are these possible assumptions?

(d) Consider the steady flow of a fluid satisfying the assumptions in part (a) of this exercise. If the body force is gravity, then the quantity $p/\rho + \frac{1}{2}u^2 + gz$ is constant along certain curves in the fluid. Are these curves always streamlines? For what flows is it necessary for these curves to be streamlines?

### Exercise 1.10

Consider the two-dimensional steady flow of an inviscid, constant-density fluid with no body forces, given by the stream function

$\psi = k \ln r + m\theta,$

where $r$, $\theta$ are cylindrical polar coordinates, and $k$, $m$ are constants.

This represents a source combined with a vortex. (See *Unit 5* Section 3.)

(a) Find the velocity field corresponding to this stream function.

(b) Show that the flow is irrotational.

(c) Find the pressure distribution $p(r,\theta)$ by using a suitable form of Bernoulli's equation, given that $\lim_{r \to \infty} p(r,\theta) = p_\infty$ (a constant).

### Exercise 1.11

Figure 1.11 shows a diagram of the cross-section of an aeroplane wing in a wind tunnel in the form of a parallel-walled channel. The flow of air past the wing, which has a flat bottom, can be modelled as the two-dimensional steady flow of an inviscid, constant-density fluid. Explain qualitatively, in terms of Bernoulli's equation, why there is a net force on the wing in the direction of the arrow.

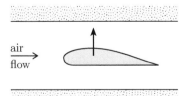

air flow

*Figure 1.11*

# 2 Applications of Bernoulli's equation

Despite the modelling assumptions of an inviscid, constant-density fluid, Bernoulli's equation can be used to analyse many physical situations. For some, it is possible to derive quantitative relationships, such as the formula for the shape of the water jet out of a tap (Example 1.1). Other applications can only be explained descriptively.

This section contains a further selection of applications of Bernoulli's equation. The first (in Subsection 2.1) considers the flow out of a tank through a small orifice, and the second (in Subsection 2.2) studies the effects of the flow through a pipe with a contraction. In each of these examples, there is no knowledge of a formula for the velocity field, and it cannot be assumed that the flows are irrotational. However, in each case the flows are steady, and an idea of the streamline pattern is known, so Bernoulli's equation along a streamline can be used.

Subsection 2.3 considers an important application of Bernoulli's equation, namely, finding the pressure distribution on solid boundary surfaces that are immersed in a fluid. Integrating this pressure distribution gives the net surface force on such a boundary due to the fluid. The velocity field is known for these flows.

## 2.1 Flow through an orifice

Figure 2.1 illustrates the physical situation that will be investigated in this subsection. Consider a large tank containing an inviscid liquid of constant density, $\rho$ say, at a constant depth. The free surface is then at rest, and at that surface $p = p_0$, atmospheric pressure. In the side of the tank is a small orifice (hole), through which the liquid flows out. The depth of liquid in the tank is kept constant by adding liquid at the same rate as it leaves through the orifice (though this is not shown in Figure 2.1).

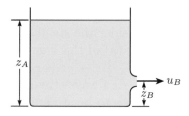

*Figure 2.1*

The problem is to derive a formula for the speed of the liquid as it emerges from the orifice.

The liquid leaves the tank as a jet; assume that the cross-sectional area of this jet at the point of exit is the same as the area of the orifice. This area is sufficiently small that changes in the potential pressure, $\rho gz$, across the jet are negligible.

Suppose that the height of the free surface of the liquid is $z_A$ (a constant, wherever the point $A$ is chosen on the surface), that the height of the orifice is $z_B$ (with $B$ being a point at the orifice), and that the speed of the liquid as it leaves the tank is $u_B$ (assumed to be constant across the orifice), as shown in Figure 2.1.

The liquid is inviscid and of constant density, the flow is steady, and the only body force is gravity, which is conservative. Hence Procedure 1.1 can be used.

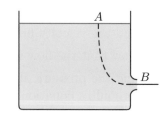

*Figure 2.2*

To apply Bernoulli's equation, select two points on the same streamline, say $A$ on the free surface and $B$ at the orifice (see Figure 2.2). It is not necessary to identify the positions of the two points exactly, since there is a streamline from any point in the free surface to some point at the orifice. Applying Bernoulli's equation along the streamline between $A$ and $B$ gives

$$\frac{p_A}{\rho} + \tfrac{1}{2}u_A^2 + gz_A = \frac{p_B}{\rho} + \tfrac{1}{2}u_B^2 + gz_B.$$

Step (a): Choose a suitable curve in the fluid and two points on it.

Step (b): Apply Bernoulli's equation.

Now, at the free surface,

$$p_A = p_0 \quad \text{and} \quad u_A = 0.$$

At the orifice, assume that the streamlines are parallel, so the pressure is uniform across the jet and equal to atmospheric pressure. Then we have $p_B = p_0$. Bernoulli's equation becomes

$$\frac{p_0}{\rho} + 0 + gz_A = \frac{p_0}{\rho} + \tfrac{1}{2}u_B^2 + gz_B.$$

Subtracting $p_0/\rho$ from each side of this equation, and rearranging, we obtain

$$u_B = \sqrt{2g(z_A - z_B)}. \qquad (2.1)$$

This simple formula shows that the speed of the jet depends only on the height of the liquid surface at $A$ above the orifice, a result that is, perhaps, intuitively clear (though the exact form of the relationship is not).

The derivation of the formula for $u_B$ did not require use of the continuity equation. To retain a constant depth of liquid, the tank has to be replenished with liquid at the same volume flow rate as that leaving the orifice, in order that the mass of liquid is conserved. Conservation of mass is the physical law from which the continuity equation is derived.

The physical situation described above provides the basis for simple experiments which validate Bernoulli's equation as a model to describe certain flow situations. For different volume flow rates (though with the water surface stationary for each pair of measurements), Equation (2.1) predicts that $u_B^2$ is proportional to $z_A - z_B$, which is found to match experimental data closely.

Although in Figure 2.1 the liquid is drawn as emerging in a horizontal jet, the speed $u_B$ predicted by Bernoulli's equation is the same regardless of orientation of the jet, provided that the difference in height between the liquid surface in the tank and the orifice is the same (see Figure 2.3).

Since the free surface is stationary, $u_A = 0$.

This result was first derived by Evangelista Torricelli (1608–47), an Italian physicist and mathematician, and is known as *Torricelli's formula*.

Step (c): Use the continuity equation (not needed here).

Since $u_B$ is not easy to measure directly, it is the volume flow rate which is measured. This is equal to $S_B u_B$, where $S_B$ is the (constant) area of the orifice.

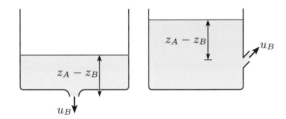

*Figure 2.3*

### Exercise 2.1

(a)  Determine the speed of the jet from the orifice if the liquid surface is 3 metres above the level of the orifice.

(b)  If the orifice is circular, with radius 1 cm, what is the volume flow rate?

### Exercise 2.2

Consider the flow of an inviscid liquid through an orifice out of a tank which is *not* replenished, and let the speed of the free surface be $u_A$ (see Figure 2.4).

(a) Are the assumptions for the use of Bernoulli's equation as in the text satisfied in this case?

(b) Suppose that you could use Bernoulli's equation along a streamline between points $A$ and $B$ (see Figure 2.4). Find a relationship between $u_A$, $u_B$, $z_A$ and $z_B$.

(c) Use the continuity equation to write down a relationship between the speeds $u_A$, $u_B$ and the areas $S_A$, $S_B$ of the free surface and of the orifice, respectively.

(d) Hence, by eliminating $u_A$, show that

$$u_B = \sqrt{\frac{2g(z_A - z_B)}{1 - (S_B/S_A)^2}}.$$

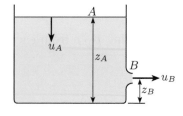

*Figure 2.4*

In Exercise 2.2(a), the flow is not steady, so that one of the assumptions in the derivation of Bernoulli's equation does not apply, and the formula for $u_B$ derived in part (d) may not be justified.

In fact, it can be shown that neglecting the unsteadiness of the flow is justifiable, provided the area of the free surface $S_A$ is sufficiently large compared to that of the orifice $S_B$ (in which case, the rate $u_A$ at which the free surface falls is very small compared with $u_B$). Neglecting the unsteadiness, of course, leads us back to Equation (2.1) as the expression for $u_B$, which may be obtained from the formula for $u_B$ in Exercise 2.2(d) by letting $S_B/S_A \to 0$.

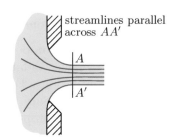

*Figure 2.5*

More important is the shape of the orifice. Only if the orifice is smoothly shaped at the entry is there good agreement between theory and experiment. Figure 2.5 illustrates the pattern of the streamlines near a sharp-edged orifice. Liquid approaching the orifice converges towards it in smooth streamlines. Because these lines cannot suddenly change direction, they continue to converge beyond the orifice, until they become parallel at the section $AA'$, known as the *vena contracta*.

One of the assumptions in modelling the flow in Figure 2.1 (on page 80) is that the streamlines are parallel at the orifice, $B$. This can be achieved by a 'bell-shaped' entry to the orifice as shown in Figure 2.6. For an orifice of this shape, the analysis is valid.

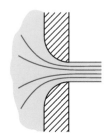

*Figure 2.6*

## 2.2 Flow through a contraction in a pipe

In Subsection 1.3, Bernoulli's equation was interpreted as a qualitative law,

> high (low) speed implies low (high) pressure,

and this was used to explain two of the experiments in the audio session for *Unit 1*. A simple experiment to demonstrate this law can be carried out using the apparatus shown in Figure 2.7. A uniform circular horizontal pipe has a short length of reduced diameter. Three vertical tubes are connected to the pipe, one to the section of reduced diameter and one on either side, and these tubes lead down to a small reservoir of liquid. When the situation is static, the air pressure above the liquid is the same throughout and so the liquid surfaces in the three tubes are at the same horizontal level. When air flows through the pipe, from left to right, the flow speed at $B$, in the section with reduced diameter, will be greater than that at $A$ (by the continuity equation). Bernoulli's equation then predicts that the air pressure $p_B$ at $B$ will be less than the air pressure $p_A$ at $A$. This should show up through the column of liquid at $B$ being higher than that at $A$, as shown in Figure 2.7. In fact, since the liquid pressure is the same at all points on the horizontal level through $D$ (and since the air pressure will not vary along the tubes, where there is no air flow), we have

$$p_A = p_B + \rho g h, \qquad \text{or} \qquad p_B = p_A - \rho g h,$$

where $\rho$ is the density of the liquid and $h$ is the height of the liquid column in the central tube above $D$.

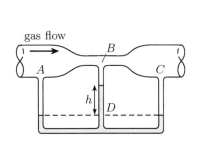

Figure 2.7

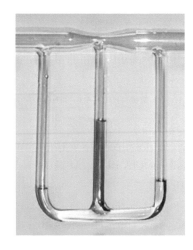

Figure 2.8

The photograph in Figure 2.8 shows this predicted effect quite clearly. (Bernoulli's equation also predicts that the pressure at $C$ in Figure 2.7 should be the same as that at $A$, since the pipe has the same diameter at the right as at the left. However, Figure 2.8 demonstrates that the air pressure beyond the contraction is slightly lower than before. This pressure drop is due to viscous effects which are ignored in the derivation of the equation in Section 1.)

This phenomenon of lower flow pressure in a pipe contraction underlies the operation of a paint spray (see Figure 2.9).

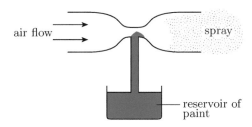

Figure 2.9

Air is pumped through a tube which has a contraction in it. At the contraction, there is a small tube which dips into a paint reservoir. As the air goes through the contraction, its speed is increased and hence the pressure at the top of the tube is reduced. This causes the paint to travel up the tube; it is injected into the air flow, where it forms droplets.

We now study in more detail the flow in a pipe with a contraction. The following exercise contains the preliminary steps in the theory.

The type of paint spray shown in Figure 2.9 can be bought as an accessory for a household cylinder vacuum cleaner, which can be used to blow air out as well as to suck air in.

### Exercise 2.3

A horizontal circular pipe of diameter $3\,\mathrm{cm}$ at $A$ contracts to half of this diameter at $B$, and carries water whose speed at any point on the cross-section at $A$ is $1\,\mathrm{m\,s^{-1}}$. Figure 2.10 shows a vertical cross-section of the pipe.

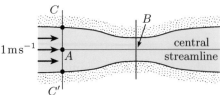

*Figure 2.10*

(a) Use Procedure 1.1 to find an expression for the pressure difference between points $A$ and $B$ along the horizontal central streamline. (Take the density of water to be $10^3\,\mathrm{kg\,m^{-3}}$.)

(b) Find the pressure difference between the points $C$ and $C'$ at section $A$.

---

Consider the flow of a liquid of constant density $\rho$ in a horizontal pipe with a contraction, in which the speed increases from $u_A$ at $A$ to $u_B$ at $B$, and the pressure decreases from $p_A$ to $p_B$.

The solution to Exercise 2.3 suggests that, typically, the pressure difference *across* the pipe (i.e. $p_{C'} - p_C$) is much less than the pressure differences *along* the pipe (i.e. $p_A - p_B$); for the flow in this exercise, $p_{C'} - p_C$ is about 4% of $p_A - p_B$. We use this to simplify Bernoulli's equation, by *assuming* that the pressure is uniform across each of sections $A$ and $B$, neglecting variations in pressure due to height. So along *any* streamline between sections $A$ and $B$,

$$\frac{p_A}{\rho} + \tfrac{1}{2}u_A^2 = \frac{p_B}{\rho} + \tfrac{1}{2}u_B^2. \tag{2.2}$$

The continuity equation gives

$$S_A u_A = S_B u_B, \tag{2.3}$$

where $S_A$, $S_B$ are the cross-sectional areas at $A$, $B$. Eliminating $u_B$ from Equations (2.2) and (2.3) gives the equation

$$p_B = p_A + \tfrac{1}{2}\rho u_A^2 \left(1 - \frac{S_A^2}{S_B^2}\right). \tag{2.4}$$

Now, the upstream conditions (at section $A$) are given, so Equation (2.4) can be thought of as giving the pressure $p_B$ as a function of $S_B$. Figure 2.11 shows a graph of this function. From Equation (2.4) and the graph, the following three deductions can be made.

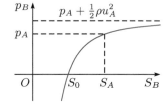

*Figure 2.11*

As $S_B$ increases beyond $S_A$ (which is fixed), the pipe expands, not contracts.

(i) As $S_B$ increases indefinitely, the pressure at section $B$ approaches its maximum value, $p_A + \tfrac{1}{2}\rho u_A^2$, which is the stagnation pressure (i.e. the pressure where $u_B = 0$, at a stagnation point).

(ii) Mathematically, $S_B$ can tend towards zero, and then Equation (2.4) predicts that the pressure at section $B$ becomes large and negative.

(iii) The pressure at $B$ is zero when

$$p_A + \tfrac{1}{2}\rho u_A^2 \left(1 - \frac{S_A^2}{S_B^2}\right) = 0, \quad \text{or} \quad S_B = \frac{S_A u_A}{\sqrt{u_A^2 + 2p_A/\rho}} = S_0, \text{ say.}$$

Now, in reality, negative pressures cannot exist, and this means that our mathematical model describes a real physical situation only for non-negative values of $p_B$. For flow through a contraction, the minimum cross-sectional area reduction for which the model still applies is given by

$$\frac{S_0}{S_A} = \frac{u_A}{\sqrt{u_A^2 + 2p_A/\rho}} \qquad \text{(i.e. when } S_B = S_0\text{)}.$$

This refers to *absolute* pressures. Negative *gauge* pressures (measured relative to the local atmospheric pressure) are possible. The two types of pressure measurement were discussed in *Unit 1* Subsection 3.2.

Of course, physically it is possible to have a pipe with a contraction for which $S_B < S_0$, but a new model would have to be developed in order to predict values of the flow variables at section $B$.

For the flow of a liquid, difficulties arise before the pressure actually reaches zero. At low pressures, a liquid will vaporise, and pockets or *cavities* of liquid vapour are formed. Sometimes, these cavities can also contain air sucked in from the liquid/air surface. This phenomenon of cavity formation is known as *cavitation*.

Cavitation can be a serious problem in pumps and propellers and, if severe enough, it will reduce performance, and create noise and vibration. Most damaging of all, cavitation can erode the surface of a solid boundary. The cavities may suddenly collapse, and the forces then exerted by the liquid rushing into the cavities cause very high localised surface stresses.

As well as damaging a solid surface in contact with a liquid, the presence and collapse of cavitation bubbles disturbs the flow and can reduce the efficiency of hydraulic machinery.

## 2.3    The pressure distribution on solid boundaries

Many problems in fluid mechanics involve the flow of a fluid around a solid object, and it is often important to determine the force produced on a solid boundary by fluid flowing past it. A solid body immersed in a fluid experiences two types of force: there is the net body force, such as its weight, and the net surface force exerted by the fluid. For example, if a small marble is dropped into a bottle of a viscous fluid such as cooking oil, the marble will experience two forces. These are (see Figure 2.12)

(i)   the weight **W** of the sphere (of magnitude $mg$, acting downwards), and

(ii)  the net surface force **R** (acting upwards) due to the viscous and pressure forces. (This net surface force provides resistance to the marble's downward motion.)

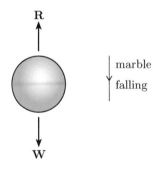

*Figure 2.12*

The inviscid model of a fluid neglects the viscous forces, so that the net surface force is due solely to the pressure. A strategy for finding the net surface force was outlined in the Introduction to *Unit 5*. To summarise what was said there: first find the velocity vector field, then apply Euler's equation to obtain the pressure distribution in the fluid, and finally, by evaluating a surface integral involving the pressure, find the net surface force on a solid boundary. In *Unit 5* Subsection 5.2, the first two stages in this strategy were worked through. For flows of fluids satisfying certain assumptions, the various integrals of Euler's equation of motion (i.e. Bernoulli's equations) provide the pressure distribution directly.

The following example and exercises illustrate how this leads to finding the pressure distribution on a solid boundary, beginning with the case of two-dimensional flow past a cylinder.

The evaluation of the surface force is left until *Unit 7*.

### Example 2.1

Model the steady, two-dimensional flow of an inviscid, constant-density fluid past a cylinder of radius $a$ by a combination of a uniform stream $U\,\mathbf{i}$ and a doublet of strength $-2\pi a^2 U\,\mathbf{i}$, for which the stream function is

$$\psi = U \sin\theta \left(\frac{r^2 - a^2}{r}\right).$$

Find the pressure distribution on the surface of the cylinder, given that there are no body forces, and that far from the cylinder the pressure is $p_0$.

### Solution

To find the pressure distribution on the surface of the cylinder, we need to choose the appropriate form of Bernoulli's equation, depending on whether the flow is irrotational or not. Hence we start by evaluating $\mathbf{curl\,u}$, to see whether the velocity field is irrotational.

For the given stream function, the velocity vector field is given by

$$\mathbf{u} = U \cos\theta \left(1 - \frac{a^2}{r^2}\right) \mathbf{e}_r - U \sin\theta \left(1 + \frac{a^2}{r^2}\right) \mathbf{e}_\theta.$$

From *Unit 5* Subsection 2.1,
$$u_r = \frac{1}{r}\frac{\partial\psi}{\partial\theta}, \quad u_\theta = -\frac{\partial\psi}{\partial r}.$$

Hence

$$\begin{aligned}
\mathbf{curl\,u} &= \frac{1}{r}\left(\frac{\partial}{\partial r}(r u_\theta) - \frac{\partial u_r}{\partial\theta}\right) \mathbf{e}_z \\
&= \frac{1}{r}\left(-U\sin\theta\left(1 - \frac{a^2}{r^2}\right) + U\sin\theta\left(1 - \frac{a^2}{r^2}\right)\right)\mathbf{e}_z = \mathbf{0},
\end{aligned}$$

The formula for **curl** in cylindrical polar coordinates is from *Unit 4* Subsection 4.1. Recall that $\mathbf{e}_z = \mathbf{k}$.

so that in this case the flow is irrotational (and steady), and the form of Bernoulli's equation that can be used is

$$\frac{p}{\rho} + \tfrac{1}{2}u^2 = \text{constant along } any \text{ curve.}$$

See Table 1.2 on page 77. Here there are no body forces, so $\Omega = 0$.

Figure 2.13 shows a curve coming from a long way upstream, where the pressure is $p_0$ and the speed is $U$, to a general point $B$ on the cylinder, with polar coordinates $(a, \theta)$ (since $r = a$ on the surface of the cylinder). The flow velocity at $B$ is

$$\begin{aligned}
\mathbf{u}_B = \mathbf{u}(a,\theta) &= \left[U\cos\theta\left(1 - \frac{a^2}{r^2}\right)\mathbf{e}_r - U\sin\theta\left(1 + \frac{a^2}{r^2}\right)\mathbf{e}_\theta\right]_{r=a} \\
&= -2U\sin\theta\,\mathbf{e}_\theta,
\end{aligned}$$

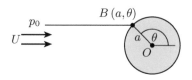

*Figure 2.13*

and so $u_B^2 = |\mathbf{u}_B|^2 = 4U^2\sin^2\theta$. Bernoulli's equation along this curve gives

$$\frac{p_B}{\rho} + \tfrac{1}{2}(4U^2\sin^2\theta) = \frac{p_0}{\rho} + \tfrac{1}{2}U^2,$$

which can be rearranged to give an equation for the pressure on the cylinder, as

$$\begin{aligned}
p_B &= p_0 + \tfrac{1}{2}\rho U^2(1 - 4\sin^2\theta) \\
&= p_0 + \tfrac{1}{2}\rho U^2(2\cos(2\theta) - 1).
\end{aligned}$$

The second form for $p_B$ is more amenable to integration.

(Note that at the stagnation points, where $\theta = 0$ and $\theta = \pi$, the pressure on the cylinder takes a maximum value $p_0 + \tfrac{1}{2}\rho U^2$, as observed in Subsection 1.1.)  ∎

The solution to Example 2.1 provides an expression for the distribution of pressure, $p$, round the cylinder. For the inviscid, steady flow considered,

$$p = p_0 + \tfrac{1}{2}\rho U^2 (2\cos(2\theta) - 1).$$

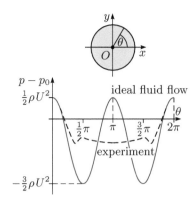

Figure 2.14 shows a graph of $p - p_0$ against $\theta$. The pressure is symmetrical about both the $x$-axis ($\theta = 0, \pi$) and the $y$-axis ($\theta = \tfrac{1}{2}\pi, \tfrac{3}{2}\pi$), and so the net surface force on the cylinder is zero. This result is expected from considering the symmetry of the streamline pattern. The force on the upper half of the cylinder will be balanced by the force on the lower half. This predicted pressure distribution conflicts with the experimental results, which are indicated by the broken curve in Figure 2.14. It is the inviscid assumption that leads to this discrepancy between the prediction from the model and reality.

*Figure 2.14*

### Exercise 2.4

The stream function for a source of strength $2\pi m$ at the point $(0, b)$, where $b > 0$, outside a wall along the $x$-axis is

$$\psi = m\left( \arctan\left( \frac{y - b}{x} \right) + \arctan\left( \frac{y + b}{x} \right) \right).$$

The fluid can be modelled as inviscid and of constant density, the flow is irrotational, and there are no body forces. Find the pressure at any point of the wall, if the pressure is $p_0$ far from the wall.

This is the same problem as in Exercise 5.3 of *Unit 5*. Compare the two solutions to see how the use of Bernoulli's equation is more convenient.

### Exercise 2.5

Consider the two-dimensional unsteady flow field of a constant-density, inviscid liquid, given by

$$\mathbf{u} = 2yt\,\mathbf{i} - 2x\,\mathbf{j},$$

with body force per unit mass $\mathbf{F} = 2y\,\mathbf{i}$. Can one of the forms of Bernoulli's equation be used to find the pressure distribution in the fluid? Explain your answer.

---

The problem in Exercise 2.5 is the same as that investigated in Example 5.1 of *Unit 5*. By integrating Euler's equation, the pressure distribution was found there to be $p = 2(x^2 + y^2)\rho t + g(t)$. No form of Bernoulli's equation can be applied to this problem, because

- the body force is not conservative, and
- the flow is unsteady and rotational (i.e. **curl u** $\neq$ **0**).

Thus, in some problems, Bernoulli's equation will not provide a simple formula for finding the pressure distribution. In such cases, Euler's equation may be used to find **grad** $p$, leading to integration of the two simultaneous partial differential equations involving $\partial p / \partial x$ and $\partial p / \partial y$.

## *End-of-section exercises*

### *Exercise 2.6*

Consider the flow of water (assumed inviscid and of constant density) from an orifice of area $S$ in the base of a reservoir. The depth $H$ of water in the reservoir is constant (see Figure 2.15). Derive an equation for the area of the cross-section of the jet at a distance $h$ below the base of the reservoir, in terms of $h$, $H$ and $S$.

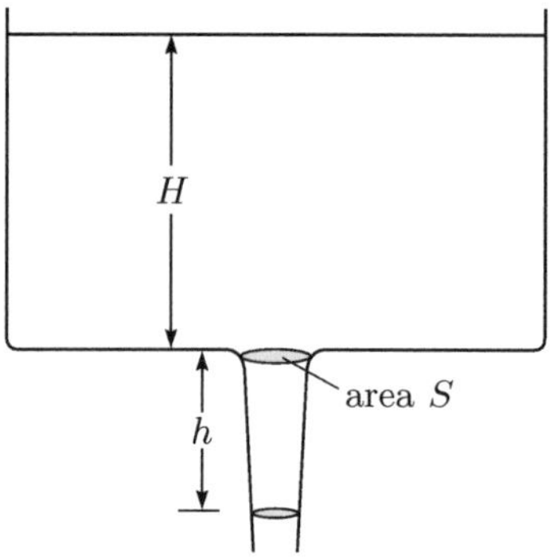

### *Exercise 2.7*

Consider the steady flow of an inviscid, constant-density fluid in the horizontal circular pipe shown in Figure 2.16. The cross-sectional areas of sections $A$, $B$, $C$ and $D$ are $S$, $\frac{1}{4}S$, $\frac{1}{2}S$ and $\frac{3}{4}S$ respectively. Sketch graphs showing the variation with distance $x$ along the central streamline of the following.

(a) the speed, $u$     (b) the pressure, $p$     (c) the stagnation pressure

### *Exercise 2.8*

Consider the steady flow of an inviscid, constant-density liquid past a sphere of radius $a$. In spherical polar coordinates, the velocity field is

$$\mathbf{u} = U\cos\theta\left(1 - \frac{a^3}{r^3}\right)\mathbf{e}_r - U\sin\theta\left(1 + \frac{a^3}{2r^3}\right)\mathbf{e}_\theta.$$

Find the pressure distribution on the surface of the sphere, assuming that there are no body forces and that the pressure is $p_0$ far from the sphere.

*Figure 2.15*

*Figure 2.16*

The formula for **curl** in spherical polar coordinates is in *Unit 4* Subsection 4.1, or at the back of the *Handbook*.

# 3    *Open channel flows*

This section considers the flow of liquid in a channel for which the uppermost boundary is a free surface. In contrast to the flow in a pipe, discussed in Subsection 2.2, the cross-section of the flow in a channel is not completely determined by the shape of the solid boundary forming the channel, but is free to change. Such flows are called **open channel flows**. The free surface is usually open to the atmosphere, so the pressure at every point on the free surface is equal to atmospheric pressure. If this pressure is assumed constant, then, by Bernoulli's equation, changes in the flow of liquid are caused by the effects of gravity as the channel bed changes level, or by changes in the width of the channel.

There are many applications of open channel flow. Natural streams and rivers, artificial canals and irrigation ditches are familiar examples. The flow of water with a free surface exposed to the atmosphere presents to the hydraulic engineer perhaps the most common problems of fluid mechanics. The flows of liquids in partly-filled pipes and tunnels (e.g. sewers) are other examples which can be modelled as open channel flows.

The pressure difference over the depth of the channel is *not* negligible. This contrasts with the situation in Subsection 2.2 (see the discussion following Exercise 2.3 on page 84).

The flow in an open channel is difficult to model, and so the following simplifying assumptions are made in order to make progress.

(i) The liquid flowing in the channel is *inviscid* and of *constant density*. (Frictional forces become important only if there are changes of depth over a long length of channel, and if the flow is close to boundaries.)

(ii) The flow is *steady*. (In most problems, the flow in an open channel is reasonably steady, although unsteady flows do arise if there is a surge wave travelling through the liquid.)

(iii) The channel is *straight*, and of *rectangular vertical cross-section* with *constant width*.

(iv) The flow is *uniform*, in that at every point of a vertical cross-section, the speed takes the same value.

An example of a surge wave in a river is the Severn bore.

The channel is deep enough for the liquid not to spill over.

With these assumptions, Bernoulli's equation is used along a streamline in the free surface of the liquid, along which the pressure does not change. By using the continuity equation and Bernoulli's equation, it is possible to identify the possible flows that can occur in an open channel.

## 3.1  Classification of the flow

Consider the steady, uniform flow of an inviscid, constant-density liquid in an open channel with a rectangular cross-section of constant width (see Figure 3.1). If the depth of liquid in the channel is $h$ and the width of the channel is $b$, then the volume flow rate $V$ through any cross-section is given by

$$V = hbu,$$

where $u$ is the speed of the liquid. The continuity equation states that $V$ is constant, since there is no net accumulation of liquid in any part of the channel. With the assumptions of uniform flow ($u$ is constant across a cross-section) and the channel having constant width ($b$ is constant), the consequence of $V$ being constant is that the volume flow rate per unit width, that is, $V/b = hu$, is constant along the channel. If $Q$ denotes the volume flow rate per unit width, then

Here $h$ and $u$ may vary from section to section.

$$Q = hu = \text{constant}. \tag{3.1}$$

Consider $Q$ to be a given quantity; it is, in a sense, the 'input' to the channel from some source. For example, if the channel under consideration is a sewer carrying water from a drain, then $Q$ is the amount of water (per unit width) per unit time that enters at one end and leaves at the other.

*Figure 3.1*

Now apply Bernoulli's equation along a streamline in the free surface of the liquid in a flat-bottomed channel, to obtain

$$\frac{p_0}{\rho} + \tfrac{1}{2}u^2 + gh = \text{constant},$$

where $p_0$ is atmospheric pressure, $\rho$ is the density, and the datum level $z = 0$ is chosen as the bottom of the channel (see Figure 3.2). Subtracting the constant $p_0/\rho$ from each side of this equation provides a relationship between possible flow speeds and possible depths of liquid in the channel,

$$\tfrac{1}{2}u^2 + gh = \text{constant}.$$

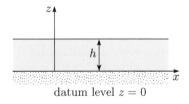

*Figure 3.2*

In open channel flow problems, it is convenient to write Bernoulli's equation in an amended form. Dividing this last equation by $g$, we have

$$\frac{u^2}{2g} + h = \text{constant} = E, \text{ say}. \tag{3.2}$$

The quantity $E = u^2/(2g) + h$ is usually called the **specific energy**.

For a channel with a *horizontal* floor, as above, $E$ is a constant of the flow. This is an important point. If the channel floor is not horizontal, for example, supposing that it slopes upwards as in Figure 3.3, then Bernoulli's equation along a line in the free surface is

$$\frac{p_0}{\rho} + \tfrac{1}{2}u^2 + gz = \text{constant},$$

from which (since $z = h + r$)

$$\frac{u^2}{2g} + h + r = \text{constant} = H, \text{ say.}$$

The constant $H$ is usually called the **total energy**. The specific energy (referred to the channel floor) is $E = u^2/(2g) + h$, and is now *not* a constant. As you will see, it is still more convenient to work with $E$. In this subsection the channel is always horizontal, so that $r = 0$, and for a given flow $E$ is constant.

Sometimes $E$ is called the *specific head*; it has the dimensions of length (energy per unit weight).

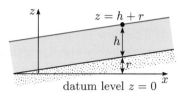

*Figure 3.3*

Sometimes $H$ is called the *total head*; it has the dimensions of length.

In fact, $E = H - r$, where $H$ is constant and $r$ increases if the channel floor rises.

### Exercise 3.1

Consider an open channel flow in which water flows to a depth of $1\,\text{m}$ with speed $2\,\text{m}\,\text{s}^{-1}$. Calculate the value of the specific energy, $E$, and the volume flow rate per unit width, $Q$, for this flow. Starting with these values of $Q$ and $E$, find any other values of $u$ and $h$ that satisfy Equations (3.1) and (3.2). Take $g = 10\,\text{m}\,\text{s}^{-2}$.

*Hint:* To factorise a cubic $f(h)$ for which one root $\alpha$ is known, first write

$$f(h) = (h - \alpha)(h^2 + ah + b)$$

and find values for $a$, $b$ by equating coefficients of $h$.

Exact results are not required here, so calculations are simplified in this section by taking $g = 10\,\text{m}\,\text{s}^{-2}$. You will always be told if you are to use a value for $g$ other than $9.81\,\text{m}\,\text{s}^{-2}$.

The solution to Exercise 3.1 shows that, for this particular channel flow problem, there are two possible flows that have the same values for the constants $E$ and $Q$. It is possible to generalise this result. Using Equation (3.1), we have $u = Q/h$, and substituting for $u$ in Equation (3.2) gives

$$E = \frac{Q^2}{2gh^2} + h, \tag{3.3}$$

that is,

$$h^3 - Eh^2 + \frac{Q^2}{2g} = 0.$$

A cubic may have either three real roots (including possible repeated roots) or just one. In fact, just one of the roots in this case is always negative and hence is physically meaningless. (The cubic expression on the left-hand side above is positive for $h = 0$ and negative when $h$ is large and negative; hence it must have a negative root. Since the expression is increasing for $h < 0$, there can be only one negative root.) So, for a *given* $E$ (and $Q$), there are either two feasible values of $h$, one (repeated) or none.

Now, instead of thinking of $E$ as fixed, consider Equation (3.3) as describing the specific energy, $E$, as a function of the depth $h$ ($> 0$). Figure 3.4 shows a graph of $E$ against $h$ (with $Q$ given a constant value); it is called the **specific energy function curve**. Its general shape follows from the fact that $E$ becomes large as $h$ becomes small (where $E \simeq Q^2/(2gh^2)$) and as $h$ becomes large (where $E \simeq h$).

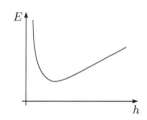

*Figure 3.4*

From the graph in Figure 3.4 you can see that, given a value of $h$, there is a unique value for $E$. However, if the value of $E$ is known, then the value of $h$ may not be unique; there are three cases to consider.

(i) If $E > E_{\min}$, then two flows are possible, at different depths $h_1$, $h_2$ and corresponding speeds $u_1$, $u_2$; see Figure 3.5. Now, $h_1 < h_2$, and since $Q = h_1 u_1 = h_2 u_2$, then $u_1 > u_2$. So one flow is 'shallow and fast' ($h = h_1$) and the other is 'deep and slow' ($h = h_2$).

(ii) If $E = E_{\min}$, then the flow is unique; see Figure 3.6. The liquid flows with depth $h_c$ and speed $u_c = Q/h_c$, where $h_c$, $u_c$ are called the **critical depth** and **critical speed**, respectively.

(iii) If $E < E_{\min}$, then no flow is possible; see Figure 3.7.

The critical conditions, $h = h_c$ and $u = u_c$, are key values that facilitate the classification of flows in open channels.

Since the critical depth, $h_c$, occurs at a minimum of the specific energy function, an equation relating $h_c$ to $Q$ can be found in the usual way, by differentiating $E$ with respect to $h$ and then equating the result to zero. From Equation (3.3), this gives

$$\left[\frac{dE}{dh}\right]_{h=h_c} = \left[1 - \frac{Q^2}{gh^3}\right]_{h=h_c} = 1 - \frac{Q^2}{gh_c^3} = 0.$$

Solving this equation gives

$$h_c = \left(\frac{Q^2}{g}\right)^{1/3}, \tag{3.4}$$

so that also

$$Q^2 = h_c^3 g. \tag{3.5}$$

The minimum value of the specific energy, $E_{\min}$, for which flow is possible is then

$$E_{\min} = \left[h + \frac{Q^2}{2gh^2}\right]_{h=h_c} = h_c + \frac{h_c^3 g}{2gh_c^2} = \tfrac{3}{2}h_c.$$

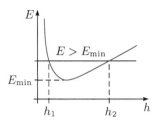

*Figure 3.5*

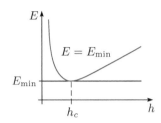

*Figure 3.6*

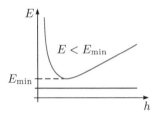

*Figure 3.7*

These equations for $h_c$ and $E_{\min}$ hold only for channels of rectangular cross-section.

### Exercise 3.2

Consider the channel flows described in Exercise 1.7, where there were two horizontal, rectangular channels in which the depths and speeds were $1.2\,\text{m}$, $2.5\,\text{m s}^{-1}$ and $0.6\,\text{m}$, $12.5\,\text{m s}^{-1}$, respectively. Calculate the critical depth for each of these channels, and classify the flows as 'shallow and fast' or 'deep and slow'. Take $g = 10\,\text{m s}^{-2}$.

Note that $Q$ is not the same in the two channels, since they have different widths.

Since $u = Q/h$, the critical speed, $u_c$, may be determined in terms of the critical depth, $h_c$, by substituting for $Q$ from Equation (3.5). This gives

$$u_c = \frac{\sqrt{h_c^3 g}}{h_c} = \sqrt{h_c g},$$

from which it follows that

$$\frac{u_c}{\sqrt{gh_c}} = 1. \tag{3.6}$$

The ratio $u/\sqrt{gh}$ is one of the many dimensionless quantities in fluid mechanics that has been given a special name. It is called the **Froude number** (usually denoted by $Fr$), after William Froude (1810–79), who first introduced it. The Froude number is often important for flows in which the viscous forces are negligible.

Froude was a pioneer in the study of naval architecture.

Wave motion caused by the passage of a ship through water is an example of such a flow. Another example is open channel flow, the subject of this section. Equation (3.6) illustrates an application of the Froude number in this case. When the critical flow conditions ($u = u_c$, $h = h_c$) occur in an open channel flow then, by Equation (3.6),

$$Fr = \frac{u}{\sqrt{gh}} = 1.$$

In Exercise 3.2 the flow in each channel was classified by comparing the flow levels to the critical height. The Froude number provides an alternative method of classification.

The Froude number here is $Fr = u/\sqrt{gl}$, where $l$ is the length of the ship, and for ships, $Fr < 1$. For example, for a tanker of length 400 m moving at 12 knots, $Fr \simeq 0.1$, and for a fast warship of length 100 m moving at 25 knots, $Fr \simeq 0.4$.

1 knot $\simeq 1.15$ mph $\simeq 0.51$ m s$^{-1}$.

## Exercise 3.3

(a) Use Equations (3.1) and (3.4) to show that

$$Fr = \left(\frac{h_c}{h}\right)^{3/2}.$$

(b) Show that 'deep and slow' flows (those for $h > h_c$) occur for $Fr < 1$, and that 'shallow and fast' flows (those for $h < h_c$) occur for $Fr > 1$.

$Fr$ can also be written in terms of $u_c$, as

$$Fr = \left(\frac{u}{u_c}\right)^{3/2},$$

so that $Fr > 1$ corresponds to $u > u_c$, i.e. 'fast' flow.

The solution to Exercise 3.3 provides a method of classifying the flow in a (rectangular) open channel. Corresponding to a given flow rate per unit width, $Q$, there is a critical depth, $h_c$, for which the specific energy is the minimum necessary to sustain flow. If the specific energy is greater than this minimum value, then there are two possible flow states.

(i) If $Fr \left(= u/\sqrt{gh}\right) < 1$, then the flow is 'deep and slow', and is referred to as **subcritical flow** (because $Fr < 1$, whereas $Fr = 1$ corresponds to the critical values of $h$ and $u$).

(ii) If $Fr \left(= u/\sqrt{gh}\right) > 1$, then the flow is 'shallow and fast' and is referred to as **supercritical flow**.

Flow with $Fr = 1$ is called **critical flow**.

The critical speed $u_c = \sqrt{gh_c}$ reappears in *Unit 12*, in the discussion of water waves, where it represents the speed of propagation of small surface waves on a shallow liquid. When the flow speed is less than this critical value, i.e. $Fr = (u/u_c)^{3/2} < 1$, it is possible for a small surface wave to travel upstream against the flow. However, if the flow speed is greater than the critical value, i.e. $Fr > 1$, then the liquid is travelling downstream faster than a small wave can be propagated upstream. Since a wave can be thought of as a 'messenger' carrying information, if $u < u_c$ then it is possible to send messages upstream by means of the wave, so that the liquid upstream can be informed of any disturbances downstream. However, for the other case, $u > u_c$, messages cannot be passed upstream, so that the flow cannot be influenced by downstream disturbances. The significance of these ideas will become apparent in the next two subsections, where the flow is influenced by obstacles.

The Froude number is similar to the dimensionless *Mach number*, which is a measure of speed relative to the speed of sound in a fluid.

Imagine a pedestrian walking with speed $u_c$ against the motion of a downward-moving escalator that has speed $u$. If $u < u_c$, then the pedestrian succeeds in travelling up the escalator. However, if $u > u_c$, then the escalator carries the pedestrian down with it.

## Exercise 3.4

In a long open channel of width 3 m, the specific energy is 2.2 m and the volume flow rate is 12 m$^3$s$^{-1}$. Show that $h = 2$ m is one possible depth of flow, and calculate the other possible depth. What are the corresponding speeds of flow and Froude numbers? Take $g = 10$ m s$^{-2}$.

A summary of the classification of channel flows is given below.

### Channel flow classification

Froude number: $Fr = \dfrac{u}{\sqrt{gh}} = \left(\dfrac{u}{u_c}\right)^{3/2} = \left(\dfrac{h_c}{h}\right)^{3/2}.$

Subcritical flow: $Fr < 1, \quad h > h_c \text{ ('deep')}, \quad u < u_c \text{ ('slow')}.$

Critical flow: $Fr = 1, \quad h = h_c = \left(\dfrac{Q^2}{g}\right)^{1/3}, \quad u = u_c = (Qg)^{1/3}.$

Supercritical flow: $Fr > 1, \quad h < h_c \text{ ('shallow')}, \quad u > u_c \text{ ('fast')}.$

The details here apply only to channels with uniform rectangular cross-section. However, the same principles can be applied to other shapes of cross-section, as you will see in Exercise 3.7.

For critical flow, using Equation (3.4), we have
$$u_c = (h_c g)^{1/2}$$
$$= ((Q^2/g)^{1/3}g)^{1/2}$$
$$= (Qg)^{1/3}.$$

## 3.2 Flow over a weir

So far in this section, the flow considered has been in a channel which has a level horizontal floor. For a given specific energy and volume flow rate per unit width, there are then often two possible flows.

Next we investigate channel flow where there is a raised portion in the floor. The channel has a rectangular cross-section, as before, and the raised portion of its floor extends across the full width of the stream. Such an obstruction is called a *weir*. Figure 3.8 shows two designs of weirs, and the flows over them. This subsection will investigate the flow over a broad-crested weir. The upstream and downstream edges of such a weir are rounded, so as to avoid the formation of vortices and the resulting loss of mechanical energy. The smooth streamline pattern suggested by Figure 3.8(b) means that Bernoulli's equation will apply. Weirs provide a method of estimating the volume flow rate in rivers, and are also used to maintain the level of a river upstream; weirs are also a good model for the changes in floor level that occur naturally in streams and rivers.

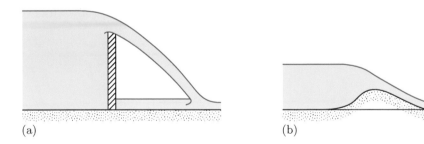

(a)          (b)

*Figure 3.8*  (a)  A sharp-crested weir    (b)  A broad-crested weir

We begin by investigating the flow in a channel with a small inclined step in the floor, which separates two horizontal sections. Denote upstream conditions by the subscript 1 ($u_1$ and $h_1$), and downstream conditions by the subscript 2 ($u_2$ and $h_2$). In all diagrams, upstream is to the left and downstream to the right.

### Example 3.1

Figure 3.9 shows two sections of a horizontal channel of constant width, separated by a small step of height 0.2 m. In the upstream section of the channel, the depth of steady flow of an inviscid, constant-density liquid is 2 m, and the speed is $2\,\mathrm{m\,s^{-1}}$. Determine the depth and speed of flow in the downstream section of the channel. Compare the Froude numbers in each section. Take $g = 10\,\mathrm{m\,s^{-2}}$.

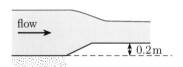

*Figure 3.9*

93

### Solution

The volume flow rates per unit width in each section of the channel are equal, by the continuity equation. Using the given upstream values to evaluate $Q$, we have

$$Q = u_1 h_1 = 2 \times 2 = 4\,\mathrm{m^2 s^{-1}};$$

and then, in the downstream channel section, $Q = u_2 h_2 = 4\,\mathrm{m^2 s^{-1}}$.

Applying Bernoulli's equation along a streamline in the free surface, on which $p = p_0$, we obtain

$$\frac{u_2^2}{2g} + h_2 + r = \frac{u_1^2}{2g} + h_1 = \frac{4}{2g} + 2 = 2.2, \qquad (3.7)$$

where $z$ is measured from the horizontal level of the upstream channel floor and $r$ is the rise in the channel floor (see Figure 3.10). Substituting $r = 0.2$, $g = 10$ and $u_2 = 4/h_2$ gives

$$\frac{0.8}{h_2^2} + h_2 + 0.2 = 2.2.$$

Thus $h_2$ is a solution of the cubic equation

$$s^3 - 2s^2 + 0.8 = 0. \qquad (3.8)$$

To solve this cubic equation for $s$, we use the Newton–Raphson method to determine the value of the root near $s = 2$. (Intuitively, the level of the liquid would not be expected to increase or decrease by much from the upstream value, $h_1 = 2\,\mathrm{m}$, so this is taken as the first iterate, $s_0$.)

This root is (see the calculation in the margin) $s = h_2 \simeq 1.734$. The value of the speed corresponding to this depth is

$$u_2 = \frac{Q}{h_2} = \frac{4}{1.734} \simeq 2.307\,\mathrm{m\,s^{-1}}.$$

The Froude numbers for the upstream and downstream sections of the channel are, respectively,

$$\frac{2}{\sqrt{2g}} \simeq 0.45 \qquad \text{and} \qquad \frac{2.307}{\sqrt{1.734 \times g}} \simeq 0.55.$$

The subcritical flow upstream of the step remains subcritical downstream, but at a lower depth and faster speed.  ■

---

### Exercise 3.5

Consider a flow in the same channel as in Example 3.1, with the same volume flow rate per unit width, $Q = 4\,\mathrm{m^2 s^{-1}}$, and upstream specific energy, $E_1 = 2.2\,\mathrm{m}$. The supercritical flow possible for these conditions upstream has depth $h_1 = 0.740\,\mathrm{m}$ (as found in Exercise 3.4). Show that, for this case, the downstream depth, $h_2$, is given as before by a solution of the cubic equation (3.8).

Determine the root of this equation near $s = h_1 = 0.740$. Compare the Froude numbers in each section of the channel. Take $g = 10\,\mathrm{m\,s^{-2}}$.

---

For the above example and exercise, the subcritical and supercritical flows upstream remain in those states downstream. In the subcritical case (Example 3.1), the depth of liquid falls, whereas in the supercritical case (Exercise 3.5), the depth of liquid increases. In each case, the cubic equation for $h_2$ is the same. This is because the specific energies and volume flow rates are identical. (The two upstream flows are the solutions of Exercise 3.4, for which $E = 2.2\,\mathrm{m}$ and $Q = 4\,\mathrm{m^2 s^{-1}}$.)

---

Bernoulli's equation here can be written as

$$\frac{p_0}{\rho g} + \frac{u^2}{2g} + z = \text{constant}.$$

Hence the specific energy upstream is $E_1 = 2.2\,\mathrm{m}$.

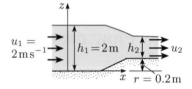

Figure 3.10

The *Newton–Raphson method* is discussed in MS221 *Chapter C1*. To solve the equation $f(s) = 0$, it is based on the iteration formula

$$s_{n+1} = s_n - \frac{f(s_n)}{f'(s_n)}.$$

For the cubic equation (3.8), the calculation is below:

$$s_{n+1} = s_n - \frac{s_n^3 - 2s_n^2 + 0.8}{3s_n^2 - 4s_n}.$$

| $n$ | $s_n$ |
|-----|-------|
| 0 | 2 |
| 1 | 1.8 |
| 2 | 1.740 |
| 3 | 1.734 |
| 4 | 1.734 |

Here 'downstream' means, as in Example 3.1, beyond the rise of 0.2 m in the channel floor.

A problem of this type requires the solution of a cubic equation for the downstream depth, $h_2$. However, the conditions of the flow over a rise in the channel floor can be deduced from the specific energy function curve. Although this approach will not give an accurate value for the depth, it does allow a qualitative prediction of how the flow will change. Furthermore, for the flow over a step, consideration of the specific energy function can explain why subcritical flow does not usually become supercritical, or vice versa.

Consider again the flows in Example 3.1 and Exercise 3.5. In each case, as in Equation (3.7), Bernoulli's equation gives

$$\frac{u_1^2}{2g} + h_1 = \frac{u_2^2}{2g} + h_2 + r \tag{3.9}$$

(see Figure 3.11). From the continuity equation,

$$Q = h_1 u_1 = h_2 u_2 \ (= \text{constant}).$$

Eliminating $u_1$ and $u_2$ from Equation (3.9) gives

$$\frac{Q^2}{2gh_1^2} + h_1 = \frac{Q^2}{2gh_2^2} + h_2 + r. \tag{3.10}$$

The specific energy (relative to the floor of the channel) was defined by

$$E = \frac{u^2}{2g} + h = \frac{Q^2}{2gh^2} + h.$$

See Equation (3.3).

Now, for the channel of Example 3.1 and Exercise 3.5, $E_1 = 2.2\,\text{m}$ and $Q = 4\,\text{m}^2\text{s}^{-1}$, so that in this case (with $g = 10\,\text{m s}^{-2}$)

$$E_2 = \frac{0.8}{h_2^2} + h_2 \quad \text{and, from Equation (3.10),} \quad E_1 = E_2 + r = 2.2.$$

This equation shows that, although $E_1$ is the constant upstream value of $E$, if the channel floor rises by an amount $r$ then the downstream specific energy, $E_2$, is less than $E_1$ by the same amount, $r$. Figure 3.12 shows a graph of $E$ plotted against $h$, incorporating the above conditions.

Often in the literature, the graphs of specific energy curves such as this are plotted with the $E$-axis horizontal and the $h$-axis vertical. This sometimes enables the graph to be aligned with a diagram representing the channel.

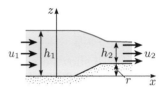

*Figure 3.11*

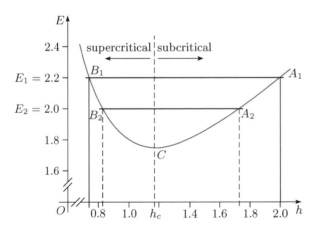

*Figure 3.12*

The upstream conditions are represented by the point $A_1$ or $B_1$ (on the line $E = E_1 = 2.2$), and the critical conditions occur at point $C$. Now, if the floor rises by $r = 0.2\,\text{m}$, the specific energy decreases by $r = 0.2\,\text{m}$. This new value of $E$ $(= E_2 = 2.0)$ corresponds to the point $A_2$ or $B_2$.

Starting with the upstream conditions at $A_1$, i.e. $h_1 = 2$ and $E_1 = 2.2$, a step of height 0.2 m leads to the downstream conditions at $A_2$, i.e. a decrease in the depth to 1.73 m. Both points $A_1$ and $A_2$ lie on the subcritical $(h > h_c)$ parts of the curve. So the subcritical flow at $A_1$

Example 3.1

95

remains subcritical at $A_2$. Similarly, if the upstream conditions are those at $B_1$, i.e. $h_1 = 0.74$ and $E_1 = 2.2$, then the step leads to the downstream conditions at $B_2$, i.e. an increase in the depth to 0.83 m.

Consider the general case for which there is a rise in the channel floor and the upstream conditions are subcritical. Suppose that the volume flow rate per unit width is $Q$, the upstream specific energy is $E_1$ and the channel floor rises by an amount $r$. Then (as before)

$$E_1 = \frac{Q^2}{2gh_1^2} + h_1 = \frac{Q^2}{2gh_2^2} + h_2 + r = E_2 + r.$$

Figure 3.13 shows a sketch of $E$ against $h$, i.e. a sketch of the function $E(h) = Q^2/(2gh^2) + h$, and the point $A_1$ represents the specific energy level, $E_1$, for an upstream flow which is subcritical. If the bed rises by a height $r$, then the specific energy, $E$, decreases by the same amount $r$ from $E_1$ to $E_2$. This decrease in $E$ leads to a lower depth in the downstream channel, as represented by the point $A_2$ on the specific energy curve. The downstream conditions remain subcritical.

Exercise 3.5

Subcritical flows are the normal conditions prevailing in applications of open channel flows such as rivers.

As stated in Figure 3.13, we assume here that

$$r < E_1 - E_{\min}.$$

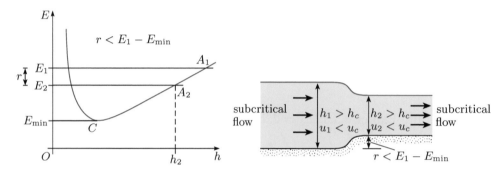

Figure 3.13

Now if $r = E_1 - E_{\min}$, then the point $A_2$ lies at the critical point, $C$, for which $h = h_c = (Q^2/g)^{1/3}$ (see Figure 3.14). The downstream flow is then critical, and this value of $E$ $(= E_{\min})$ is the smallest possible to sustain the steady flow.

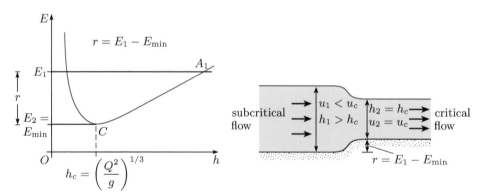

Figure 3.14

Imagine now that $r$, the rise in the channel floor, is increased beyond the value $E_1 - E_{\min}$, the upstream conditions still being subcritical with $E = E_1$. What happens? Initially, the upstream conditions $h_1$ and $u_1$ are not sufficient to sustain the critical flow downstream, and the steady flow of Figure 3.14 breaks down. This 'information' is fed back upstream (because all the fluid cannot pass over the rise), and the upstream flow conditions will change, the depth increasing (but the volume flow rate remaining constant) so as to re-establish critical flow downstream. This situation is shown in Figure 3.15.

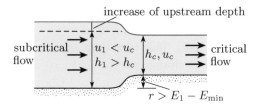

*Figure 3.15*

To summarise, a steady subcritical flow in the upstream section of the channel either remains subcritical or becomes critical downstream of a rise in the channel bed.

### Exercise 3.6

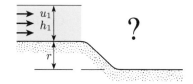

*Figure 3.16*

Consider the flow of an inviscid, constant-density liquid in a channel with a drop of $r$ metres separating the two horizontal sections (see Figure 3.16). Use the specific energy curve to predict the downstream conditions if the upstream flow is (a) subcritical; (b) supercritical.

As you might expect, and as the solution to this exercise shows, lowering the channel floor produces the reverse effect of that which occurs for a rise in the channel floor. The flow after a drop in the channel floor becomes further from critical. We now combine the results for a flow over a rise and over a drop, to investigate the flow over a rounded weir.

### Example 3.2

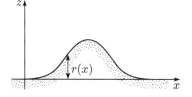

*Figure 3.17*

Suppose that the upstream flow approaching the rounded weir shown in Figure 3.17 is subcritical. Determine the possible flows downstream.

### Solution

According to the discussion above, when a subcritical flow approaches a rise in the channel floor, the flow becomes nearer critical. There are two cases to consider. At the crest of the weir, the flow is either subcritical or critical, depending on the step size, $r$.

If $r$ is too large, then the upstream conditions change so that the flow is critical at the crest.

(a) For subcritical flow at the crest, the downstream flow after the drop becomes further from critical (see Exercise 3.6(a)). The flow returns to its original depth downstream, i.e. $h_2 = h_1$; see Figure 3.18.

(b) For critical flow at the crest, consider the change in $h$ over the front half of the weir (i.e. the rise). The solid curve for the liquid surface in Figure 3.19 shows $h = h_1 > h_c$ before the crest and $h = h_c$ at the crest.

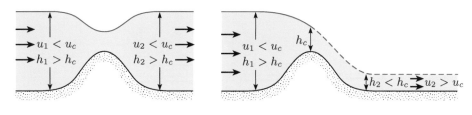

*Figure 3.18*          *Figure 3.19*

At the crest, the flow is critical and the gradient of $h(x)$ is negative (this is justified on the next page). With the assumption that there are no sudden changes in $h$, it should follow that the depth continues to fall (shown by the broken curve in Figure 3.19), so beyond the crest the flow becomes supercritical. ■

The two possible downstream flows for Example 3.2 are shown in Figures 3.18 and 3.19. For the first case, there is a minimum value for $h$ at the crest, corresponding to the maximum for $r$ at the crest. This property can be verified mathematically, by considering the rate of change of the total energy, $E + r$, over the weir. In general, the depth of the liquid, $h$, and the height of the channel bed, denoted by $r$, are functions of $x$, so that Bernoulli's equation gives

*Choose $z = 0$ for the channel bed on either side of the weir.*

$$E(x) + r(x) = \frac{Q^2}{2g\,[h(x)]^2} + h(x) + r(x) = \text{constant}.$$

*See Equation (3.3).*

Differentiating with respect to $x$, and abbreviating $h(x)$ and $r(x)$ to $h$ and $r$ respectively, gives

$$\frac{dE}{dx} + \frac{dr}{dx} = -\frac{Q^2}{gh^3}\frac{dh}{dx} + \frac{dh}{dx} + \frac{dr}{dx} = 0. \qquad (3.11)$$

Now $Q^2/g = h_c^3$ and $Fr = (h_c/h)^{3/2}$, so

*See Equation (3.4) and Exercise 3.3.*

$$\frac{Q^2}{gh^3} = \frac{h_c^3}{h^3} = Fr^2.$$

Equation (3.11) can then be written as

$$\left(1 - Fr^2\right)\frac{dh}{dx} + \frac{dr}{dx} = 0. \qquad (3.12)$$

At the crest of the weir, $dr/dx = 0$; so either $dh/dx = 0$ or $1 - Fr^2 = 0$. If $dh/dx = 0$ and $Fr \neq 1$ at the crest, then the minimum value of $h$ occurs at the crest; this is case (a) in Example 3.2.

*If both $dh/dx = 0$ and $Fr = 1$ at the crest, this analysis does not predict whether the downstream flow will be subcritical or supercritical.*

If $dh/dx \neq 0$ at the crest, then $1 - Fr^2 = 0$, that is, $Fr = 1$ and the flow is critical at the crest. Just before the crest, the flow is subcritical ($Fr < 1$) and $dr/dx > 0$, so Equation (3.12) implies that $dh/dx < 0$, that is, the depth is decreasing. At the crest, $dh/dx \neq 0$, and so, assuming that $h(x)$ is a continuous function with continuous derivatives, $dh/dx$ is still negative. Physically, this means that the depth of flow continues to fall beyond the crest of the weir. This is case (b) in Example 3.2.

In both cases, the downstream values of $Q$ and $E$ are the same as the upstream values. The two possible depths and corresponding speeds of flow downstream of the weir can be found from the same cubic equation in $h$ (as in Subsection 3.1). The two possible flows in a channel for given values $E$ and $Q$ are achievable by inserting an obstruction into the flow. The type of downstream flow depends on the shape of the weir. Broad-crested weirs are commonly used for measuring the flow rates in open channels. In particular, if the flow is critical at the crest of the weir, a measure of $h_c$ will give the flow rate by using Equation (3.5), $Q^2 = h_c^3 g$.

Experiments validate the predictions made here for flows over a weir.

## 3.3  *The hydraulic jump*

There is one situation that has not been discussed in Subsection 3.2. Suppose that the upstream flow in a channel is supercritical and the channel floor is raised an amount $r$. This raising of the channel floor decreases $E$ from $E_1$ to $E_2 = E_1 - r$, and the depth of flow increases (see Figure 3.20). The flow remains supercritical, provided that $r < E_1 - E_{\min}$. If $r = E_1 - E_{\min}$, then the downstream flow becomes critical. If $r$ were to be increased further, then the point $A_2$ would be forced to go lower than the critical point, at which the specific energy is $E = E_{\min}$.

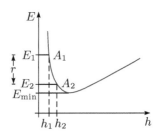

*Figure 3.20*

A flow is not possible for $E < E_{\text{min}}$. Physically, however, it is possible to have a supercritical flow approaching such a large rise in the channel floor, by, for example, a combination of two weirs (see Figure 3.21).

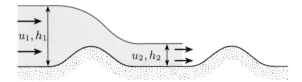

*Figure 3.21*

So what happens? In the analogous situation of a subcritical upstream flow, the liquid could send information upstream to inform the approaching liquid of the rise in the floor. The depth of the liquid ahead of the rise increases by exactly the correct amount to sustain a critical flow at the crest.

For a supercritical upstream flow (with $u = u_1$, $h = h_1$), the information about the rise cannot be transmitted to the approaching fluid, because the liquid is flowing too fast. To accommodate the large rise, $r > E_1 - E_{\text{min}}$, the approaching fluid changes to subcritical flow (with $u = u_3$, $h = h_3$) of such a specific energy level as to retain critical flow at the following crest. In this change, represented by the line $A'A''$ in Figure 3.22, there is a loss of energy, and Bernoulli's equation is no longer valid. This occurs across a sudden jump in the liquid level called a **hydraulic jump**. A smooth transition from fast to slow flow is not possible.

For video of a hydraulic jump, see the *Media Guide*.

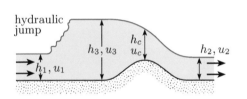 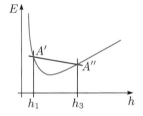

*Figure 3.22*

In a river, hydraulic jumps occur naturally at the back of weirs and other obstructions. The weir causes the flow to become supercritical, and the water is then fast-flowing in the downstream part of the river. It is important to arrange for a hydraulic jump to occur behind the weir so that the flow becomes subcritical further downstream. This avoids the severe scouring of the river bed and damage to the river banks that fast flows can cause. A hydraulic jump decelerates the flow, transferring unwanted kinetic energy into thermal energy.

A hydraulic jump can be created very easily in a kitchen sink (see Figure 3.23). After falling onto the sink, the water streams away at high speed. The sides of the sink act like a weir, slowing the flow to a critical value. In between, there is a sharp transition from supercritical (fast) flow to subcritical (slow) flow across a hydraulic jump.

*Figure 3.23*

# *End-of-section exercises*

## *Exercise 3.7*

The cross-section of a horizontal channel is an isosceles triangle with a constant angle of $2\alpha$ at the apex, as shown in Figure 3.24.

(a) Write down an expression for the volume flow rate, $V$, in terms of the flow speed, $u$, the vertical height of the triangle, $h$, and the angle $\alpha$.

(b) By using Bernoulli's equation, show that the specific energy function $E = u^2/(2g) + h$ is constant.

(c) For a given constant volume flow rate, $V$, find an expression for the critical depth, $h_c$, in terms of $V$, $g$ and $\alpha$. Hence determine a relationship between the critical speed and the critical depth.

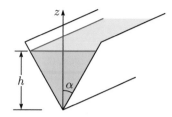

*Figure 3.24*

## *Exercise 3.8*

An inviscid, constant-density liquid flows steadily along an open flat-bottomed channel of *variable* breadth $b$, as shown in plan view in Figure 3.25. Each cross-section of the channel is rectangular.

(a) Show that the rates of change of breadth, $b(x)$, and depth, $h(x)$, are related by the equation

$$\frac{db}{dx} = \left( \frac{1}{Fr^2} - 1 \right) \frac{b}{h} \frac{dh}{dx},$$

where $Fr$ is the Froude number and the $x$-axis is in the direction of the flow. (Denote the volume flow rate by $V$.)

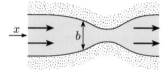

*Figure 3.25*

(b) Deduce the two possible conditions on the depth of flow at the throat.

(c) Suppose that the upstream conditions are subcritical. Draw a diagram showing the depth of the liquid surface above the channel bed if

   (i) $Fr < 1$ at the throat;     (ii) $Fr = 1$ at the throat.

# *Outcomes*

After studying this unit you should be able to:

- integrate Euler's equation to obtain Bernoulli's equation, under given assumptions;
- decide which form of Bernoulli's equation to use in a particular situation;
- use Bernoulli's equation to solve appropriate fluid flow problems;
- explain why Bernoulli's equation implies that higher fluid speed implies lower pressure, and vice versa;
- explain the difference between static, stagnation and dynamic pressures;
- specify the underlying assumptions for modelling channel flow;
- use Bernoulli's equation to solve channel flow problems;
- explain what is meant by subcritical, critical and supercritical flow, and how these relate to the Froude number;
- explain what occurs to the flow when there is a weir in the channel;
- recall how basic mathematical techniques can be useful in solving real problems;
- appreciate how mathematics can be applied in modelling.

# *Acknowledgements*

Grateful acknowledgement is made to the following for permission to reproduce photographs in this text:

Figure 1.3: `istockphoto.co.uk`;

Figure 2.8: Taken from `http://hyperphysics.phy-astr.gsu.edu`;

Figure 3.23: © Ken Kerr/Alamy.

Every effort has been made to contact copyright holders. If any have been inadvertently overlooked the publishers will be pleased to make the necessary arrangements at the first opportunity.

# Solutions to the exercises

## Section 1

### Solution 1.1

From the definition of $\Omega$,
$$\mathbf{F} = \nabla\Omega = \frac{\partial\Omega}{\partial x}\mathbf{i} + \frac{\partial\Omega}{\partial y}\mathbf{j} + \frac{\partial\Omega}{\partial z}\mathbf{k},$$
and for the body force of gravity,
$$\mathbf{F} = -g\,\mathbf{k}.$$
Thus $\dfrac{\partial\Omega}{\partial x} = 0,\quad \dfrac{\partial\Omega}{\partial y} = 0\quad$ and $\quad \dfrac{\partial\Omega}{\partial z} = -g.$

The first two of these three equations show that $\Omega$ is independent of $x$ and $y$. Integrating the third equation gives
$$\Omega = -gz + c, \quad \text{where } c \text{ is an arbitrary constant.}$$
Using this form for $\Omega$ in Bernoulli's equation (1.4), we have
$$\frac{p}{\rho} + \tfrac{1}{2}u^2 - (-gz + c) = \text{constant along a streamline}$$
or
$$\frac{p}{\rho} + \tfrac{1}{2}u^2 + gz = \text{constant along a streamline.}$$

### Solution 1.2

Using dimensional analysis methods, we have
$$\left[\frac{p}{\rho}\right] = \frac{[p]}{[\rho]} = \frac{\text{ML}^{-1}\text{T}^{-2}}{\text{ML}^{-3}} = \text{L}^2\text{T}^{-2}.$$
The dimensions of kinetic energy per unit mass are
$$\left[\frac{\tfrac{1}{2}mu^2}{m}\right] = [u^2] = [u]^2 = (\text{L T}^{-1})^2 = \text{L}^2\text{T}^{-2}.$$
Hence $p/\rho$ has the dimensions of energy per unit mass.

### Solution 1.3

The diagram below shows the pipe and the streamline through the points $A$ and $B$.

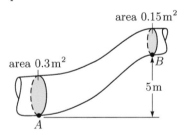

area $0.15\,\text{m}^2$

area $0.3\,\text{m}^2$

$B$

$5\,\text{m}$

$A$

Label the speeds at $A$ and $B$ by $u_A$, $u_B$, and the pressures by $p_A$, $p_B$. From the question,
$$u_A = 1.8\,\text{m s}^{-1} \quad \text{and} \quad p_A = 1 \times 10^5\,\text{Pa}.$$

**(a)** Use the continuity equation, from *Unit 5* Subsection 4.3, in the form

volume flow rate = area × average speed = constant.

This gives (in SI units)
$$0.3 \times 1.8 = 0.15 \times u_B.$$
Solving for $u_B$ gives
$$u_B = 3.6\,\text{m s}^{-1}.$$

**(b)** Assume that water is inviscid and of constant density, and that the flow is steady. Then, applying Bernoulli's equation along the streamline $AB$, we obtain
$$\frac{p_A}{\rho} + \tfrac{1}{2}u_A^2 + gz_A = \frac{p_B}{\rho} + \tfrac{1}{2}u_B^2 + gz_B,$$
since the only body force is due to gravity. Rearranging this gives
$$p_B = p_A + \tfrac{1}{2}\rho(u_A^2 - u_B^2) + \rho g(z_A - z_B).$$
Now $z_B - z_A = 5$ (point $B$ is $5\,\text{m}$ above point $A$), $\rho = 10^3$ and $g = 9.81$, so that
$$p_B = (1 \times 10^5) + 10^3(\tfrac{1}{2}(1.8^2 - 3.6^2) - 9.81 \times 5)$$
$$\simeq 4.61 \times 10^4.$$
The pressure at $B$ is $4.61 \times 10^4\,\text{Pa}$.

### Solution 1.4

Euler's equation is
$$\frac{\partial\mathbf{u}}{\partial t} + \nabla\left(\tfrac{1}{2}u^2\right) - \mathbf{u} \times (\nabla \times \mathbf{u}) = \nabla\left(-\frac{p}{\rho} + \Omega\right).$$
If the flow is irrotational, then $\nabla \times \mathbf{u} = \mathbf{0}$, and so the term $\mathbf{u} \times (\nabla \times \mathbf{u})$ is zero. Further, $\mathbf{u}$ can be written as $\mathbf{u} = \nabla\phi$, and then the first term becomes
$$\frac{\partial}{\partial t}(\nabla\phi) = \nabla\left(\frac{\partial\phi}{\partial t}\right),$$
on changing the order of the differentiations.

On substitution, Euler's equation can be written as
$$\nabla\left(\frac{\partial\phi}{\partial t} + \tfrac{1}{2}u^2 + \frac{p}{\rho} - \Omega\right) = \mathbf{0}.$$

### Solution 1.5

If the flow is steady, then $\partial\phi/\partial t = 0$ and $f(t) = \text{constant}$. If the only body force is gravity, then $\Omega = -gz + c$ (see Exercise 1.1). Hence, from Equation (1.10), Bernoulli's equation for a steady, irrotational flow of an inviscid, constant-density fluid, where the only body force is gravity, is
$$\frac{p}{\rho} + \tfrac{1}{2}u^2 + gz = \text{constant along any curve.}$$

### Solution 1.6

Each flow field must be classified as steady or unsteady, and as rotational or irrotational.

**(a)** If $\mathbf{u} = (k/r)\,\mathbf{e}_\theta$ then
$$\mathbf{curl\,u} = \frac{1}{r}\left(\frac{\partial}{\partial r}(ru_\theta) - \frac{\partial u_r}{\partial\theta}\right)\mathbf{e}_z = \mathbf{0},$$
so this velocity vector field is irrotational. Furthermore, it is steady since $k$ is constant. Bernoulli's equation can be used in the form
$$\frac{p}{\rho} + \tfrac{1}{2}u^2 + gz = \text{constant along } any \text{ curve.}$$

**(b)** If $\mathbf{u} = (A/r)\,\mathbf{e}_r + B\,\mathbf{e}_\theta$ then $\mathbf{curl\,u} = (B/r)\,\mathbf{e}_z$, which is non-zero, so this velocity vector field is rotational. It is steady since $A$ and $B$ are constant. Bernoulli's equation can be used in the form

$$\frac{p}{\rho} + \tfrac{1}{2}u^2 + gz = \text{constant along } \textit{a streamline}.$$

(In this case, since all streamlines lie in horizontal planes $z = \text{constant}$, the '$+gz$' term may be omitted from the left-hand side.)

**(c)** If $\mathbf{u} = (mt^2/r)\,\mathbf{e}_r$, then $\mathbf{curl\,u} = \mathbf{0}$, so this velocity vector field is irrotational. Furthermore, the flow is unsteady. Thus Bernoulli's equation can be used in the form

$$\frac{p}{\rho} + \tfrac{1}{2}u^2 + gz + \frac{\partial \phi}{\partial t} = f(t) \text{ along } \textit{any curve}.$$

## Solution 1.7

Since the flow is irrotational and steady, Bernoulli's equation can be applied along any curve, but it is better to choose a streamline.

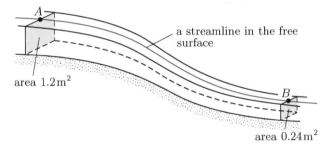

Step (a):  Choose a streamline in the free surface, along which the pressure has a constant value, $p_0$. Select two points $A$ and $B$ on such a streamline, as shown in the figure above.

Step (b):  Since the flow is steady and the fluid can be modelled as inviscid and of constant density, use Bernoulli's equation

$$\frac{p_0}{\rho} + \tfrac{1}{2}u_A^2 + gz_A = \frac{p_0}{\rho} + \tfrac{1}{2}u_B^2 + gz_B,$$

where $z_A$ and $z_B$ are the heights of $A$ and $B$ measured from some horizontal level. Hence

$$z_A - z_B = \frac{1}{2g}\left(u_B^2 - u_A^2\right). \tag{S.1}$$

Step (c):  Use the continuity equation, in the form

  volume flow rate = area × average speed = constant.

For this problem, we have

$$1.2 \times u_A = 0.24 \times u_B,$$

where $u_A = 2.5\,\mathrm{m\,s^{-1}}$. Thus, $u_B = 5u_A = 12.5\,\mathrm{m\,s^{-1}}$.

Step (d):  Substituting for $u_A$, $u_B$ in Equation (S.1) gives

$$z_A - z_B = \frac{1}{2g}(12.5^2 - 2.5^2) = \frac{75}{g}$$

$$\simeq 7.65\,\mathrm{m}.$$

This is the difference in surface height of the water. Hence the difference in height of the channel floors is

$$(z_A - 1.2) - (z_B - 0.6) = z_A - z_B - 0.6$$

$$\simeq 7.05\,\mathrm{m}.$$

## Solution 1.8

As air is blown down through the cotton reel and over the card, the speed of the air over the card is increased and, according to Bernoulli's equation, this creates a pressure $p_1$ which is lower than the static atmospheric pressure $p_0$ beneath the card. The net effect on the card is an upward force.

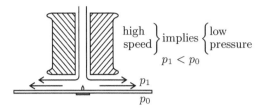

## Solution 1.9

**(a)** The fluid is inviscid and of constant density.

**(b)** The body force is conservative.

**(c)** The three sets of flow assumptions considered are: steady and rotational; unsteady and irrotational; steady and irrotational.

**(d)** These curves must be streamlines if the flow is rotational. For irrotational flows, the choice can be any curve in the fluid.

## Solution 1.10

**(a)** The velocity vector is given (from *Unit 5* Subsection 2.1) by

$$\mathbf{u} = \frac{1}{r}\frac{\partial \psi}{\partial \theta}\,\mathbf{e}_r - \frac{\partial \psi}{\partial r}\,\mathbf{e}_\theta.$$

If $\psi = k \ln r + m\theta$, then

$$\mathbf{u} = \frac{m}{r}\,\mathbf{e}_r - \frac{k}{r}\,\mathbf{e}_\theta.$$

**(b)** For $\mathbf{u} = (m/r)\,\mathbf{e}_r - (k/r)\,\mathbf{e}_\theta$, we have

$$\mathbf{curl\,u} = \frac{1}{r}\left(\frac{\partial}{\partial r}(ru_\theta) - \frac{\partial u_r}{\partial \theta}\right)\mathbf{e}_z = \mathbf{0},$$

so this velocity vector field is irrotational.

**(c)** Since the flow is irrotational and steady, and there is no body force, use Bernoulli's equation in the form

$$\frac{p}{\rho} + \tfrac{1}{2}u^2 = \text{constant along any curve}.$$

Now

$$u = |\mathbf{u}| = \sqrt{\frac{m^2}{r^2} + \frac{k^2}{r^2}} = \frac{\sqrt{m^2 + k^2}}{r};$$

hence Bernoulli's equation becomes

$$\frac{p}{\rho} + \frac{m^2 + k^2}{2r^2} = \text{constant}.$$

To evaluate the constant, consider what happens for large $r$; we have

$$\lim_{r \to \infty}\left(\frac{p}{\rho} + \frac{m^2 + k^2}{2r^2}\right) = \frac{p_\infty}{\rho}.$$

Hence the pressure distribution is

$$p(r, \theta) = p_\infty - \frac{\rho(m^2 + k^2)}{2r^2}.$$

## Solution 1.11

A diagram of the wing cross-section is below.

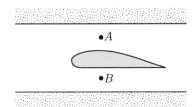

Above the wing, at $A$, the narrowing gap leads to an increase in the speed of the air and, according to Bernoulli's equation, this creates a lower pressure at $A$ than at $B$, where there is no narrowing. Hence the net effect on the wing is an upward force from $B$ to $A$.

(A similar explanation of lift on the wing, with air speed above greater than air speed below, applies even in the absence of walls.)

# Section 2

## Solution 2.1

(a)  According to Equation (2.1), the speed of the jet from the orifice is
$$u_B = \sqrt{2g(z_A - z_B)}.$$
Substituting $g = 9.81$ and $z_A - z_B = 3$ gives
$$u_B = \sqrt{6g} \simeq 7.67\,\mathrm{m\,s^{-1}}.$$

(b)  The volume flow rate $V$ through the orifice is
$$V = \text{area} \times \text{speed} = \pi(0.01)^2 \times 7.67$$
$$\simeq 0.0024\,\mathrm{m^3 s^{-1}}.$$

## Solution 2.2

(a)  No. Here the flow is unsteady, because the depth of liquid in the tank depends on time. (However, the liquid surface may descend only slowly.)

(b)  Apply Bernoulli's equation along a streamline between points $A$ and $B$ (as in Figure 2.4 on page 82) to give
$$\frac{p_0}{\rho} + \tfrac{1}{2}u_A^2 + gz_A = \frac{p_0}{\rho} + \tfrac{1}{2}u_B^2 + gz_B$$
(the pressure at the points $A$ and $B$ is atmospheric pressure, $p_0$). Thus
$$u_B^2 = u_A^2 + 2g(z_A - z_B). \tag{S.2}$$

(c)  If the area of the free surface is $S_A$ and the area of the orifice is $S_B$, then the continuity equation gives
$$S_A u_A = S_B u_B.$$

(d)  Substituting for $u_A$ in Equation (S.2) gives
$$u_B^2 = \left(\frac{S_B}{S_A}u_B\right)^2 + 2g(z_A - z_B);$$
that is,
$$u_B = \sqrt{\frac{2g(z_A - z_B)}{1 - (S_B/S_A)^2}}, \qquad \text{as required.}$$

## Solution 2.3

(a)  Procedure 1.1 can be used because the flow is steady, the fluid is inviscid and of constant density, and the only body force is gravity (conservative).

Using Procedure 1.1 gives the following.

Step (a):   The 'suitable' curve for this problem is given in the question as the central streamline.

Step (b):   Applying Bernoulli's equation along this streamline gives
$$\frac{p_A}{\rho} + \tfrac{1}{2}u_A^2 + gz_A = \frac{p_B}{\rho} + \tfrac{1}{2}u_B^2 + gz_B.$$
Now $z_A = z_B$, since $A$ and $B$ are on the same horizontal level, so Bernoulli's equation becomes
$$\frac{p_A}{\rho} + \tfrac{1}{2}u_A^2 = \frac{p_B}{\rho} + \tfrac{1}{2}u_B^2.$$

Step (c):   The continuity equation yields
$$\pi r_A^2 u_A = \pi r_B^2 u_B.$$

Step (d):   Substituting for $u_B$ in Bernoulli's equation, and rearranging the terms, gives a formula for the pressure difference as
$$p_A - p_B = \tfrac{1}{2}\rho(u_B^2 - u_A^2) = \tfrac{1}{2}\rho u_A^2\left(\frac{r_A^4}{r_B^4} - 1\right).$$
Since $u_A = 1$ and $r_B = \tfrac{1}{2}r_A$, we have
$$p_A - p_B = \tfrac{1}{2} \times 10^3 \times 1^2 \times (2^4 - 1)$$
$$= 7.5 \times 10^3\,\mathrm{Pa}.$$

(b)  The pressure difference across the pipe at section $A$ is due only to gravity: since $CC' = h = 0.03\,\mathrm{m}$, it is
$$p_{C'} - p_C = \rho g h = 10^3 \times 9.81 \times 0.03 \simeq 2.94 \times 10^2\,\mathrm{Pa}.$$
(This is the same as in the static fluid case, because all fluid motion is in a horizontal direction.)

## Solution 2.4

For the stream function
$$\psi = m\left(\arctan\left(\frac{y-b}{x}\right) + \arctan\left(\frac{y+b}{x}\right)\right),$$
we have
$$\mathbf{u} = \frac{\partial \psi}{\partial y}\mathbf{i} - \frac{\partial \psi}{\partial x}\mathbf{j}$$
$$= m\left(\frac{x}{x^2 + (y-b)^2} + \frac{x}{x^2 + (y+b)^2}\right)\mathbf{i}$$
$$+ m\left(\frac{y-b}{x^2 + (y-b)^2} + \frac{y+b}{x^2 + (y+b)^2}\right)\mathbf{j}.$$
Since the flow is steady and irrotational, apply Bernoulli's equation along any curve in the flow. In particular, take a curve from the wall to 'infinity', which gives
$$\frac{p}{\rho} + \tfrac{1}{2}u^2 = \frac{p_0}{\rho} + 0.$$
On the wall, we have $y = 0$ and
$$\mathbf{u} = \frac{2mx}{x^2 + b^2}\mathbf{i}, \qquad u = |\mathbf{u}| = \frac{2m|x|}{x^2 + b^2}.$$
The pressure at any point on the wall is then
$$p(x,0) = p_0 - \tfrac{1}{2}\rho u^2 = p_0 - \frac{2\rho m^2 x^2}{(x^2 + b^2)^2}.$$

## Solution 2.5

To be able to use a form of Bernoulli's equation, there are conditions on the flow and on the fluid which must be satisfied. These are as follows.

(a) On the fluid: inviscid and of constant density. These are both satisfied in this case.

(b) On the flow: unsteady and irrotational, or steady. In this case the fluid velocity depends on $t$, so that the flow is unsteady. Further, $\mathbf{curl\,u} = (-2 - 2t)\,\mathbf{k} \neq \mathbf{0}$, so that the flow is not irrotational.

Hence Bernoulli's equation cannot be used here.

Another condition that is not satisfied applies to the body force. Since $\mathbf{curl\,F} = -2\,\mathbf{k} \neq \mathbf{0}$, the body force is *not* conservative.

## Solution 2.6

Consider the streamline through points $A$, $B$ and $C$ shown in the figure below.

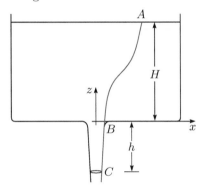

The pressure at each of these points is atmospheric pressure, $p_0$. The flow is assumed to be steady.

(a) Applying Bernoulli's equation to points $A$ and $B$ gives an equation for $u_B$.

(b) Applying Bernoulli's equation to points $B$ and $C$, and the continuity equation between the sections at $B$ and $C$, leads to an equation for the area at $C$.

Step (a): $\dfrac{p_B}{\rho} + \tfrac{1}{2}u_B^2 + gz_B = \dfrac{p_A}{\rho} + \tfrac{1}{2}u_A^2 + gz_A,$

where $z$ is measured upwards from the base of the reservoir.

Now $p_B = p_A = p_0$, $z_B = 0$, $u_A = 0$ and $z_A = H$. Hence, we have $u_B = \sqrt{2gH}$ (which could also have been deduced directly from Torricelli's formula, Equation (2.1)).

Step (b): $\dfrac{p_C}{\rho} + \tfrac{1}{2}u_C^2 + gz_C = \dfrac{p_B}{\rho} + \tfrac{1}{2}u_B^2 + gz_B.$

With $z_B = 0$, $z_C = -h$, $p_C = p_B = p_0$ and $u_B = \sqrt{2gH}$, this gives

$$u_C^2 = u_B^2 - 2gz_C = 2g(H + h).$$

The continuity equation gives

(area at $C$) $\times\, u_C =$ (area at $B$) $\times\, u_B = Su_B.$

Substituting for $u_B$ and $u_C$ gives a formula for the cross-sectional area of the jet at $C$, namely,

$$\frac{S\sqrt{2gH}}{\sqrt{2g(H+h)}} = \frac{S}{\sqrt{1 + h/H}}.$$

## Solution 2.7

In each part of the pipe for which the walls are parallel, the pressure and speed are constant. In the converging and diverging parts, these variables change.

(a) The continuity equation will give the values of $u_B$, $u_C$ and $u_D$ in terms of $u_A$; that is,

$$Su_A = \tfrac{1}{4}Su_B = \tfrac{1}{2}Su_C = \tfrac{3}{4}Su_D,$$

so $u_B = 4u_A$, $u_C = 2u_A$ and $u_D = \tfrac{4}{3}u_A$. A sketch graph for the speed along the pipe is below.

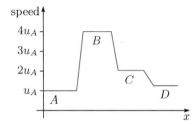

(b) If Bernoulli's equation is applied along the central streamline (ignoring the term involving gravity, since each point is at the same horizontal level), then

$$\frac{p_A}{\rho} + \tfrac{1}{2}u_A^2 = \frac{p_B}{\rho} + \tfrac{1}{2}u_B^2 = \frac{p_C}{\rho} + \tfrac{1}{2}u_C^2 = \frac{p_D}{\rho} + \tfrac{1}{2}u_D^2.$$

Substituting for $u_B$, $u_C$ and $u_D$ in turn gives

$$p_B = p_A - \tfrac{15}{2}\rho u_A^2,$$

$$p_C = p_A - \tfrac{3}{2}\rho u_A^2,$$

$$p_D = p_A - \tfrac{7}{18}\rho u_A^2.$$

A sketch graph for the pressure along the pipe follows.

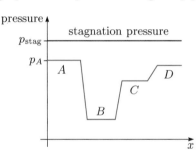

(c) The stagnation pressure $p_{\text{stag}}$ is the combination of $p$ and $u$ given by $p_{\text{stag}} = p + \tfrac{1}{2}\rho u^2$. Along the central streamline, this takes the same value at each point, i.e. $p_A + \tfrac{1}{2}\rho u_A^2$. The sketch in part (b) includes a graph of the stagnation pressure.

## Solution 2.8

In spherical polar coordinates (from *Unit 4* Subsection 4.1), we have

$$\mathbf{curl\,u} = \frac{1}{r^2 \sin\theta} \begin{vmatrix} \mathbf{e}_r & r\,\mathbf{e}_\theta & r\sin\theta\,\mathbf{e}_\phi \\ \partial/\partial r & \partial/\partial\theta & \partial/\partial\phi \\ u_r & r\,u_\theta & r\sin\theta\,u_\phi \end{vmatrix},$$

where $u_\phi = 0$ and

$$u_r = U\cos\theta\left(1 - \frac{a^3}{r^3}\right), \qquad u_\theta = -U\sin\theta\left(1 + \frac{a^3}{2r^3}\right).$$

Hence **curl u** here is

$$\frac{1}{r}\left[-U\sin\theta\frac{\partial}{\partial r}\left(r+\frac{a^3}{2r^2}\right)-U\left(1-\frac{a^3}{r^3}\right)\frac{\partial}{\partial\theta}(\cos\theta)\right]\mathbf{e}_\phi$$

$$=\frac{U\sin\theta}{r}\left(-1+\frac{2a^3}{2r^3}+1-\frac{a^3}{r^3}\right)\mathbf{e}_\phi=\mathbf{0},$$

showing that the flow is irrotational.

The flow is steady, and the fluid is inviscid and of constant density. So Bernoulli's equation can be used in the form

$$\frac{p}{\rho}+\tfrac{1}{2}u^2=\text{constant along }any\text{ curve}$$

(there are no body forces).

Consider a curve between a point on the sphere with coordinates $(a, \theta, \phi)$ and a point far from the sphere, where $r$ is very large. Then

(a) on the sphere $(r = a)$, $p = p(a, \theta, \phi)$ and

$$\mathbf{u}=-\tfrac{3}{2}U\sin\theta\,\mathbf{e}_\theta,\quad\text{so}\quad u=|\mathbf{u}|=\tfrac{3}{2}U\sin\theta;$$

(b) where $r$ is very large, $p = p_0$ and

$$\mathbf{u}=U\cos\theta\,\mathbf{e}_r-U\sin\theta\,\mathbf{e}_\theta,\quad\text{so}\quad u=|\mathbf{u}|=U.$$

Substituting for these values in Bernoulli's equation,

$$\frac{p}{\rho}+\tfrac{1}{2}\left(\tfrac{9}{4}U^2\sin^2\theta\right)=\frac{p_0}{\rho}+\tfrac{1}{2}U^2,$$

which yields

$$p(a,\theta,\phi)=p_0+\tfrac{1}{2}\rho U^2\left(1-\tfrac{9}{4}\sin^2\theta\right).$$

This is the pressure distribution on the sphere. It depends only on $\theta$.

# Section 3

## Solution 3.1

Equation (3.2) gives (taking $g = 10\,\mathrm{m\,s^{-2}}$)

$$E=\frac{u^2}{2g}+h=\frac{2^2}{2\times10}+1=1.2\,\mathrm{m}.$$

The volume flow rate per unit width is

$$Q=uh=2\,\mathrm{m^2s^{-1}}.$$

These values for $Q$ and $E$ give two equations relating $u$ and $h$,

$$uh=2\quad\text{and}\quad\frac{u^2}{2g}+h=1.2.$$

Eliminating $u$ between these two equations, we obtain

$$\frac{4}{2gh^2}+h=1.2,$$

that is,

$$h^3-1.2h^2+0.2=0.$$

This cubic equation for $h$ has one or three real roots. One root ($h = 1$) is known, so $h - 1$ is a factor of $h^3 - 1.2h^2 + 0.2$. Factorising (and using the hint) gives

$$(h-1)(h^2-0.2h-0.2)=0.$$

The other two roots for $h$ are solutions of

$$h^2-0.2h-0.2=0;$$

thus

$$h=\frac{0.2\pm\sqrt{(0.2)^2+4\times0.2}}{2}$$

$$=0.1\pm0.46\quad\text{(to 2 d.p.)}.$$

The three possible values of $h$ are

$$h_1=1,\ h_2=0.56\text{ and }h_3=-0.36,$$

but the negative value of $h_3$ is physically meaningless, and so is discounted.

For the values $Q = 2$ and $E = 1.2$, there are two possible flows: $h = 1\,\mathrm{m}$ and $u = 2\,\mathrm{m\,s^{-1}}$, or $h \simeq 0.56\,\mathrm{m}$ and $u = 2/h \simeq 3.58\,\mathrm{m\,s^{-1}}$.

## Solution 3.2

In the upper channel,

$$u=2.5\,\mathrm{m\,s^{-1}}\qquad\text{and}\qquad h=1.2\,\mathrm{m};$$

therefore $Q = uh = 3\,\mathrm{m^2s^{-1}}$.

For this flow, the critical depth is

$$h_c=\left(\frac{Q^2}{g}\right)^{1/3}\simeq0.97\,\mathrm{m}.$$

Since $h > h_c$, the flow is 'deep and slow'.

In the lower channel,

$$u=12.5\,\mathrm{m\,s^{-1}}\qquad\text{and}\qquad h=0.6\,\mathrm{m};$$

therefore $Q = uh = 7.5\,\mathrm{m^2s^{-1}}$.

For this flow, the critical depth is

$$h_c=\left(\frac{Q^2}{g}\right)^{1/3}\simeq1.78\,\mathrm{m}.$$

Since $h < h_c$, the flow is 'shallow and fast'.

## Solution 3.3

**(a)** The Froude number is defined by

$$Fr=\frac{u}{\sqrt{gh}}.$$

Applying Equation (3.1) gives $u = Q/h$, so

$$Fr=\frac{Q}{h^{3/2}g^{1/2}}.$$

From Equation (3.4), $Q/g^{1/2} = h_c^{3/2}$, so that

$$Fr=\left(\frac{h_c}{h}\right)^{3/2}.$$

**(b)** For 'deep and slow' flows, $h > h_c$. Thus $Fr < 1$ in this case.

For 'shallow and fast' flows, $h < h_c$. Thus $Fr > 1$ in this case.

## Solution 3.4

For a channel of width $3\,\mathrm{m}$ and volume flow rate $12\,\mathrm{m^3s^{-1}}$, we have $Q = 12/3 = 4\,\mathrm{m^2s^{-1}}$. The specific energy is given as $E = 2.2\,\mathrm{m}$. If $u$ and $h$ are the possible speed and depth of flow corresponding to these values of $Q$ and $E$, then

$$Q=uh=4\qquad\text{and}\qquad E=h+\frac{u^2}{2g}=2.2.$$

Eliminating $u$ gives the equation

$$h+\frac{16}{2gh^2}=2.2,$$

that is,

$$h^3-2.2h^2+0.8=0.$$

Now $h = 2$ is a root of this equation, since
$$2^3 - 2.2 \times 2^2 + 0.8 = 0.$$
Then factorisation leads to
$$h^3 - 2.2h^2 + 0.8 = (h - 2)(h^2 - 0.2h - 0.4) = 0.$$
Solving the quadratic equation $h^2 - 0.2h - 0.4 = 0$ gives
$$h = 0.1 \pm 0.640 \quad \text{(to 3 d.p.)}.$$
The two physically meaningful values for $h$ are $2\,\text{m}$ and $0.740\,\text{m}$. The corresponding speeds of flow are $2\,\text{m}\,\text{s}^{-1}$ and $5.40\,\text{m}\,\text{s}^{-1}$. The corresponding Froude numbers can be found using the formula $Fr = u/\sqrt{gh}$, which gives $Fr_1 = 0.45$ (deep and slow) and $Fr_2 = 1.99$ (shallow and fast).

## Solution 3.5

The volume flow rate per unit width is $Q = u_1 h_1 = 4$, and the upstream specific energy is
$$E_1 = \frac{u_1^2}{2g} + h_1 = 2.2.$$
In terms of the downstream values, $u_2$ and $h_2$, we have
$$Q = u_2 h_2 = 4 \quad \text{and} \quad E_2 = \frac{Q^2}{2gh_2^2} + h_2,$$
where $E_2$ is the downstream specific energy. From Equation (3.7),
$$E_2 + r = E_1. \tag{S.3}$$
Substituting $r = 0.2$, $Q = 4$ and $E_1 = 2.2$ in Equation (S.3) gives
$$\frac{0.8}{h_2^2} + h_2 + 0.2 = 2.2.$$
Thus $h_2$ is a solution of the cubic equation (3.8),
$$s^3 - 2s^2 + 0.8 = 0.$$
Using the Newton–Raphson method with $s_0 = 0.74$ (seeking a solution close to $h_1 = 0.740$) gives the following table of values for successive iterations.

| $n$ | 0 | 1 | 2 | 3 |
|-----|------|-------|-------|-------|
| $s_n$ | 0.74 | 0.824 | 0.825 | 0.825 |

The downstream depth is $h_2 \simeq 0.825\,\text{m}$. The speeds in the upstream and downstream sections of the channel are
$$u_1 = \frac{4}{0.740} \simeq 5.41\,\text{m}\,\text{s}^{-1}, \quad u_2 = \frac{4}{0.825} \simeq 4.85\,\text{m}\,\text{s}^{-1},$$
respectively. The corresponding Froude numbers are $Fr_1 = 1.99$ and $Fr_2 = 1.69$. (The supercritical flow upstream remains supercritical downstream, but the speed decreases and the depth increases.)

## Solution 3.6

In this case, the equation relating $E_1$, $E_2$ and $r$ is $E_1 = E_2 - r$. The specific energy curve is shown in the following figure.

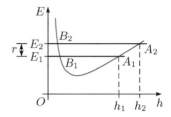

(a) Point $A_1$ represents a subcritical upstream flow. If the channel flow drops by $r$ metres, then $E$ is increased by the same amount, from $E_1$ to $E_2 = E_1 + r$. The downstream conditions are represented by point $A_2$ on the graph, with an increased depth and decreased speed. The flow becomes further from critical.

(b) For a supercritical upstream flow (point $B_1$), the depth of flow decreases with a drop in the channel bed (point $B_2$). The speed of flow increases and the flow becomes further from critical.

## Solution 3.7

(a) The volume flow rate is the product of the area $A$ of the triangle and the flow speed, $u$. So the volume flow rate is
$$V = uh^2 \tan \alpha. \tag{S.4}$$

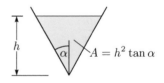

(b) The specific energy function is
$$E = \frac{u^2}{2g} + h. \tag{S.5}$$
Applying Bernoulli's equation along a streamline in the free surface gives
$$\frac{p_0}{\rho g} + \frac{u^2}{2g} + h = \text{constant}.$$
Since $p_0/(\rho g)$ is constant, this gives
$$E = \frac{u^2}{2g} + h = \text{constant}.$$

(c) Substituting $u = V/(h^2 \tan \alpha)$ from Equation (S.4) in Equation (S.5) gives
$$E = h + \frac{V^2}{2gh^4 \tan^2 \alpha}.$$
Critical conditions occur at the minimum value for $E$, i.e. where $dE/dh = 0$. So we find
$$\frac{dE}{dh} = 1 - \frac{2V^2}{gh^5 \tan^2 \alpha} = 0.$$

Solving for $h$ gives

$$h_c = \left(\frac{2V^2}{g\tan^2\alpha}\right)^{1/5},$$

which is the critical depth. Putting $V = u_c h_c^2 \tan\alpha$ gives a relationship between $u_c$ and $h_c$, as

$$h_c = \left(\frac{2u_c^2 h_c^4 \tan^2\alpha}{g\tan^2\alpha}\right)^{1/5}.$$

Simplifying this gives

$$h_c = \frac{2u_c^2}{g} \qquad \text{or} \qquad u_c = \sqrt{\tfrac{1}{2}gh_c}.$$

## Solution 3.8

**(a)** For a streamline in the free surface,

$$E = \frac{u^2}{2g} + h = \text{constant},$$

and the volume flow rate is

$$V = uhb = \text{constant}.$$

Here, $u$, $h$ and $b$ depend on $x$. Substituting $u = V/(hb)$ gives

$$E = \frac{V^2}{2gh^2 b^2} + h = \text{constant}.$$

Differentiating with respect to $x$ gives

$$\frac{dE}{dx} = -\frac{V^2}{gh^3 b^2}\frac{dh}{dx} - \frac{V^2}{gh^2 b^3}\frac{db}{dx} + \frac{dh}{dx} = 0.$$

Rearrange this to obtain

$$\frac{db}{dx} = \left(1 - \frac{V^2}{gh^3 b^2}\right)\frac{gh^2 b^3}{V^2}\frac{dh}{dx}$$

$$= \left(\frac{gh^3 b^2}{V^2} - 1\right)\frac{b}{h}\frac{dh}{dx}. \qquad \text{(S.6)}$$

Now, the Froude number is

$$Fr = \frac{u}{\sqrt{gh}} = \frac{V}{bg^{1/2}h^{3/2}},$$

so that $V = bg^{1/2}h^{3/2}Fr$. Writing $V$ in terms of the Froude number in Equation (S.6) gives

$$\frac{db}{dx} = \left(\frac{1}{Fr^2} - 1\right)\frac{b}{h}\frac{dh}{dx}, \qquad \text{as required.}$$

**(b)** At the throat, $db/dx = 0$; so either $Fr = 1$ or $dh/dx = 0$.

If $dh/dx = 0$, there is a minimum value for the depth $h$.

If $Fr = 1$, the flow is critical at the throat, and $V = b_c g^{1/2}h_c^{3/2}$ (where $b = b_c$ at the throat), that is,

$$h_c = \left(\frac{V}{b_c g^{1/2}}\right)^{2/3} = \left(\frac{V^2}{b_c^2 g}\right)^{1/3}.$$

**(c)** For a subcritical flow upstream, $Fr < 1$ and $db/dx < 0$, so that $dh/dx < 0$ and the depth of flow falls up to the throat.

**(i)** If $Fr < 1$ at the throat, then the depth of liquid has a minimum and is shown by the curve $AB$ in the figure below.

**(ii)** If $Fr = 1$ at the throat, then the depth along the channel continues to fall beyond the throat. A possible variation of the surface level is shown by the curve $AB'$ in the figure below.

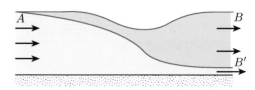

# UNIT 7   Vorticity

## Study guide

Sections 2 and 3 contain ideas that may appear difficult and abstract. However, it is worth studying these sections carefully, because Sections 4 and 5 make extensive use of the ideas. The latter sections have relatively few exercises. However, these could be regarded as the most important parts of the unit, since they discuss the flow of real fluids, based on the theoretical concepts introduced earlier.

Much of the mathematics in this unit relates to line, surface and volume integrals of vector and scalar quantities, as introduced in *Unit 4*. Also the curl of a vector and Stokes' Theorem will be called upon. Section 4 uses dimensional analysis, as covered in MST209 *Unit 16* and revisited in Section 5 of the *Revision Booklet*.

Section 1 should take about one and a half hours to study. Section 2 will require about three hours of study. Section 3 will also take about three hours, and the remaining sections about two hours each.

Subsection 2.3 contains an audio session.

## Introduction

The angular velocity (about an axis) of a rigid body is a familiar idea. It arises in many everyday occurrences: for example, the rolling of a wheel, the closing of a door, the spinning of an ice-skater, the turning of a screw. Rigid bodies that rotate have two significant properties: first, the distance between two given particles of a rigid body is assumed to be constant; second, the angular velocity is the same for every particle of the body.

See MST209 *Unit 20*.

The situation for fluids can be quite different. It is indeed possible to conceive of flows where a fluid rotates as a rigid body, but it is also possible to observe flows in which the angular velocity differs from point to point, and where the distance between a pair of fluid elements changes. For instance, hurricanes in the atmosphere contain regions of air that have considerable angular velocities, while the neighbouring air is relatively still. On a smaller scale, if you move a teaspoon (but do not rotate it) in a cup of coffee or tea you should observe, for a short period of time, two regions in which the angular velocities are of relatively large magnitude, the rest of the fluid being nearly still.

In fluids, therefore, angular velocity has a strongly local aspect. This aspect of angular velocity manifests itself in the fact that it is not usual to refer to the angular velocity of fluids; instead, the term *vorticity* is used. A region of fluid where the magnitude of angular velocity is (locally) high is known as a *vortex*.

Vorticity is of fundamental importance in fluid mechanics, for two reasons. First, the understanding of the manner in which it is generated and propagated can be useful when modelling fluid motions, because it is sometimes possible to use the highly convenient assumption that the vorticity is zero in some regions of a moving fluid. Second, the occurrence of vorticity in a fluid is itself responsible for, or is associated with, important phenomena: for example, hurricanes, the lift on an aircraft wing, the swaying of factory chimneys and the collapse of bridges.

In this unit, much time is spent discussing the properties of vorticity in inviscid fluids. While the inviscid model (with its neglect of viscosity) is an idealisation, the flow of a real fluid can often be modelled by it, at least in parts. Against this, it is pointed out that the viscosity of a fluid plays a crucial role in the generation and destruction of vorticity.

Section 1 begins by modelling a tornado. Much of the later work of that section is concerned with developing the idealised *line vortex*. This model of vorticity is used in Section 2 to study the flow of an inviscid fluid around a circular cylinder. A good deal of effort in later sections is directed towards reconciling the results of that theoretical investigation with the experimental results obtained during studies of the flow of real fluids.

In *Unit 4*, vorticity was defined as **curl u**, where **u** is the velocity field, and in *Unit 5* a vortex was described as having the velocity field $\mathbf{u} = (k/r)\,\mathbf{e}_\theta$. The vorticity for this field is found in Section 1. In MST209 *Unit 24* it is shown that **curl u** is a measure of local rotation.

Be careful not to confuse vorticity and viscosity. Viscosity is a property of a fluid which acts like a sort of internal friction. As you will see, vorticity is a feature of the flow pattern of a fluid.

A tornado is a naturally occurring phenomenon that demonstrates the presence of vorticity.

# 1 Vorticity and circulation

Vorticity is a commonly occurring feature of fluid flows. By *vorticity* we essentially mean angular velocity, which may vary from point to point in the fluid. To be specific, we consider some examples.

(i) Next time you take a bath, place your hand in the bath-water when it is quite still. Then move your hand slowly through the water, with the palm perpendicular to the direction of travel. You should observe, for a short period of time, two regions of fluid in which the angular velocities are of relatively large magnitude, detaching themselves from your hand. The same effect can be observed in a washbasin, or even in a cup of coffee or tea with a spoon moving through it.

The same experiment was described in *Unit 1* Section 2, where a ruler was used to generate vorticity.

(ii) Some time after the plug is pulled out of a bath or washbasin containing water, a region of vorticity is observed around the plughole; the fluid is seen to swirl vigorously.

(iii) A characteristic feature of tornadoes is that they contain relatively narrow and almost vertical columns, in which the air is rotating about the vertical axis (see Figure 1.1). Outside the narrow column, the air is relatively still. The vertical columns move about, causing great havoc and destruction. Tornadoes provide excellent examples of fluid motions possessing vorticity.

One obvious conclusion to be drawn from these examples is that vorticity occurs in fluid flows of such differing length scales as coffee cups and tornadoes.

We start analysing vorticity by considering tornadoes further.

## 1.1  A model for a tornado

This subsection attempts to develop a simple model for a tornado, as a first step in developing the standard theory of vorticity.

### Example 1.1

In a tornado:

(a)  there is a core of fluid forming an essentially vertical cylindrical column, in which the air is undergoing rapid rotation;

(b)  outside the column, the air speed drops off rapidly, being undisturbed at large distances from the core.

Find an expression for the velocity field that models these two main features of a tornado.

### Solution

To reflect features (a) and (b) in the model, assume that the velocity field consists of two parts, inside and outside the core of radius $a$.

We use cylindrical polar coordinates, $r$, $\theta$, $z$, with $r = 0$ as the axis of rotation. In the core ($r \leq a$), the air rotates as a rigid body, a simple model for which is

$$\mathbf{u} = \Omega_1 r\, \mathbf{e}_\theta \qquad (r \leq a), \qquad \text{where } \Omega_1 \text{ is a constant.}$$

Outside the core ($r > a$), the velocity is small at large distances. Also, assume that the velocity in this region is in the direction of $\mathbf{e}_\theta$, since this velocity is induced by the rotation of the core. One model is

$$\mathbf{u} = \frac{\Omega_2}{r}\, \mathbf{e}_\theta \qquad (r > a), \qquad \text{where } \Omega_2 \text{ is a constant.}$$

So $\mathbf{u}$ is given by

$$\mathbf{u} = \begin{cases} \Omega_1 r\, \mathbf{e}_\theta & (r \leq a), \\ \dfrac{\Omega_2}{r}\, \mathbf{e}_\theta & (r > a), \end{cases}$$

as shown in Figure 1.2. Note that this velocity field $\mathbf{u}$ satisfies the continuity equation, $\operatorname{div} \mathbf{u} = 0$.

The model must also satisfy continuity of the velocity vector $\mathbf{u}$ at $r = a$, that is,

$$\Omega_1 a\, \mathbf{e}_\theta = \frac{\Omega_2}{a}\, \mathbf{e}_\theta.$$

It follows that

$$\Omega_2 = \Omega_1 a^2,$$

and so the proposed model velocity field can be written as

$$\mathbf{u} = \begin{cases} \Omega_1 r\, \mathbf{e}_\theta & (r \leq a), \\ \dfrac{\Omega_1 a^2}{r}\, \mathbf{e}_\theta & (r > a). \end{cases} \tag{1.1}$$

*Figure 1.1*   A tornado over the sea (often called a 'waterspout')

The motion is anticlockwise, viewed from above, if $\Omega_1 > 0$, and clockwise if $\Omega_1 < 0$.

Later it is shown that this specification for $\mathbf{u}$ implies the existence of vorticity in the core but not outside it.

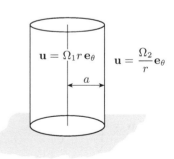

$\mathbf{u} = \Omega_1 r\, \mathbf{e}_\theta$     $\mathbf{u} = \dfrac{\Omega_2}{r}\mathbf{e}_\theta$

$a$

*Figure 1.2*

**Exercise 1.1**

Typical data for a tornado are: radius of core 100 m, maximum wind speed $50\,\text{m}\,\text{s}^{-1}$ (at $r = a$). Find the values of the parameters $\Omega_1$ and $\Omega_2$ in this case, and hence write down the velocity field.

As mentioned earlier, a tornado is an example occurring in nature of a motion possessing vorticity, i.e. rotation that is essentially local in nature. This motion is modelled by supposing that the associated velocity field consists of two parts: an inner rigid-body rotation, and an outer rotation whose magnitude decreases with increasing radial distance from the centre. It is worth noting that, while the model represents a *large-scale* fluid motion possessing vorticity, much of the analysis was independent of the scale of the motion. Indeed, that scale was allowed for only in determining values for the parameters $\Omega_1$ and $\Omega_2$ in Exercise 1.1. It follows, therefore, that Equation (1.1) could be used to model two-dimensional motion with a region of vorticity on any scale. In particular, this equation could model the motions shown in Figures 1.3–1.5.

These figures illustrate three motions with a local region of significant vorticity. A region in which the magnitude of the vorticity is relatively high is called a **vortex**, the plural of which is vortices.

Figure 1.3 shows two vortices, Figure 1.4 one vortex, and Figure 1.5 two vortices. The vortices in these figures may all be modelled by a velocity field as given by Equation (1.1), with different values for $\Omega_1$ and $a$. In summary, this is a *mathematical model* for real-life vortices.

The model has at least one shortcoming, however. The purpose of any model is either to obtain a greater understanding of known experimental results or to predict the results that would be obtained in other experimental situations.

Consider the prediction problem. The model contains two independent parameters, namely $\Omega_1$ and $a$. In order to use this model in calculations to simulate real flows, it is necessary to assign values to $\Omega_1$ and $a$. These values would have to be obtained by measurement and estimation from experimental results. In some cases this process may not be difficult, but it could often be laborious. It is a matter of experience that the fitting of *one* parameter value is an easier exercise. Thus the aim in the next subsection is to derive a one-parameter model for a vortex.

## 1.2   The line vortex

The intention here is to explore whether it is possible to describe the velocity field

$$\mathbf{u} = \begin{cases} \Omega r\, \mathbf{e}_\theta & (r \le a), \\ \dfrac{\Omega a^2}{r}\, \mathbf{e}_\theta & (r > a) \end{cases}$$

by a *single* parameter rather than by the two parameters $\Omega$ and $a$. (Note that the subscript 1 has now been dropped from $\Omega$.) It would be reasonable to expect that the single parameter will be some combination of $\Omega$ and $a$.

To make progress, recall the *mathematical* definition of vorticity given in *Unit 4*, namely

vorticity = **curl u**,    where **u** is the velocity vector.

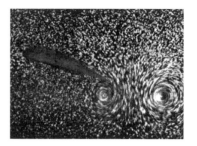

*Figure 1.3*  The 'starting' and 'stopping' vortices shed from an aerofoil which has been brought suddenly from rest to steady motion (from right to left) and then stopped suddenly

*Figure 1.4*  A vortex shed at a salient edge soon after the fluid motion (from left to right) is begun

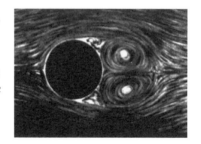

*Figure 1.5*  Two 'bound' vortices produced behind a cylinder (these are discussed in Section 4)

See *Unit 4* Subsection 4.3.

Further, recall the result known as Stokes' Theorem: for an open surface $S$ whose perimeter curve is $C$,

$$\int_S (\mathbf{curl\,F}) \cdot \mathbf{n}\,dA = \oint_C \mathbf{F} \cdot d\mathbf{r}$$

for any vector field $\mathbf{F}$ (see Figure 1.6). Writing $\mathbf{u}$ instead of $\mathbf{F}$, we have

$$\int_S (\mathbf{curl\,u}) \cdot \mathbf{n}\,dA = \oint_C \mathbf{u} \cdot d\mathbf{r}.$$

In a fluid mechanics context, this means that the summing of the normal component of $\mathbf{curl\,u}$ over an open surface equals the line integral of the velocity vector around the perimeter curve.

In other words, to assess the amount of vorticity in a region (of fluid), it is sufficient to evaluate an appropriate line integral over the boundary curve of the region. It appears, then, that the line integral of the velocity vector over closed curves may be of some importance in understanding vorticity. This line integral is given a special name, as follows.

See *Unit 4* Subsection 4.2 for details of Stokes' Theorem.

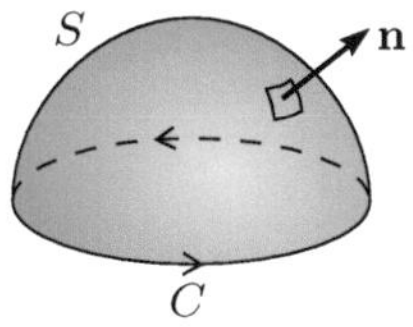

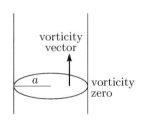

*Figure 1.6*

### Definition

The integral $\oint_C \mathbf{u} \cdot d\mathbf{r}$ is called the **circulation** of the velocity vector $\mathbf{u}$ around the closed curve $C$. This is abbreviated to 'the circulation around $C$', where it is implied that the integral of the velocity vector field is calculated.

Circulation around a closed curve is defined for *any* vector field.

You are now asked to apply some of the concepts and techniques introduced in *Unit 4*.

### Exercise 1.2

Given that

$$\mathbf{u} = \begin{cases} \Omega r\,\mathbf{e}_\theta & (r \le a), \\[2mm] \dfrac{\Omega a^2}{r}\,\mathbf{e}_\theta & (r > a), \end{cases}$$

and working in cylindrical polar coordinates, find $\mathbf{curl\,u}$.

*Hint:* You should obtain two expressions for $\mathbf{curl\,u}$, one for $0 < r < a$ and the other for $r > a$.

See *Unit 4* Subsection 4.1, or the back of the *Handbook*, for the expression for $\mathbf{curl\,u}$.

The vorticity is not defined at $r = a$, since the derivative $\partial u_\theta/\partial r$ is not defined there.

Note that in one part of the fluid ($r < a$), the vorticity vector is non-zero and parallel to the unit vector $\mathbf{e}_z$, and in the other part the vorticity is zero (see Figure 1.7).

Now check the implications of Stokes' Theorem. The aim is to show that Stokes' Theorem may be regarded as demonstrating that the circulation around a simple closed curve gives a measure of the vorticity contained in a region enclosed by it. This statement is, of necessity, imprecise; precision will be achieved later, when the details are considered.

A *simple* curve is one which does not cross itself.

Recall that inside the circle $r = a$, the vorticity is non-zero (it is $2\Omega\,\mathbf{e}_z$), while outside $r = a$, the vorticity is zero (see Figure 1.8(a), overleaf). Let $C_1$ be the circle $r = a$, and let $C_2$ be the circle $r = b$ (where $b > a$); see Figure 1.8(b) (overleaf). Let $D_1$ and $D_2$ be the discs bounded by $C_1$ and $C_2$, respectively. Then, by Stokes' Theorem,

$$\int_{D_i} (\mathbf{curl\,u}) \cdot \mathbf{n}\,dA = \oint_{C_i} \mathbf{u} \cdot d\mathbf{r} \qquad (i = 1, 2). \tag{1.2}$$

*Figure 1.7*

113

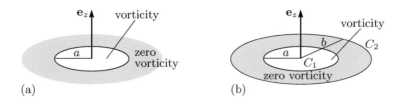

*Figure 1.8*

One deduction can be made immediately. Since **curl u** = **0** outside the circle $C_1$, it follows that

$$\int_{D_2} (\mathbf{curl\, u}) \cdot \mathbf{n}\, dA = \int_{D_1} (\mathbf{curl\, u}) \cdot \mathbf{n}\, dA.$$

It then follows from Equation (1.2) that

$$\oint_{C_2} \mathbf{u} \cdot d\mathbf{r} = \oint_{C_1} \mathbf{u} \cdot d\mathbf{r}. \qquad (1.3)$$

This follows since

$$\int_{D} (\mathbf{curl\, u}) \cdot \mathbf{n}\, dA = 0,$$

where $D$ is the region between $C_1$ and $C_2$.

### Exercise 1.3

Verify Equation (1.3) by evaluating the two line integrals, where

$\mathbf{u} = \Omega a\, \mathbf{e}_\theta$   on the circle $C_1$ $(r = a)$, and

$\mathbf{u} = \dfrac{\Omega a^2}{b}\, \mathbf{e}_\theta$   on the circle $C_2$ $(r = b,$ where $b > a)$.

---

Both line integrals in Exercise 1.3 give the value $2\pi\Omega a^2$, which is a measure of the total vorticity of the flow with velocity field

$$\mathbf{u} = \begin{cases} \Omega r\, \mathbf{e}_\theta & (r \le a), \\ \dfrac{\Omega a^2}{r}\, \mathbf{e}_\theta & (r > a). \end{cases}$$

The vorticity for this flow is localised to the region $r < a$. Now extend this localised aspect by letting both $a \to 0$ and $\Omega \to \infty$, in such a way that the circulation, $2\pi\Omega a^2$, remains constant. Let $\kappa = 2\pi\Omega a^2$. Then, in the limit, the model will have the velocity field

$$\mathbf{u} = \frac{\kappa}{2\pi r}\, \mathbf{e}_\theta \qquad (r \ne 0),$$

which involves one parameter, $\kappa$, defined in terms of $\Omega$ and $a$.

Figure 1.9 shows the velocity vector at distance $r$ from the $z$-axis, and indicates by a curved arrow the concentration of vorticity along that axis.

The main features of this model are as follows.

(a) The motion modelled is a two-dimensional motion around the $z$-axis.

(b) The motion is not defined at $r = 0$.

(c) **curl u** = **0**, except at $r = 0$ where **u** is undefined.

(d) The circulation around any circle in a plane perpendicular to the $z$-axis and with centre on that axis, traversed anticlockwise, is equal to $\kappa$.

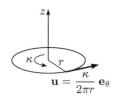

*Figure 1.9*   Here $\kappa > 0$

You showed in Exercise 1.2 that

$$\mathbf{curl}\left(\frac{\Omega a^2}{r}\, \mathbf{e}_\theta\right) = \mathbf{0}.$$

### Exercise 1.4

Check statement (d) above.

---

The model developed above is for a two-dimensional motion where the vorticity is concentrated along the $z$-axis. This model, with velocity field $\mathbf{u} = \kappa/(2\pi r)\,\mathbf{e}_\theta\ (r \neq 0)$, is called a **line vortex**.

In Exercise 1.4, you showed that the circulation is $\kappa$ for all circles centred on the $z$-axis in planes perpendicular to that axis. Also, it has been suggested that the circulation $\kappa$ indicates the strength of vorticity (of the line vortex) enclosed by the circle. It would be useful if this could be extended to *any* simple curve enclosing the $z$-axis, because it would then be meaningful to describe the concentration of vorticity (along the $z$-axis) as giving rise to a circulation, $\kappa$, which represents the strength of the vorticity concentration. The next aim, therefore, is to show that the circulation is $\kappa$ around *all* simple curves enclosing the $z$-axis.

Firstly, consider two curves, $C_1$ and $C_2$, each enclosing the line vortex concentrated along the $z$-axis (see Figure 1.10, where the $z$-axis is perpendicular to the page). We shall use Stokes' Theorem to show that

$$\oint_{C_1} \mathbf{u}\cdot d\mathbf{r} = \oint_{C_2} \mathbf{u}\cdot d\mathbf{r},$$

where the curves are traversed in the same sense.

Make a small cut in $C_1$ and $C_2$, and join them with lines $A_1A_2$ and $B_1B_2$, as shown in Figure 1.11. Then consider the closed circuit $A_1A_2D_2B_2B_1D_1A_1$, as shown, calling it $C$ for convenience. The strategy is then as follows. The circuit $C$ does not enclose the line vortex, in the sense that it can be unwrapped from around the line vortex without breaking or passing through $O$. Stokes' Theorem, applied to the circuit $C$ and to any open surface $S$ bounded by it which does not intersect the $z$-axis, states that

$$\oint_C \mathbf{u}\cdot d\mathbf{r} = \int_S (\mathbf{curl\,u})\cdot \mathbf{n}\,dA.$$

You are asked to show in the next exercise that this reduces to

$$\oint_{C_1} \mathbf{u}\cdot d\mathbf{r} = \oint_{C_2} \mathbf{u}\cdot d\mathbf{r}.$$

In *Unit 5* such a velocity field, with $k$ for $\kappa/(2\pi)$, was described as just a vortex. The new terminology here is better, since it is a reminder that, for this model, the vorticity is concentrated along the line of the $z$-axis.

The expression from *Unit 5* for the vortex strength, $2\pi k$, is now equal to $\kappa$.

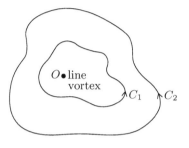

*Figure 1.10*   Curves $C_1$, $C_2$

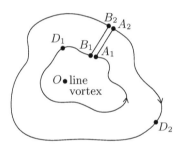

*Figure 1.11*   The circuit $C = A_1A_2D_2B_2B_1D_1A_1$

### Exercise 1.5

Let $\mathbf{u}$, $C$ and $S$ be as defined above.

(a) What is the value of $\mathbf{curl\,u}$ at any point on $S$?

(b) Deduce from Stokes' Theorem for this situation that

$$\oint_C \mathbf{u}\cdot d\mathbf{r} = 0.$$

(c) Express $\oint_C \mathbf{u}\cdot d\mathbf{r}$ as a sum of the separate contributions along

$$A_1A_2,\ A_2D_2B_2,\ B_2B_1 \text{ and } B_1D_1A_1.$$

(d) Let $B_1 \to A_1$ and $B_2 \to A_2$. Hence deduce that

$$\oint_{C_1} \mathbf{u}\cdot d\mathbf{r} = \oint_{C_2} \mathbf{u}\cdot d\mathbf{r},$$

where both curves are traversed in the same sense.

115

The deduction from Exercise 1.5 is that the circulation is $\kappa$ for all simple closed curves enclosing the line vortex. It follows, therefore, that the line vortex described by the velocity field $\mathbf{u} = \kappa/(2\pi r)\,\mathbf{e}_\theta$ may prove useful in modelling situations which require the presence of non-zero circulation. This last statement may seem puzzling, because until now the mathematical concept of circulation has been interpreted as measuring, in some sense, the amount of vorticity in a region of fluid. Now the suggestion is that it has some fundamental importance in its own right, and that circulation may have to be modelled in some situations.

This will be resolved in Sections 3 and 5, where the concept of circulation is considered in more detail, showing that flows of some *real* fluids may be explained in terms of the generation of circulation.

Having established, from Exercise 1.5, that the value of the circulation is $\kappa$ for all simple closed curves that enclose the axis of the line vortex and are traversed anticlockwise, it now makes sense to call $\kappa$ the **strength** of the line vortex. Note that *positive* strength ($\kappa > 0$) corresponds to an *anticlockwise* rotation about the axis of the vortex, and *negative* strength ($\kappa < 0$) corresponds to a *clockwise* rotation (see Figure 1.12).

The next section develops the line vortex model further, on the way to building up models of real flows. Later in that section, a line vortex is combined with a uniform flow, or 'streaming motion', to model a flow with circulation around a cylindrical obstacle.

Note that the preceding argument applies whether or not $C_1$ and $C_2$ are planar curves. It is assumed here that the curves are traversed anticlockwise.

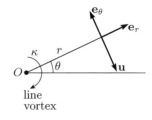

*Figure 1.12*   Here $\kappa < 0$

## *End-of-section exercise*

### *Exercise 1.6*

A line vortex of strength $\kappa$ is directed along the $z$-axis, as shown in Figure 1.13. The stream function is given in Cartesian coordinates by

$$\psi = -\frac{\kappa}{4\pi}\ln\left(x^2 + y^2\right).$$

Using $u_1 = \partial\psi/\partial y$, $u_2 = -\partial\psi/\partial x$, find the velocity components in Cartesian coordinates. Verify by integration that

$$\oint_C \mathbf{u}\cdot d\mathbf{r} = \kappa,$$

where $C$ is a square of side $2a$ in the $(x, y)$-plane with its centre at the origin, and the integration is in the anticlockwise sense, as indicated in Figure 1.13.

$$\left(\text{Note that } \int \frac{a}{x^2 + a^2}\,dx = \arctan\left(\frac{x}{a}\right) + \text{constant.}\right)$$

You met stream functions in *Unit 5* Section 2.

This result is established in the next section.

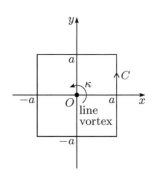

*Figure 1.13*

# 2 Inviscid flow around an obstacle

The first aim in this section is to explore in more depth the properties of the line vortex model for motions possessing a high local concentration of vorticity. The development will include some of the ideas introduced in *Unit 5*, in particular, the concept of stream function and modelling by combining basic flow patterns.

See *Unit 5* Sections 2 and 3.

## 2.1 The stream function of a line vortex

In *Unit 5* the stream function for the velocity field $\mathbf{u} = (k/r)\,\mathbf{e}_\theta$ was shown to be $\psi = -k \ln r$. In this unit, we put $k = \kappa/(2\pi)$.

See Exercise 2.2(a) of *Unit 5*.

### Exercise 2.1

Recall that the stream function $\psi$ is given in terms of $\mathbf{u} = u_r\,\mathbf{e}_r + u_\theta\,\mathbf{e}_\theta$ by

$$u_r = \frac{1}{r}\frac{\partial \psi}{\partial \theta}, \qquad u_\theta = -\frac{\partial \psi}{\partial r}.$$

Verify, by differentiation, that

$$\text{if } \psi = -\frac{\kappa}{2\pi}\ln r, \text{ then } \mathbf{u} = \frac{\kappa}{2\pi r}\,\mathbf{e}_\theta,$$

that is, $\psi$ as given here is the stream function for a line vortex of strength $\kappa$.

---

Exercise 2.1 verifies that a line vortex of strength $\kappa$, directed along the $z$-axis, with velocity field

$$\mathbf{u} = \frac{\kappa}{2\pi r}\,\mathbf{e}_\theta,$$

has stream function

$$\psi = -\frac{\kappa}{2\pi}\ln r + \text{constant}.$$

It was demonstrated in *Unit 5* that knowledge of stream functions associated with uniform streams, sinks and sources can be useful in modelling various real flow situations. These remarks apply also to line vortices. For instance, consider a vortex of strength $\kappa$ directed along the $z$-axis, for convenience. Then the streamlines are known to be circles in planes perpendicular to the $z$-axis, their centres lying on that axis. Figure 2.1 (overleaf) shows some of these streamlines (for $\kappa < 0$), the $z$-axis being directed perpendicularly out of the plane of the page. Suppose that all streamlines for which $r = a$ are considered. These streamlines lie on the surface of a circular cylinder of radius $r = a$, whose axis is the $z$-axis. That imaginary cylindrical surface could be replaced by a real surface without affecting the (inviscid) flow in any way whatsoever. Further, the flow *outside* the cylinder is unaffected by supposing that the cylinder is a solid one. Thus the use of a line vortex models a flow outside a circular cylinder (see Figure 2.2, overleaf). This rotating flow is associated with circulation $\kappa$ around all simple curves enclosing the cylinder, traversed anticlockwise. For curves not enclosing the cylinder, the circulation is zero (see Figure 2.3, overleaf).

Stream functions for line vortices directed along axes parallel to the $z$-axis will be considered shortly.

This is because the surface is formed by streamlines across which there is no flow (by definition); see *Unit 5* Subsection 2.3.

Later sections will show that circulation is of fundamental importance.

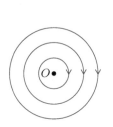

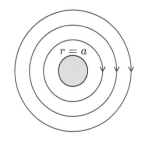

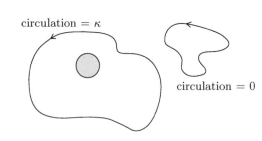

*Figure 2.1*          *Figure 2.2*          *Figure 2.3*

To sum up, a rotating motion of circulation $\kappa$ outside a circular cylinder whose axis is along the $z$-axis can be modelled by a line vortex along that axis, i.e. by the stream function

$$\psi = -\frac{\kappa}{2\pi}\ln r + \text{constant}.$$

The presence of an arbitrary constant is a feature of all stream functions. In the present case, it is convenient to choose the constant to be $\kappa/(2\pi)\ln a$, so that

$$\psi = -\frac{\kappa}{2\pi}\ln r + \frac{\kappa}{2\pi}\ln a = -\frac{\kappa}{2\pi}\ln\left(\frac{r}{a}\right).$$

Then the boundary of the cylinder $(r = a)$ corresponds to the streamline $\psi = 0$.

Note that $\mathbf{curl\,u} = \mathbf{0}$ everywhere except along $r = 0$, where it is undefined.

The constant disappears when velocity components are obtained by differentiation.

## 2.2  Combinations of line vortices

The use of combinations of line vortices enables the modelling of more complicated flows. First, we generalise the result for the stream function given earlier, by considering a line vortex through an arbitrary point, not necessarily the origin, which was used before.

Consider a line vortex of strength $\kappa$, passing through a general point $O'$ with Cartesian coordinates $(a, b, 0)$, as shown in Figure 2.4. The streamlines are circles in planes perpendicular to the axis of the line vortex, with centres on the line $(a, b, z)$, parallel to the $z$-axis.

As before, the line vortex is directed perpendicular to the plane of the paper.

It is convenient to give the stream function in terms of Cartesian coordinates. For a line vortex directed along the $z$-axis, we have

$$\psi = -\frac{\kappa}{2\pi}\ln r + \text{constant} = -\frac{\kappa}{2\pi}\ln(OP) + \text{constant}$$

$$= -\frac{\kappa}{4\pi}\ln(x^2 + y^2) + \text{constant},$$

since $r = OP = (x^2 + y^2)^{1/2}$.

For a line vortex which passes through the point $O'\,(a, b, 0)$ and which is in the direction parallel to the $z$-axis (see Figure 2.4), the stream function is

$$\psi = -\frac{\kappa}{2\pi}\ln(O'P) + \text{constant}$$

$$= -\frac{\kappa}{4\pi}\ln\left((x-a)^2 + (y-b)^2\right) + \text{constant}.$$

The following example makes use of this change of position of the line vortex, when two line vortices are considered.

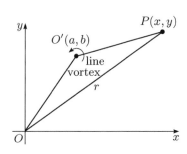

*Figure 2.4*

## Example 2.1

Find the stream function for a pair of line vortices of equal and opposite strengths $\pm\kappa$, passing through the points $(0, \pm a, 0)$, and parallel to the $z$-axis. Show that the $x$-axis is a streamline, and deduce the stream function for the motion due to a line vortex of strength $\kappa$ near a plane wall. Sketch enough streamlines to give an overall picture of the flow.

## Solution

If $r_1$ and $r_2$ denote the radial distances of a general point $P(x, y)$ from the vortices (see Figure 2.5), the stream function is

$$\psi = -\frac{\kappa}{2\pi}\ln r_1 + \frac{\kappa}{2\pi}\ln r_2 + \text{constant},$$

or

$$\psi = -\frac{\kappa}{2\pi}\ln\left(\frac{r_1}{r_2}\right) + \text{constant}.$$

Here we apply the Principle of Superposition, as in *Unit 5* Subsection 3.1.

The constant is arbitrary, and for convenience we set it to zero. Then

$$\psi = -\frac{\kappa}{2\pi}\ln\left(\frac{r_1}{r_2}\right).$$

At all points on the $x$-axis, $r_1 = r_2$; in this case,

$$\psi = -\frac{\kappa}{2\pi}\ln 1 = 0.$$

Thus the $x$-axis is a streamline ($\psi = 0$), and could be replaced by a solid boundary since there is no flow across a streamline. A velocity field for a line vortex in the presence of a plane solid boundary can therefore be obtained by placing an equal and opposite line vortex at the *image point* in the boundary, and removing the boundary (see Figure 2.6).

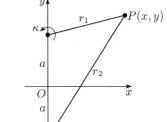

*Figure 2.5*

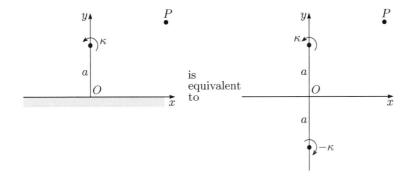

*Figure 2.6*

The equation of the streamlines, $\psi = \text{constant}$, reduces to

$$\frac{r_1}{r_2} = \text{constant} = M, \text{ say}.$$

Since $r_1 > 0$ and $r_2 > 0$, it follows that $M > 0$.

It is convenient to represent the streamlines in Cartesian coordinates. Then $r_1^2 = M^2 r_2^2$ becomes

$$x^2 + (y - a)^2 = M^2(x^2 + (y + a)^2),$$

that is,

$$(M^2 - 1)(x^2 + y^2) + 2a(M^2 + 1)y + (M^2 - 1)a^2 = 0.$$

Note that
$$r_1^2 = x^2 + (y - a)^2,$$
$$r_2^2 = x^2 + (y + a)^2.$$

119

If $M \neq 1$, this can be written as

$$x^2 + \left[y + \left(\frac{M^2+1}{M^2-1}\right)a\right]^2 = -a^2 + \left(\frac{M^2+1}{M^2-1}\right)^2 a^2,$$

or

$$x^2 + \left[y + \left(\frac{M^2+1}{M^2-1}\right)a\right]^2 = \frac{4M^2a^2}{(M^2-1)^2}.$$

If $M \neq 1$, this represents

$$\text{a circle with centre at } \left(0, \frac{(M^2+1)a}{1-M^2}\right) \text{ and radius } \left|\frac{2Ma}{M^2-1}\right|.$$

The streamlines are the circles shown in Figure 2.7; for $0 < M < 1$, these are above the $x$-axis, and for $M > 1$, they are below the $x$-axis.

Notice that if the $x$-axis is a solid boundary, and the flow above the boundary is due to the vortex at $(0, a, 0)$ — see Figure 2.7 — then the streamlines *below* the $x$-axis have no physical significance, since they are beyond the wall. ■

In using line vortices to model flows, it is assumed that the effect of a line vortex is to set up a rotating flow on parts of the fluid *other than itself*. Thus, for instance, the velocity field due to a line vortex of strength $\kappa$ directed along the $z$-axis is given by

$$\mathbf{u} = \frac{\kappa}{2\pi r}\,\mathbf{e}_\theta \qquad (r \neq 0),$$

and the assumption is that no motion is induced by the line vortex on particles situated on the $z$-axis. In other words, left to itself, the line vortex will not move. When two line vortices are present in a fluid, however, each will move sideways under the action of the other. Thus, the line vortices at $A$ and $B$ in Figure 2.8 will move in the same direction, as shown.

### Exercise 2.2

A line vortex of strength $-\kappa$ is situated outside a plane wall, as shown in Figure 2.9. The wall is given by $y = 0$, while the line vortex passes through $(0, a, 0)$ and is parallel to the $z$-axis. Find the direction and magnitude of the velocity of the vortex.

*Hint:* Use the model in Example 2.1.

### Exercise 2.3

Is it possible to model the effect of a line vortex in fluid contained within a solid cylindrical boundary, where the direction of the line vortex is parallel to but not coincident with the axis of the cylinder?

(Only a general answer is required here. You may find Figure 2.7 of use.)

The case $M = 1$ gives the $x$-axis.

Recall that

$$(x - A)^2 + (y - B)^2 = R^2$$

is the equation of a circle with centre $(A, B)$ and radius $|R|$.

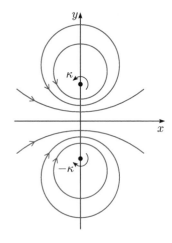

*Figure 2.7*

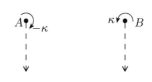

*Figure 2.8*

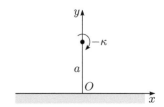

*Figure 2.9*

## 2.3  *Flow with swirl past an obstacle (audio)*

This subsection attempts to model a more realistic flow, using a uniform flow and a line vortex. The model leads to some interesting observations. The flow in question is that of a fluid streaming past a circular cylinder, around which there is a swirling of the fluid (see Figure 2.10).

*Figure 2.10*

The flow is uniform far upstream and downstream.

It is assumed that the fluid is inviscid, that body forces may be ignored, that the cylinder is infinitely long, and that the flow is two-dimensional, being in planes perpendicular to the axis of the cylinder. The fluid swirls around the obstacle.

The strategy will be to model the effect of the streaming past the cylinder by the stream function given in *Unit 5*, and the swirling motion by a line vortex. The main aim of the investigation is to calculate the force exerted on the obstacle as a result of the streaming and swirling fluid motion.

From Example 2.5 of *Unit 5*, this stream function is
$$\psi = U \sin\theta \left( \frac{r^2 - a^2}{r} \right).$$
In Example 2.1 of *Unit 6*, by finding the pressure distribution for this flow, it was deduced that the net force on the cylinder without swirl is zero.

This subsection features an audio session. Before starting this session, however, some preliminary results relating to swirling flow around a cylinder are required. The objective here is two-fold:

(i)  to set up a model for the swirling flow around the cylinder;

(ii) to calculate the force on the cylinder.

The audio session considers the combination of streaming and swirling flow.

Pursuing the first objective, the stream function for a line vortex of strength $-\kappa$, directed along the $z$-axis, is

$$\psi = \frac{\kappa}{2\pi} \ln r + \text{constant}.$$

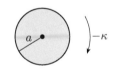

*Figure 2.11*

As pointed out previously, the corresponding streamlines are circles in planes perpendicular to the $z$-axis, and a good model for the flow outside a circular cylinder is by means of this stream function. We shall use this line vortex to model the swirling flow outside the cylinder.

With $\kappa > 0$, as will be assumed throughout this subsection, the line vortex of strength $-\kappa$ models a *clockwise* flow (see Figure 2.11). The corresponding circulation around any simple curve $C$ that encloses the cylinder is $-\kappa$ if $C$ is traversed in the usual anticlockwise sense, but the circulation is $\kappa$ if $C$ is traversed clockwise. The reason for this choice of sign for the strength will become evident later.

The second objective is to find the force on the cylinder due to the swirling flow. Intuitively, it is expected that the fluid exerts no net force on the cylinder due to the swirling flow alone, because this flow is symmetric around the cylinder.

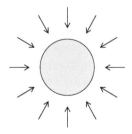

*Figure 2.12*

The force on the cylinder is found by summing the effects of the fluid pressure over the cylinder's surface (see Figure 2.12). The pressure at the surface is found by means of Bernoulli's equation. Thus, since Bernoulli's equation involves fluid speed, the first step in the calculation involves the determination of speed.

The summation process is integration.

Bernoulli's equation was considered in *Unit 6*.

The velocity field due to the line vortex alone is given by

$$\mathbf{u} = -\frac{\kappa}{2\pi r}\,\mathbf{e}_\theta.$$

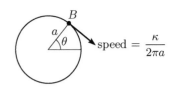

The speed $u$ at the surface $r = a$ is, therefore, $\kappa/(2\pi a)$. From Bernoulli's equation, the pressure $p = p(a, \theta)$ at a point $B$ (see Figure 2.13) on the surface of the cylinder satisfies

$$p + \tfrac{1}{2}\rho u^2 = p + \tfrac{1}{2}\rho\left(\frac{\kappa}{2\pi a}\right)^2 = M,$$

*Figure 2.13*

where $\rho$ is the density (assumed constant), and $M$ is a constant. Then

$$p(a, \theta) = M - \frac{\rho\kappa^2}{8\pi^2 a^2} = \text{constant}.$$

The next part of the argument is valid whether or not $p(a, \theta)$ is constant.

The force due to the fluid pressure, on a small surface element of area $\delta A$ immersed in a fluid, is easily found. Its magnitude is $p\,\delta A$, since pressure is the normal component of force per unit area. The associated direction is from the fluid into the surface, and is therefore given by $-\mathbf{n}$, where $\mathbf{n}$ is the unit normal vector to the surface pointing into the fluid (see Figure 2.14). Thus

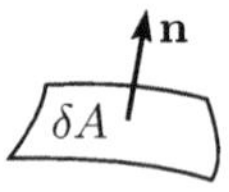

$$\text{force on surface element} = -p\,\mathbf{n}\,\delta A.$$

*Figure 2.14*

The force on the cylinder's surface is found by summing over all the surface elements and letting $\delta A \to 0$. In the limit,

$$\text{force on cylinder} = -\int_S p\,\mathbf{n}\,dA,$$

where $S$ is the surface of the cylinder. Note that, on this surface, the unit vector $\mathbf{n}$ is the same as $\mathbf{e}_r$, and is given in terms of the Cartesian unit vectors $\mathbf{i}$ and $\mathbf{j}$ by

$$\mathbf{n} = \cos\theta\,\mathbf{i} + \sin\theta\,\mathbf{j} \qquad \text{(see Figure 2.15).}$$

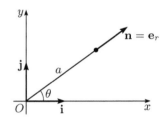

Again, it is convenient to find the force *per unit length* on the cylinder, which is

$$-\int_{-\pi}^{\pi} p(\cos\theta\,\mathbf{i} + \sin\theta\,\mathbf{j})\,a\,d\theta,$$

*Figure 2.15*

or

$$-\mathbf{i}\int_{-\pi}^{\pi} pa\cos\theta\,d\theta - \mathbf{j}\int_{-\pi}^{\pi} pa\sin\theta\,d\theta.$$

Here $\delta A = 1 \times a\,\delta\theta$. Hence the integration over unit length of the surface reduces to integration over $\theta$.

This last part of the argument is summarised as follows.

For any pressure distribution $p(a, \theta)$ around a circular cylinder of radius $a$, the components of the force per unit length in the $\mathbf{i}$- and $\mathbf{j}$-directions are, respectively,

$$-\int_{-\pi}^{\pi} pa\cos\theta\,d\theta \qquad \text{and} \qquad -\int_{-\pi}^{\pi} pa\sin\theta\,d\theta.$$

These results will be used again later in this section.

In the present example, the component of force in the $\mathbf{i}$-direction is

$$-\int_{-\pi}^{\pi} pa\cos\theta\,d\theta = -\int_{-\pi}^{\pi}\left(M - \frac{\rho\kappa^2}{8\pi^2 a^2}\right)a\cos\theta\,d\theta = 0.$$

Similarly, the component of force in the $\mathbf{j}$-direction is

$$-\int_{-\pi}^{\pi} pa\sin\theta\,d\theta = -\int_{-\pi}^{\pi}\left(M - \frac{\rho\kappa^2}{8\pi^2 a^2}\right)a\sin\theta\,d\theta = 0.$$

Here the constant value of

$$p(a, \theta) = M - \frac{\rho\kappa^2}{8\pi^2 a^2}$$

has no effect on the integration.

Hence there is no force on the cylinder in a swirling flow of inviscid fluid.

This result, in itself, is less important than the various steps followed in order to establish it:

(a) calculation of the speed at the cylinder's surface;

(b) use of Bernoulli's equation to find the pressure at the cylinder's surface, given the speed;

(c) use of the (highlighted) results for the force components due to a pressure distribution.

These same steps are used again in the audio session, to find the force on the cylinder due to a more interesting flow. The flow in question is a combination of streaming and swirling.

The modelling of the fluid is by an inviscid fluid of constant density, so the viscosity of the fluid is neglected. Also, body forces are ignored.

Note that the streaming flow of fluid past a cylinder (in the *absence* of swirl) was considered in *Units 5* and *6*. The following analysis will use some of the ideas introduced there.

Finally, here is a comment on the word 'swirl'. 'Swirl' is an everyday term which has the connotation of fluid moving around an obstacle, or just rotating; that certainly covers the situation described here. Later, the swirling formulation will be related to a more formal description involving the concept of circulation that was discussed earlier in this unit.

While the fluid rotates around an obstacle, we have avoided saying that the flow is 'rotational'. This is because 'rotational' means not irrotational, and irrotational has been defined precisely: a flow is irrotational at a point if $\mathbf{curl\, u} = \mathbf{0}$ there. For the flows with swirl considered in this subsection, despite the overall rotating sense of the motion, the flow is in fact irrotational at each point.

***When you are ready, start the audio at Track 34 of CD1.***

The earlier intuition, that there is no force on the cylinder, was therefore correct.

Recall that the flow was modelled by means of a line vortex.

However, as you will see later, a real flow with swirl could be generated by the action of viscosity in the region close to a rotating cylinder.

See *Unit 4* Subsection 4.3.

**1**   **Streaming flow past a cylinder without swirl**

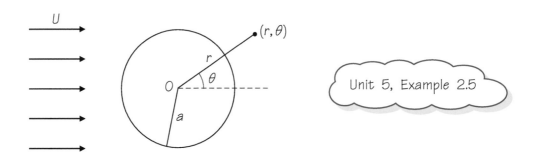

Unit 5, Example 2.5

Stream function $\psi =$ 

---

**2**   **Circulation**

Show that the flow described
in Frame 1 has zero circulation
around the cylinder.

'Circulation'
is defined in
Subsection 1.2.

(Hint: Consider $\oint_C \underline{u} \cdot d\underline{r}$ where $C$ is a circle of radius $R$, with $R \geq a$,
traversed anticlockwise)

---

**3**   **Stream function for a line vortex**

$$\underline{u} = -\frac{\kappa}{2\pi r}\underline{e}_\theta$$

See
Subsection 2.1.

Line vortex strength is $-\kappa$,
with $\kappa > 0$, for clockwise motion.

Stream function $\psi =$

**1A**   **Streaming flow past a cylinder without swirl**

Stream function is $\psi = Ur\sin\theta - \dfrac{Ua^2\sin\theta}{r}$.

 **2A**   **Circulation around cylinder**

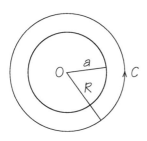

The stream function is

$$\psi = Ur\sin\theta - \frac{Ua^2\sin\theta}{r}.$$

In polar coordinates,

$$\underline{u} = u_r\,\underline{e}_r + u_\theta\,\underline{e}_\theta,$$

where $u_r = \dfrac{1}{r}\dfrac{\partial\psi}{\partial\theta}$, $\quad u_\theta = -\dfrac{\partial\psi}{\partial r}$.

*Unit 5, Section 2*

Hence $u_r = \left(U - \dfrac{Ua^2}{r^2}\right)\cos\theta$,

$$u_\theta = -\left(U + \frac{Ua^2}{r^2}\right)\sin\theta.$$

Then $\displaystyle\oint_C \underline{u}\cdot d\underline{r} = \oint_C (u_r\,\underline{e}_r + u_\theta\,\underline{e}_\theta)\cdot d\underline{r}$

$$= \int_{-\pi}^{\pi} u_\theta R\,d\theta \qquad (\text{since } \delta\underline{r} = R\,\delta\theta\,\underline{e}_\theta)$$

$$= -\int_{-\pi}^{\pi}\left(U + \frac{Ua^2}{R^2}\right)R\sin\theta\,d\theta$$

$$= -\left(U + \frac{Ua^2}{R^2}\right)R\int_{-\pi}^{\pi}\sin\theta\,d\theta = 0.$$

 **3A**   **Line vortex**

$\psi = \dfrac{\kappa}{2\pi}\ln r + \text{constant}.$

Choose constant $= -\dfrac{\kappa}{2\pi}\ln a$.

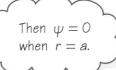

Then $\psi = 0$ when $r = a$.

So $\psi = \dfrac{\kappa}{2\pi}\ln\left(\dfrac{r}{a}\right)$.

125

### 4   Flow past a cylinder with swirl

$$\psi = Ur\sin\theta - \frac{Ua^2\sin\theta}{r} + \frac{\kappa}{2\pi}\ln\left(\frac{r}{a}\right)$$

$$u_r = \frac{1}{r}\frac{\partial\psi}{\partial\theta} = U\cos\theta - \frac{Ua^2}{r^2}\cos\theta$$

$$u_\theta = -\frac{\partial\psi}{\partial r} = -U\sin\theta - \frac{Ua^2\sin\theta}{r^2} - \frac{\kappa}{2\pi r}$$

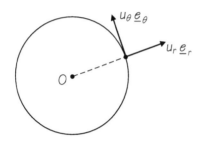

(a) Show that $u_r = 0$ when $r = a$.

(b) What is the circulation around $C$, the circle $r = R$  $(R \geq a)$, traversed anticlockwise?

### 4A   Flow past a cylinder with swirl

(a) $(u_r)_{r=a} = U\cos\theta - \frac{Ua^2}{a^2}\cos\theta = 0$

(b) Circulation $= \oint_C \underline{u}\cdot d\underline{r}$

> $C$ is a circle of radius $R \geq a$, traversed anticlockwise.

$$= \int_{-\pi}^{\pi} u_\theta R\, d\theta$$

$$= \int_{-\pi}^{\pi}\left[-U\left(1+\frac{a^2}{R^2}\right)\sin\theta - \frac{\kappa}{2\pi R}\right]R\, d\theta$$

$$= \int_{-\pi}^{\pi}\left(-\frac{\kappa}{2\pi}\right)d\theta = -\kappa.$$

**5**   **Streamlines of flow**

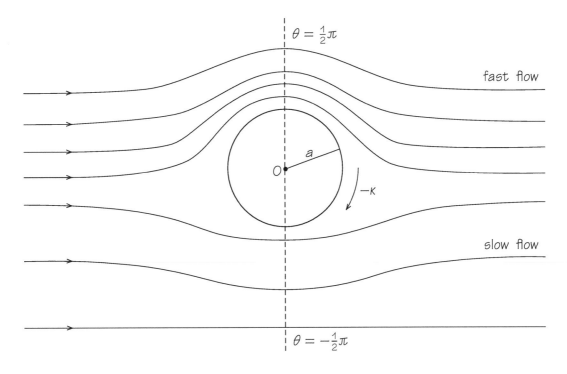

$$\psi = Ur\sin\theta - \frac{Ua^2\sin\theta}{r} + \frac{\kappa}{2\pi}\ln\left(\frac{r}{a}\right)$$

**6**   **Pressure at a point on the cylinder**

Find an expression for the pressure $p(a,\theta)$ on the cylinder at point B.

= constant

**6A**   **Pressure on cylinder**

At $B$, $r = a$; hence

$$u_r = 0$$

from Frame 4

$$u_\theta = -2U \sin\theta - \frac{\kappa}{2\pi a}.$$

The circle $r = a$ on the cylinder's surface is a streamline. Bernoulli's equation along this streamline is

$$p + \tfrac{1}{2}\rho u_\theta^2 = \text{constant}.$$

No body force

So $p + \tfrac{1}{2}\rho\left(2U\sin\theta + \dfrac{\kappa}{2\pi a}\right)^2 = M$ (constant).

Hence $p = M - \tfrac{1}{2}\rho\left(4U^2 \sin^2\theta + \dfrac{2U\kappa\sin\theta}{\pi a} + \dfrac{\kappa^2}{4\pi^2 a^2}\right).$

---

**7**   **Force on cylinder**

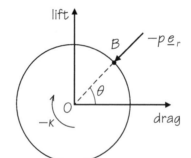

$U$ →

$$\text{Lift} = \int_{-\pi}^{\pi} (-p\sin\theta)a\,d\theta$$

$$= \int_{-\pi}^{\pi} \left( \phantom{xxxxxxxxxxxxxxxxxxxxxxxxxxxxxxxxxxxxxx} \right) a\sin\theta\,d\theta$$

$$= \boxed{\phantom{xxxxxxxxxxxxxxxxxx}}$$

$$\text{Drag} = \int_{-\pi}^{\pi} \boxed{\phantom{xxxxxxxxxxxxxxxxxx}} d\theta$$

$$= \boxed{\phantom{xxxxxxxxxxxxxxxxxx}}$$

**7A**    Force on cylinder

$$\text{Lift} = \int_{-\pi}^{\pi} (-p\sin\theta)a\,d\theta$$

$$= -\int_{-\pi}^{\pi}\left[M - \tfrac{1}{2}\rho\left(4U^2\sin^2\theta + \frac{2U\kappa\sin\theta}{\pi a} + \frac{\kappa^2}{4\pi^2 a^2}\right)\right]a\sin\theta\,d\theta$$

$$\int_{-\pi}^{\pi}\sin\theta\,d\theta = 0$$

$$\int_{-\pi}^{\pi}\sin^3\theta\,d\theta = 0$$

Both integrands are odd functions

$$= -0 + 0 + \frac{\rho U\kappa}{\pi}\int_{-\pi}^{\pi}\sin^2\theta\,d\theta + 0$$

$$= \frac{\rho U\kappa}{2\pi}\int_{-\pi}^{\pi}(1 - \cos(2\theta))\,d\theta$$

$$= \frac{\rho U\kappa}{2\pi}\left[\theta - \tfrac{1}{2}\sin(2\theta)\right]_{-\pi}^{\pi}$$

$$= \rho U\kappa$$

Integration by substitution shows that

$$\int \sin^n\theta\cos\theta\,d\theta = \frac{1}{n+1}\sin^{n+1}\theta + \text{constant};$$

can use this here with $n = 2, 1, 0$.

$$\text{Drag} = \int_{-\pi}^{\pi}(-p\cos\theta)a\,d\theta$$

$$= -\int_{-\pi}^{\pi}\left[M - \tfrac{1}{2}\rho\left(4U^2\sin^2\theta + \frac{2U\kappa\sin\theta}{\pi a} + \frac{\kappa^2}{4\pi^2 a^2}\right)\right]a\cos\theta\,d\theta$$

$$= \left[-Ma\sin\theta + \frac{2\rho U^2 a\sin^3\theta}{3} + \frac{\rho U\kappa\sin^2\theta}{2\pi} + \frac{\rho U\kappa^2\sin\theta}{8\pi^2 a}\right]_{-\pi}^{\pi}$$

$$= 0.$$

Summary

The combination of a streaming and a swirling flow around a cylinder gives rise to lift.

The model predicts that there is no drag force on the cylinder.

A summary of the results from the audio session is as follows.

(i)  The combination of a streaming flow and a swirling flow around the cylinder gives rise to a *lift*, perpendicular to the stream direction.

(ii)  The model predicts that there is no force component on the cylinder in the direction of the stream; that is, there is no *drag*.

For a streaming flow from left to right, the swirling must be in the clockwise sense for the 'lift' to be directed upwards.

It is convenient, for reasons which will become more apparent later, to regard swirling flow as modelling a flow having non-zero circulation around the cylinder. Then statement (i) above can be written as follows.

(i)  In the streaming flow past a cylinder, the presence of a non-zero circulation around the cylinder gives rise to a 'lift'.

Some interesting questions arise from these results.

(a) How can the zero drag predicted by this model be reconciled with the non-zero drag that occurs in practice?

(b) Does the relationship between lift and circulation for the model apply to the flow of real fluids past a cylinder?

(c) Associated with (b), how can circulation arise during the flow of real fluids past cylinders?

(d) For flows involving geometries other than the circle, can the observed lift force be explained in terms of circulation? One such situation, for example, is the lift force observed on an aircraft wing during the flow of air past it.

For example, such a drag is experienced visibly by a flagpole in strong winds.

A part of the remainder of this unit addresses itself to these questions.

## End-of-section exercise

### Exercise 2.4

An inviscid fluid occupies the region $(y > 0)$ above a planar plate, whose upper surface is given by $y = 0$ (see Figure 2.16). A line vortex of strength $-\kappa$ is at rest, is directed parallel to the $z$-axis and passes through the point $(0, a, 0)$. The fluid is moving such that, at large distances from the line vortex, it is streaming in the direction of the $x$-axis, with constant speed $U$. Body forces may be ignored. There is a constant pressure $p_0$ acting on the lower surface of the plate, and above the plate, the pressure approaches $p_0$ as $x \to \pm\infty$.

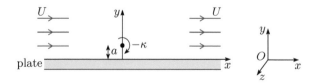

*Figure 2.16*

(a) Use the result of Example 2.1 (see Figure 2.6) to sketch a system of two line vortices which is equivalent to the given line vortex in the presence of the boundary $y = 0$. Using the result of Exercise 2.2, show that $\kappa = 4\pi a U$.

(b) Show that the magnitude of the net force on the plate, due to the presence of the line vortex, is zero.

To do this, it suffices to integrate the pressure difference over an infinite strip in the $x$-direction, lying in the plane $y = 0$ and with unit width in the $z$-direction. The following integrals will prove useful:

$$\int \frac{a}{a^2 + x^2} \, dx = \arctan\left(\frac{x}{a}\right) + c,$$

$$\int \frac{a^2}{(a^2 + x^2)^2} \, dx = \frac{1}{2a} \arctan\left(\frac{x}{a}\right) + \frac{x}{2(a^2 + x^2)} + c.$$

# 3    Kelvin's Theorem

The model predictions at the end of the previous section, concerning streaming and swirling flow past a cylinder, prompted several questions. In this section, the groundwork is laid for later attempts to answer those questions.

Much of the discussion is concerned with further exploration of the concept of circulation. However, the close connection between vorticity and circulation also necessitates further consideration of vorticity.

*See Subsection 1.2.*

Subsection 3.1 introduces the concepts of *vortex lines* and *vortex tubes*. A word of caution is appropriate here. You have already met the concept of line vortex, but the concept of vortex line is a different one, as will be seen below.

## 3.1    Vortex lines and vortex tubes

You saw in *Unit 5* that streamlines provide a pictorial representation of the fluid velocity vector field at an instant of time; streamlines are (by definition) the field lines of the velocity vector field **u**. Vortex lines are defined in an analogous way; the field lines of the vorticity vector field $\boldsymbol{\omega} = \mathbf{curl\,u}$ are called **vortex lines**. In more basic terms, a vortex line is a curve such that at each point along the curve, the tangent vector is parallel to the vorticity vector. In the same way as for streamlines, you can imagine vortex lines being drawn in the fluid.

Since, in general, **u** is a function of time, so is $\boldsymbol{\omega}$, and the pattern of vortex lines will change as time passes.

As with streamlines, vortex lines will in general be curves rather than straight lines.

For example, if

$$\mathbf{u} = u_1(x, y)\,\mathbf{i} + u_2(x, y)\,\mathbf{j}$$

represents a two-dimensional flow, then the vorticity is

$$\boldsymbol{\omega} = \mathbf{curl\,u} = \left(\frac{\partial u_2}{\partial x} - \frac{\partial u_1}{\partial y}\right)\mathbf{k},$$

which is a vector perpendicular to the direction of the motion. The vortex lines are parallel to $\boldsymbol{\omega}$, so the vortex lines here are straight lines perpendicular to the plane in which the motion occurs (i.e. they are parallel to the $z$-axis or **k**-direction, as shown in Figure 3.1 overleaf).

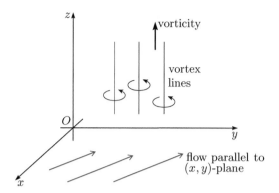

*Figure 3.1*

Cartesian coordinates have been used in the above, but it is possible also to write down expressions for the curl of a vector in other coordinate systems, using whichever system is most useful to find the vortex lines for a flow. The vortex lines are in the direction of **curl u** at every point of the flow, where **u** is the velocity vector.

See *Unit 4* Subsection 4.1.

### Exercise 3.1

Find an expression for the vorticity of the flow given by the velocity field

$$\mathbf{u} = u_z(r)\,\mathbf{e}_z,$$

in cylindrical polar coordinates. Hence sketch the vortex lines.

This could be a flow within a pipe, with axis on the $z$-axis.

Note that $\mathbf{e}_z = \mathbf{k}$; these unit vector expressions are used interchangeably.

Vortex lines appear prominently in the definition of a *vortex tube*, just as streamlines do in the definition of a streamtube.

In the pictorial representation of a fluid flow, through every point there is a vortex line, except for those points where the vorticity is zero. Consider all the vortex lines drawn through a closed curve $C$ in the fluid (see Figure 3.2). The surface of the tube so formed is called a **vortex tube**. For example, it has been shown that for a two-dimensional motion, the vortex lines are perpendicular to the plane of motion (see Figure 3.1). In this case, for a circle $C$ in the $(x, y)$-plane, the associated vortex tube is a circular cylinder with $C$ as cross-section, as shown in Figure 3.3.

The definition of a streamtube is in *Unit 5* Subsection 4.3.

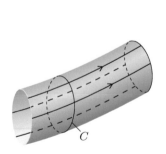

*Figure 3.2*

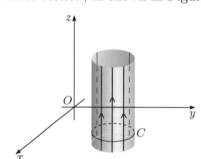

*Figure 3.3*

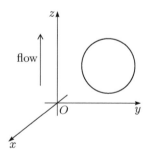

*Figure 3.4*

### Exercise 3.2

Consider again the flow from Exercise 3.1, with flow velocity

$$\mathbf{u} = u_z(r)\,\mathbf{e}_z.$$

Using the results of Exercise 3.1, sketch the vortex tube which passes through a circle in the $(y, z)$-plane $(\theta = \frac{1}{2}\pi)$, as shown in Figure 3.4.

Note that the result of Exercise 3.2 is a model for the real-life phenomenon of a smoke ring (see Figure 3.5). The smoke highlights the vortex lines, forming a closed tube (like a small tyre or doughnut), the tube moving with the general flow along its axis.

*Figure 3.5*   A smoke ring

## 3.2   The strength of a vortex tube

Consider a vortex tube passing through a plane simple closed curve $C$, as shown in Figure 3.6. Let $S$ be the plane surface whose boundary is $C$.

The flux of vorticity $\boldsymbol{\omega}$ across the surface $S$ is

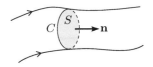

$$\int_S \boldsymbol{\omega} \cdot \mathbf{n}\, dA,$$

where $\mathbf{n}$ is the unit normal to $S$ in the direction for which $\boldsymbol{\omega} \cdot \mathbf{n} > 0$.

*Figure 3.6*   The arrowheads indicate the direction of the vorticity.

It is reasonable to ask whether the value for the flux of vorticity depends on the particular surface $S$ that is chosen. If the flux is constant along the tube, then it may be taken as a measure of the *strength* of the vortex tube, or alternatively, as a measure of the strength of vorticity in the region of fluid enclosed by the vortex tube. The flux is indeed constant, and you are asked to establish this result through a sequence of exercises.

The flux of a vector field across a surface was introduced in *Unit 4* Subsection 2.1.

The general aim is to show that the fluxes of vorticity through two arbitrary plane cross-sectional surfaces, $S_1$ and $S_2$, are the same. The strategy is to consider the region $B$ bounded by the surfaces $S_1$, $S_2$ and $S_T$, where $S_T$ is the segment of tube surface between $S_1$ and $S_2$ (see Figure 3.7). Then Gauss' Theorem, applied to the vorticity vector field $\boldsymbol{\omega}$, will lead to the required result.

See *Unit 4* Subsection 3.2.

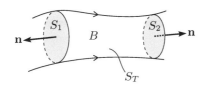

*Figure 3.7*

### Exercise 3.3

Use Gauss' Theorem to convert the volume integral $\int_B \operatorname{div} \boldsymbol{\omega}\, dV$ into the sum of three surface integrals.

*Hint:* What are the boundaries of $B$?

The volume integral has been replaced by three surface integrals:

$$\int_B \operatorname{div} \boldsymbol{\omega}\, dV = \int_{S_1} \boldsymbol{\omega} \cdot \mathbf{n}\, dA + \int_{S_2} \boldsymbol{\omega} \cdot \mathbf{n}\, dA + \int_{S_T} \boldsymbol{\omega} \cdot \mathbf{n}\, dA.$$

This equation can be simplified, as you will show in the next exercise.

Remember that **n** denotes the outward-pointing unit normal on the various surfaces.

### Exercise 3.4

Show that $\operatorname{div} \boldsymbol{\omega} = 0$, and hence that $\int_B \operatorname{div} \boldsymbol{\omega}\, dV = 0$.

*Hint:* Write down the definition of the vorticity $\boldsymbol{\omega}$ in terms of the velocity **u**, and then make use of a vector identity.

Exercise 3.4 shows that

$$0 = \int_{S_1} \boldsymbol{\omega} \cdot \mathbf{n}\, dA + \int_{S_2} \boldsymbol{\omega} \cdot \mathbf{n}\, dA + \int_{S_T} \boldsymbol{\omega} \cdot \mathbf{n}\, dA.$$

The next step is to show that the third term on the right-hand side can be eliminated.

### Exercise 3.5

Show that

$$\int_{S_T} \boldsymbol{\omega} \cdot \mathbf{n}\, dA = 0.$$

*Hint:* Remember the definitions of vortex tube and of **n**, and consider the directions of $\boldsymbol{\omega}$ and **n** at any point on $S_T$, the surface of the tube.

As a result of the previous exercises, we have

$$\int_{S_1} \boldsymbol{\omega} \cdot \mathbf{n}\, dA + \int_{S_2} \boldsymbol{\omega} \cdot \mathbf{n}\, dA = 0.$$

For both $S_1$ and $S_2$, the unit normal **n** points outwards from the region $B$ (see Figure 3.7). Now choose the normals to the surfaces in the direction for which $\boldsymbol{\omega} \cdot \mathbf{n} > 0$ (see Figure 3.8); that is, take

$$\mathbf{n}_1 = -\mathbf{n} \text{ on } S_1 \qquad \text{and} \qquad \mathbf{n}_2 = \mathbf{n} \text{ on } S_2.$$

We then have

$$\int_{S_1} \boldsymbol{\omega} \cdot (-\mathbf{n}_1)\, dA + \int_{S_2} \boldsymbol{\omega} \cdot \mathbf{n}_2\, dA = 0,$$

which becomes

$$\int_{S_1} \boldsymbol{\omega} \cdot \mathbf{n}_1\, dA = \int_{S_2} \boldsymbol{\omega} \cdot \mathbf{n}_2\, dA.$$

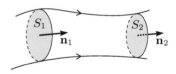

*Figure 3.8*

It follows from the above that, for any plane cross-sectional surface $S$ of a vortex tube, the quantity $\int_S \boldsymbol{\omega} \cdot \mathbf{n}\, dA$ is constant. In fact, it is not necessary to restrict $S$ to be planar; $S$ can be any 'smooth' open surface whose perimeter, $C$, lies on and encloses the vortex tube. The **strength** of a vortex tube is defined to be $\int_S \boldsymbol{\omega} \cdot \mathbf{n}\, dA$.

Here **n** is in the direction for which $\boldsymbol{\omega} \cdot \mathbf{n} > 0$.

Note that the strength of a vortex tube is given as the surface integral of the normal component of the curl of a vector over a surface. This may bring to mind a theorem from vector calculus.

$$\text{strength} = \int_S (\mathbf{curl}\, \mathbf{u}) \cdot \mathbf{n}\, dA.$$

### Exercise 3.6

Apply Stokes' Theorem to find an expression for the strength of a vortex tube in terms of a line integral around $C$, the perimeter of an open surface $S$ that spans the tube.

---

The result of Exercise 3.6 gives a more precise interpretation of the circulation (of the velocity vector) around a simple closed curve $C$.

> The circulation of the velocity around a simple closed curve $C$ is the strength of the vortex tube formed by the vortex lines that pass through $C$.

Consideration of vortex tubes and vortex lines has led back to circulation. This reinforces a previous assertion that circulation is a fundamental concept in the theory.

Some basic questions posed at the end of Section 2 concerned the occurrence of circulation: can circulation arise in practice, and if so, what is the mechanism for producing it? These questions will be discussed in Section 5. For the moment, consider a different question: how does the circulation around a curve $C$ change as the curve moves with the fluid? The answer to this question is given by Kelvin's Theorem, which is considered in the next subsection.

*Recall that, on page 130, the problem considered in the audio session was recast in terms of circulation.*

*In terms of vortex tubes, the question may be posed as: how do the strengths of vortex tubes passing through $C$ change as $C$ moves with the fluid?*

## 3.3  Kelvin's Theorem

As you will see, Kelvin's Theorem describes how the circulation around a closed curve changes, as that curve moves with the fluid. Consider the following three assumptions on the flow of a fluid.

*Assumption 1*   The fluid is inviscid, and so Euler's equation can be used.

*Assumption 2*   The fluid is incompressible. Take $\rho = \rho_0$, a constant, as the mathematical model of an incompressible fluid.

*Assumption 3*   The vector field $\mathbf{F}$ describing the body force per unit mass is conservative. So $\mathbf{F}$ can be written as $\mathbf{F} = \boldsymbol{\nabla}\Omega$, where $\Omega$ is a scalar field.

*These three assumptions apply to each form of Bernoulli's equation derived in Unit 6.*

### Kelvin's Theorem

If Assumptions 1, 2 and 3 above hold for a fluid flow, then the circulation around any closed curve $C$ moving with the fluid remains constant in time. Thus

$$\text{if } \kappa = \oint_C \mathbf{u} \cdot d\mathbf{r}, \text{ then } \frac{d\kappa}{dt} = 0.$$

Here, in general, $\mathbf{u}$ may be a function of both time and position.

*William Thomson (Lord Kelvin, 1824–1907) was an Irish physicist and engineer.*

To establish this result, we consider particles of fluid and follow their motion. The need for this approach arises out of the necessity to identify the particles forming the curve $C$ at all times. In this identification each particle is labelled by a real number $\lambda$, where $0 \le \lambda \le 1$, and $\lambda$ varies continuously as the curve $C(t)$ is traversed. The position vector of a fluid particle at some time $t$ is then $\mathbf{r}(t, \lambda)$; see Figure 3.9. As the fluid moves,

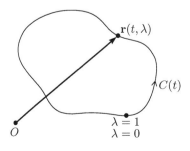

*Figure 3.9*

$\lambda$ remains constant for each marked particle on the curve $C(t)$. Note that $t$ and $\lambda$ are independent variables; a variation in $t$ describes the paths of particles, whereas a variation in $\lambda$ describes the curve $C(t)$.

Now, the circulation around $C(t)$ is

$$\kappa(t) = \oint_{C(t)} \mathbf{u} \cdot d\mathbf{r} = \oint_{C(t)} \mathbf{u}(\mathbf{r}, t) \cdot d\mathbf{r}$$

$$= \int_{\lambda=0}^{\lambda=1} \mathbf{u}(\mathbf{r}, t) \cdot \frac{d\mathbf{r}}{d\lambda} \, d\lambda,$$

Integration around the curve at a fixed time $t$ is in terms of $\lambda$.

where $\lambda$ is the chosen parameter for the curve $C(t)$. Since the limits of integration are constant, differentiating this with respect to $t$ gives

$$\frac{d\kappa}{dt} = \int_{\lambda=0}^{\lambda=1} \left[ \frac{d\mathbf{u}}{dt} \cdot \frac{d\mathbf{r}}{d\lambda} + \mathbf{u} \cdot \frac{d}{dt}\left(\frac{d\mathbf{r}}{d\lambda}\right) \right] d\lambda$$

$$= \int_{\lambda=0}^{\lambda=1} \frac{d\mathbf{u}}{dt} \cdot \frac{d\mathbf{r}}{d\lambda} \, d\lambda + \int_{\lambda=0}^{\lambda=1} \mathbf{u} \cdot \frac{d\mathbf{u}}{d\lambda} \, d\lambda.$$

Note that

$$\frac{d}{dt}\left(\frac{d\mathbf{r}}{d\lambda}\right) = \frac{d^2\mathbf{r}}{dt \, d\lambda}$$

$$= \frac{d}{d\lambda}\left(\frac{d\mathbf{r}}{dt}\right) = \frac{d\mathbf{u}}{d\lambda}.$$

Thus

$$\frac{d\kappa}{dt} = \int_{\lambda=0}^{\lambda=1} \frac{d\mathbf{u}}{dt} \cdot \frac{d\mathbf{r}}{d\lambda} d\lambda + \left[\tfrac{1}{2}u^2\right]_{\lambda=0}^{\lambda=1}.$$

Here $u = |\mathbf{u}|$.

Now $\lambda = 0$ and $\lambda = 1$ represent the same fluid particle, and as long as the velocity is a continuous function, $\left[\tfrac{1}{2}u^2\right]_{\lambda=0}^{\lambda=1} = 0$. Therefore

$$\frac{d\kappa}{dt} = \int_{\lambda=0}^{\lambda=1} \frac{d\mathbf{u}}{dt} \cdot \frac{d\mathbf{r}}{d\lambda} \, d\lambda. \tag{3.1}$$

Euler's equation gives

Here Assumption 1 is used.

$$\frac{d\mathbf{u}}{dt} = -\frac{1}{\rho}\boldsymbol{\nabla}p + \mathbf{F}. \tag{3.2}$$

Now, from Assumption 2, the density is $\rho = \rho_0$, a constant, so that

$$\frac{1}{\rho}\boldsymbol{\nabla}p = \frac{1}{\rho_0}\boldsymbol{\nabla}p = \boldsymbol{\nabla}\left(\frac{p}{\rho_0}\right);$$

and from Assumption 3, we have $\mathbf{F} = \boldsymbol{\nabla}\Omega$.

Substituting these expressions into the right-hand side of Euler's equation (3.2) gives

$$\frac{d\mathbf{u}}{dt} = -\boldsymbol{\nabla}\left(\frac{p}{\rho_0}\right) + \boldsymbol{\nabla}\Omega = \boldsymbol{\nabla}\left(-\frac{p}{\rho_0} + \Omega\right).$$

Further, using the Chain Rule for partial differentiation gives

$$\frac{d\mathbf{u}}{dt} \cdot \frac{d\mathbf{r}}{d\lambda} = \boldsymbol{\nabla}\left(-\frac{p}{\rho_0} + \Omega\right) \cdot \frac{d\mathbf{r}}{d\lambda}$$

$$= \frac{d}{d\lambda}\left(-\frac{p}{\rho_0} + \Omega\right).$$

For the details of this step, see *Unit 6*, page 70, with $\lambda$ in place of $s$.

Thus Equation (3.1) becomes

$$\frac{d\kappa}{dt} = \int_{\lambda=0}^{\lambda=1} \frac{d}{d\lambda}\left(-\frac{p}{\rho_0} + \Omega\right) d\lambda$$

$$= \left[-\frac{p}{\rho_0} + \Omega\right]_{\lambda=0}^{\lambda=1} = 0,$$

since the combination $-p/\rho_0 + \Omega$ is continuous, and $\lambda = 0$, $\lambda = 1$ represent the same fluid particle, which is, at any instant of time, at a single point in space. This establishes the result.

Kelvin's Theorem can be used to make some useful deductions concerning the nature of vortex lines and tubes in an inviscid fluid.

Start by considering a vortex tube and two closed curves $C_1$, $C_2$ formed by fluid particles and lying on the surface of the tube. The curve $C_1$ passes around the vortex tube, while the curve $C_2$ does not (see Figure 3.10).

Note that Kelvin's Theorem does not apply to viscous fluids.

### Exercise 3.7

Write down the strength of the vortex tube formed by the vortex lines passing through $C_1$. From Kelvin's Theorem, what can be said about the strengths of the vortex tubes formed by the vortex lines passing through $C_1(t)$ as it moves through the fluid?

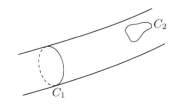

Figure 3.10

From Exercise 3.7, then, the significance of a curve $C_1$ moving with the fluid is that all the vortex tubes associated with it have the same strength. What of the curve $C_2$, which lies initially on the surface of a vortex tube but does not pass around the tube? From Kelvin's Theorem, the circulation around $C_2(t)$ will be constant as it moves through the fluid. Exercise 3.8 asks you to show that the initial value of this circulation is zero, and hence that it is zero at all subsequent times.

### Exercise 3.8

(a) Use Stokes' Theorem to relate the circulation around $C_2$ to an appropriate integral over that part of the surface of the vortex tube enclosed by $C_2$ (see Figure 3.11).

(b) What is the angle between the vorticity $\boldsymbol{\omega}$ at a point on the surface of the vortex tube and the unit normal to the tube surface at that point?

(c) Deduce from parts (a) and (b) that the circulation around $C_2(t)$ is zero at all times.

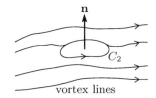

Figure 3.11

A curve which moves with the fluid is called a *material curve*. Let the simple closed material curve $C_1$ deform to the curve $C_1'$ after some time interval. Exercise 3.7 shows that the strength of the vortex tube $T$ through $C_1$ is the same as that of the vortex tube $T'$ through $C_1'$. Let $C_2$ be a simple closed material curve on the surface of the vortex tube $T$, which (unlike $C_1$) does not encircle the tube. Suppose that $C_2$ has a section in common with $C_1$, and let $C_2'$ be the deformed position of $C_2$ (see Figure 3.12). Clearly, the fluid particles which are common to $C_1$ and $C_2$ are also common to $C_1'$ and $C_2'$. Exercise 3.8 says that the circulations around $C_2$ and around $C_2'$ are zero. Since the circulation around $C_2'$ is zero, it follows that $C_2'$ lies on the surface of a vortex tube but does not encircle it. Because the section common to $C_1$ and $C_2$ can be enlarged (without it being the whole of $C_1$), the section common to $C_2'$ and $C_1'$ can also be enlarged. Hence the vortex tube on which $C_2'$ lies is the vortex tube $T'$ through $C_1'$. In fact, it can be shown that the vortex tube $T'$ through $C_1'$ is the deformed version of the vortex tube $T$ through $C_1$. That is, vortex tubes move with the fluid, and are therefore a permanent feature of the motion.

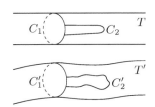

Figure 3.12

By regarding the cross-sectional area of a vortex tube as becoming vanishingly small, the limit is a vortex line. Hence vortex lines are also a permanent feature of fluid motion.

The implications of these findings for the transport and variations of vorticity in fluids are considered in the next subsection.

137

## 3.4   Transport of vorticity in inviscid fluids

The permanent nature of vortex tubes and lines gives some insight into the way vorticity is transported in an inviscid fluid, and also how changes of vorticity are caused.

Consider first the method of transport of vorticity. Since vortex tubes are a permanent feature of a fluid motion, they are transported around in a manner similar to that in which real tubes (albeit elastic ones) would be transported by the fluid. The important point is that the method of transport is on the macroscopic or large scale. Essentially, the tubes are, as it were, transported by the movement of 'lumps' of fluid. Such a method of transport on the macroscopic scale is known as *convection*, because it is due to the motion of the fluid.

An everyday example of the transport of a property in a fluid relates to the taking of a bath. The process of attaining a uniform temperature in the bath is speeded up by imposing some motion on the bath water by moving one's hands. In effect, 'lumps' of hot water are moved to colder regions, and vice versa, by the process of convection. Left to itself, a bath of hot water would take a considerable time to attain a uniform temperature throughout. In that case, the mode of transport of heat is called conduction or *diffusion*. Diffusion is a process whereby the property (heat) may be supposed to diffuse or 'leak' through the fluid via its molecules.

Note that convection is a relatively quick process compared with diffusion. The relative rates of these processes is returned to in Section 4.

In a real fluid, vorticity is diffused by the action of viscosity, operating on a microscopic scale. This contrasts with the macroscopic scale of the convection process. In an inviscid fluid, there is no diffusion of vorticity because there is no viscosity present to set up the diffusion.

Vorticity, like heat, can be convected in an inviscid fluid, and in its simplest form this involves the *translation* of vortex tubes. Since vorticity is a vector quantity, unlike heat, the effect of *rotation* on a vortex tube (not about an axis parallel to it) is to change the direction of the vorticity vector. The motion of a fluid may also lead to the *stretching* or *compressing* of vortex tubes. Recall that, as a vortex tube moves with the fluid, its strength remains constant. This does not mean, however, that the vorticity within it remains constant. The strength of a vortex tube is related to the size of a cross-section of the tube and the distribution of vorticity across it, and changes in the cross-section will be accompanied by corresponding changes in vorticity. Thus, changes in vorticity along a vortex tube (as the fluid moves) can arise owing to the stretching or compressing of the tube.

These motions are also aspects of convection.

To sum up:
(i)   vorticity can be convected in an inviscid fluid, but not diffused;
(ii)  the direction of vorticity may be changed, by supposing that the vortex tubes are rotated;
(iii) the intensity of vorticity may change as a result of the stretching or compressing of vortex tubes.

Diffusion would imply a breaking up of the vortex tubes.

The presence of these properties is demonstrated by considering a tall chimney stack in a two-dimensional stream that has some vorticity present (see Figure 3.13). The vortex tubes and lines are perpendicular to the stream. For convenience, some vortex lines, rather than tubes, are shown in Figure 3.14.

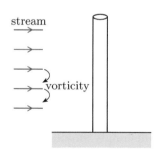

*Figure 3.13*

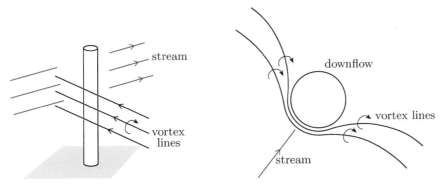

*Figure 3.14*                    *Figure 3.15*

When the vortex tubes (and lines) reach the chimney, they are unable to pass through. While the parts of the tubes not close to the chimney move with the stream, those parts in contact with the chimney are unable to move further. As a result, the vortex tubes are bent around the chimney, and therefore change direction (see Figure 3.15). This results in a 'downflow' behind the chimney which, if it captures some smoke, can result in pollution at ground level from a tall chimney (see Figure 3.16).

Note also that the intensity of the vortices behind the chimney is greater than that for the 'parent' vortices in front of the chimney. This increased intensity is due to the aligning of the vortex tubes in the general direction of the stream: the tubes are stretched, causing a reduction in cross-section and an associated increase in the intensity of vorticity.

*Figure 3.16*

It is assumed that the strength of the vortex tubes remains constant, i.e. that the inviscid model gives a good representation of a real phenomenon.

## 3.5   Persistence of irrotational motion

Kelvin's Theorem can be used to deduce an important result in the theory of inviscid fluid flow. This result will bring into focus the limitations of the inviscid model when some aspects of the flow behaviour of *real* fluids are discussed.

Kelvin's Theorem concerns the circulation around curves which move with the fluid, termed here material curves.

Suppose the fluid motion is such that at some instant ($t = 0$) the vorticity is zero everywhere, i.e. the motion is *irrotational*. Then, by Stokes' Theorem, the circulation around any closed material curve is initially zero, provided that a surface bounded by the curve lies entirely within the fluid. Thus, by Kelvin's Theorem, the circulations around all such material curves will be zero at all subsequent times. However, it follows from Stokes' Theorem that if the circulations around all closed material curves in the fluid are zero, then the vorticity is zero at all points on every open surface bounded by the curves. The conclusion is as follows.

Thus Kelvin's Theorem states that the circulation around a closed material curve remains constant in an inviscid fluid.

If an inviscid fluid motion is irrotational (vorticity-free) at any time, then it will be irrotational at all subsequent times.

That the vorticity is zero at all points also follows from the definition of curl:

$$(\mathbf{curl}\,\mathbf{u}) \cdot \mathbf{n} = \lim_{A \to 0} \frac{1}{A} \oint_C \mathbf{u} \cdot d\mathbf{r},$$

where $A$ is the area enclosed by the closed curve $C$, in a plane perpendicular to $\mathbf{n}$ (see *Unit 4* Subsection 4.1).

This argument is summarised as follows.

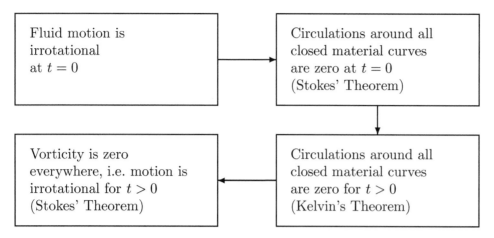

This result is known as the **persistence of irrotational motion** of an inviscid fluid. The result is not an altogether surprising one, because there is no physical mechanism available whereby rotation can be imposed on a fluid element by fluid pressure acting perpendicular to its boundary (see Figure 3.17). The setting up of a rotation would require forces tangential to the boundary, and such forces are neglected in the inviscid fluid model.

Such forces arise through the viscous properties of the fluid.

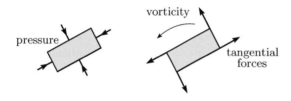

*Figure 3.17*

The persistence of irrotational motion may also be explored in terms of vortex tubes, as in the following exercise.

### Exercise 3.9

Suppose that the motion of an inviscid fluid is irrotational at a given instant.

(a) Do any vortex tubes exist at the instant in question?

(b) What are the mechanisms for transporting and changing vorticity in an inviscid fluid?

(c) Deduce the persistence of irrotational motion from your answers to parts (a) and (b).

The last two sections explored the ideas of vorticity and circulation more closely. This additional knowledge enables a more adequate understanding of the flows of real fluids to be developed in Sections 4 and 5.

See the *Media Guide* for material connected with the topics in Sections 1–3.

## *End-of-section exercises*

### *Exercise 3.10*

State whether the following statements are true or false.

(a) For a closed curve in a real fluid and moving with the fluid, the circulation around the curve does not change with time.

(b) A vortex tube moves with an inviscid fluid, and its strength may be considered to be constant at all times.

(c) The strength of a vortex tube can be found by considering the circulation around any simple closed curve on its surface.

### *Exercise 3.11*

State whether the following statements are true or false.

(a) The only method of transporting vorticity in a real fluid is by convection.

(b) For a two-dimensional motion of an inviscid fluid, the vorticity and velocity vectors are perpendicular. Thus the velocity vector cannot cause changes in the intensity of vorticity.

(c) A real fluid whose initial motion is irrotational will move such that its motion at all subsequent times will also be irrotational.

### *Exercise 3.12*

It is a matter of experience that one can create two vortices by moving an object such as one's hand through a bath of still water. Consider the initial still state to be an irrotational motion (trivially). Explain briefly why the inviscid fluid model is incapable of explaining the real phenomenon.

# 4   *Flow of real fluids*

The last section explored the manner in which vorticity is transported through a theoretical inviscid fluid. The method of transportation in question is convection. During the discussion, another method of transportation of a property of a real fluid was briefly mentioned, namely diffusion.

This section will consider empirical evidence relating to the flow of real fluids. For convenience, a long cylinder of circular cross-section is considered in an essentially two-dimensional fluid stream, the flow being at right angles to the cylinder's axis. The aim here is to explain *qualitatively* some of the phenomena that have been observed, in terms of the convection and diffusion of vorticity. In order to do so, some further consideration is given to the diffusion process.

Diffusion was introduced by discussing the way in which temperature differences were evened out in a bath of still water.

In practice, many of the experimental results obtained during the flow of real fluids are categorised according to the corresponding value of the *Reynolds number*, and that will be the case here. For that reason, the next subsection gives a brief introduction to the Reynolds number.

## 4.1 Reynolds number

Assume that the speed of the fluid a long distance away from the cylinder is $U$, that the radius of the cylinder is $a$ (see Figure 4.1), and that the density and coefficient of viscosity are $\rho$ and $\mu$, respectively. An important quantity associated with the flow is the **Reynolds number**, defined by

$$Re = \frac{\rho U a}{\mu}.$$

*Figure 4.1*

### Exercise 4.1

The coefficient of viscosity $\mu$ has SI units $\mathrm{kg\,m^{-1}\,s^{-1}}$, and therefore has dimensions $\mathrm{M\,L^{-1}\,T^{-1}}$. Show that $Re$ is dimensionless.

Dimensions were studied in MST209 *Unit 16*. See also Section 5 of the *Revision Booklet*.

The Reynolds number, $Re$, is a basic parameter in the description of fluid flows. In general, it is defined as

$$Re = \frac{\text{characteristic speed} \times \text{characteristic length} \times \text{density}}{\text{coefficient of viscosity}}$$

Note that various combinations of magnitudes of $U$, $a$, $\rho$ and $\mu$ can result in similar values of $Re$; it is found that experimental arrangements with different length and speed scales can be associated with similar magnitudes of Reynolds number (see Figure 4.2, which shows two such arrangements). Also, it is easy to see that increases in length and speed scales can be counteracted by increasing $\mu$ and/or decreasing $\rho$.

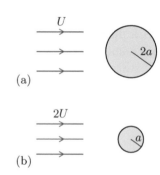

*Figure 4.2*

It is clear from the definition of Reynolds number that flows of fluids with low values of $\mu$ correspond to large Reynolds numbers. It would be reasonable to suppose, therefore, that the flow of an inviscid fluid, with its associated neglect of viscosity, should be closely related to the flows of (real) viscous fluids whose Reynolds numbers are in the higher ranges. The bonus accruing would be considerable: Bernoulli's equation, Kelvin's Theorem and the conclusions concerning vortex tubes could then be used to study real flows with complete freedom. Unfortunately, it is not always the case that the inviscid fluid is a satisfactory model when discussing the flows of real fluids with high Reynolds number. Therefore, applying the results relating to the flows of (theoretical) inviscid fluids to real situations has to be treated with caution.

The discrepancy arises because an additional condition has to be applied at the boundary for a real fluid, namely, that the fluid does not slip there. See *Unit 5* Subsection 2.3.

The next subsection describes the experimental results to be analysed.

## 4.2  *Flow past a circular cylinder: the various cases*

Consider the flow of a real fluid past a long circular cylinder. It is found experimentally that the various flow patterns are strongly dependent upon the various ranges of Reynolds number, as demonstrated in Figure 4.3.

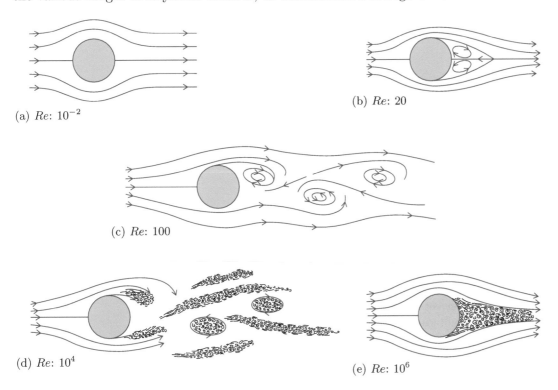

(a) *Re*: $10^{-2}$

(b) *Re*: 20

(c) *Re*: 100

(d) *Re*: $10^4$

(e) *Re*: $10^6$

*Figure 4.3*  Examples of flow patterns for various values of Reynolds number. Note that the flow upstream (to the left) is steady and uniform in each case.

The main features of flows (a)–(e) are described in the following remarks.

(a) $Re \ll 1$   For this range of Reynolds number, the flow is steady; the velocity vector at any fixed point in space is constant. The flow goes around the cylinder and is approximately symmetrical, the streamlines at the back bearing a close resemblance to the mirror image of those in front.

Recall that $\ll$ means 'much less than'.

The streamline pattern for $Re \ll 1$ appears to be similar to that for inviscid flow (see Example 2.5 of *Unit 5*), which corresponds to infinitely large *Re*. The difference is that for inviscid flow the streamline pattern is *exactly* symmetrical for all values of the speed $U$, whereas for this viscous flow the streamlines are only *approximately* symmetrical (a real fluid *cannot* slip past a boundary) and small *Re* may be thought of as corresponding to *small* values of $U$ only.

(b) $1 < Re < 30$   For this range of Reynolds number, the flow consists of two regions. In the front of the cylinder and at some distance behind it, the flow bears some resemblance to (a). However, an additional feature has appeared. Just behind the cylinder, two symmetrically placed vortices occur. The vigour of the vortices increases with Reynolds number in this range; these vortices do not move away from the cylinder, and are called *bound* vortices.

(c) $40 < Re < 4000$   When the Reynolds number reaches about 40, the character of the motion described in (b) changes abruptly. One of the vortices behind the cylinder becomes so distorted by the action of the stream that it breaks off and travels downstream with the fluid, i.e. a vortex is shed. The fluid moving around the cylinder starts to create a replacement vortex; but the other bound vortex then breaks away and a replacement for that is created. The process continues, with the temporarily attached vortices being shed alternately. The stream of vortices is called a **Kármán vortex street** (see Figure 4.4), and has been much studied in the literature. For this flow configuration, the flow is no longer steady but varies with time in a regular, periodic manner.

Theodore von Kármán (1881–1963) was a Hungarian engineer and physicist.

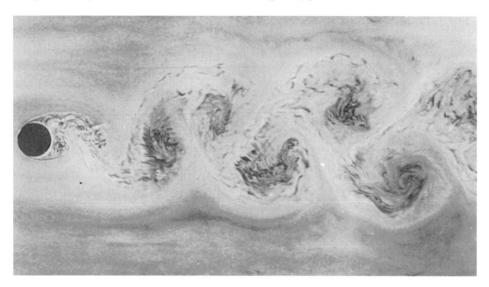

*Figure 4.4*  Photograph of a vortex street behind a cylinder. The flow visualisation was achieved by tiny bubbles of froth.

(d) $10^3 < Re < 10^4$   As the Reynolds number is increased, another change occurs. Patches of turbulent (chaotic and irregular) motion appear more frequently and ultimately spoil the regular pattern of vortices described in (c). The region behind the cylinder (the *wake*) becomes one of fully turbulent flow, and the main flow separates from the cylinder.

(e) $Re > 10^5$   For larger Reynolds numbers, the turbulent region works its way forward and reaches the point where the flow lines leave the cylinder. The turbulent region decreases in width as it progresses downstream.

See the *Media Guide* for more about the Reynolds number and flow past a cylinder.

## 4.3   Generation and transport of vorticity

Before attempting to explain the foregoing phenomena, consider how vorticity is propagated in a fluid. One mode of propagation is convection, the vorticity being transported by the movement of the fluid elements themselves. During the convection of a fluid element, the vorticity vector may be strengthened, weakened and/or rotated.

Considering the flow of those (real) fluids possessing viscous properties, vorticity is propagated in an additional way, namely, by viscous diffusion. To understand diffusion, it is useful to consider the analogy of heat conduction. By this process, heat is passed from one element to another on the molecular scale, without significant motion of the material. This lack of material motion is underlined by the fact that conduction of heat occurs in both solids and fluids. By contrast, convection is not a mechanism for heat transport in solids.

In a fluid, vorticity is diffused or spread from one region to another by the action of viscosity. The internal friction passes the motion from an element to its neighbour on the microscopic scale, compared with the macroscopic scale of the convection process.

Another important difference between diffusion and convection concerns the rates at which they occur. Convection, as mentioned earlier, is a relatively quick process compared with diffusion.

The purpose of this subsection is to give some physical explanation of the various flow regimes described in Subsection 4.2. Essentially, the various configurations will be regarded in terms of a competition between the convection and diffusion transport processes.

But how does vorticity arise in the first place? It is in fact the conditions near a boundary that give rise to vorticity.

Consider flow past a circular cylinder. For a fluid possessing viscosity, the fluid velocity is zero at the surface of the cylinder. (This contrasts with the requirement of the inviscid model, where only the normal component of the velocity is required to vanish at the boundary.) Away from the surface, there is a rapid increase in velocity, particularly in the transverse (non-radial) component. The rapid variation in velocity from zero at the boundary to the high value of the undisturbed stream results in a creation of vorticity in the neighbourhood of the surface, as depicted in Figure 4.5.

See *Unit 5* Subsection 2.3.

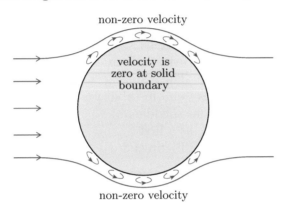

*Figure 4.5*   Creation of vorticity in the neighbourhood of a surface

The vorticity created is transported by convection and diffusion. The convection is caused by the overall flow field, and by this mechanism the vorticity is driven from the front of the cylinder to the back. Under the diffusion process, vorticity has a tendency to leak away from the layer around the cylinder towards the outer regions of the fluid (see Figure 4.6), and during this 'leaking', the vorticity loses its vigour owing to the action of the internal friction of the fluid.

Viscosity is therefore responsible for the creation, diffusion and decay of vorticity.

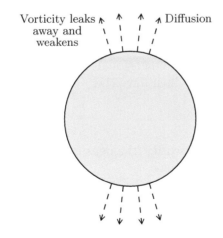

*Figure 4.6*   The transport of vorticity from a boundary

The various flow regimes can then be understood in terms of the relative strengths of the two transport mechanisms. For the sake of convenience, assume that the differences in the ranges of Reynolds number are due to differences in the range of values of the undisturbed stream speed, $U$; in other words, assume that the cylinder radius, $a$, the density, $\rho$, and the coefficient of viscosity, $\mu$, are fixed.

When the main stream is sufficiently slow, the diffusion process dominates and the vorticity spreads from the inner region near the cylinder to the outer region. The vorticity is also weakened during the process. As a result, the regime is the orderly one of Figure 4.3(a), no areas of obvious intense vortex activity being evident. (Very little vorticity is created, because there is hardly any discrepancy between the zero velocity at the boundary and the small flow velocity close to the boundary.)

As the stream becomes faster and the Reynolds number increases, the convection process becomes more important. Diffusion, being the slower process, has less time to control the situation, and the vorticity is confined to a thin layer around the cylinder called the **boundary layer**. The contributions of the (small) vortices in this boundary layer reinforce each other and lead to two major vortices at the rear of the cylinder, as indicated in Figure 4.3(b). In this situation, however, there is sufficient diffusion and associated weakening of the vortices to result in the relatively stable configuration of two vortices bound to the cylinder.

No boundary layer is shown in Figure 4.3(a) for the reason given above.

A further increase of main stream speed (and therefore of Reynolds number) further enhances the effect of convection, reducing even further the effect of diffusion and its associated decaying influence. The resulting enhancement of the mutual reinforcement of vortices leads to an instability of the two bound vortices. As a result, there is a continuous shedding of vortices from the rear of the cylinder (as in Figure 4.3(c)), as a first indication of the chaotic flow situation that will develop (see Figure 4.3(d)).

The enhancement of convection continues unremittingly with increasing Reynolds number. Ultimately, the regime becomes extremely disorderly as the decaying effect of diffusion is reduced. A marked feature of this effect is the narrowing of the disturbance due to the cylinder, as in Figure 4.3(e).

In the foregoing discussion, we introduced the concept of a boundary layer, in which the vorticity is considered to be confined near the cylinder for larger Reynolds numbers. We shall now consider this a little further.

The boundary layer is significant when convection is the dominant process of transport of vorticity. To determine which of the transport processes dominates, we need to consider the relative rates at which these processes occur, and to find appropriate time scales for the processes.

A *time scale* for a process is a time which has significance in relation to the process. Thus, for a simple pendulum, an appropriate time scale would be its period.

### Exercise 4.2

Consider the flow of a liquid past a circular cylinder. Use dimensional analysis to find possible combinations of $\mu$, $\rho$, $U$ and $a$ which have the dimension of time, in the form

$$t = \mu^\alpha \rho^\beta U^\gamma a^\delta \qquad (\alpha, \beta, \gamma, \delta \text{ constants}),$$

where $\mu$, $\rho$, $U$ and $a$ are respectively the coefficient of viscosity, the density, the undisturbed stream speed and the radius of the cylinder.

Dimensional analysis was studied in MST209 *Unit 16*; see also Subsection 5.2 of the *Revision Booklet*.

*Hint:* Express three of the powers in terms of the fourth. There are three distinct combinations to be found.

The distinct time scales arising from Exercise 4.2 are

$$\frac{a}{U}, \qquad \frac{a^2\rho}{\mu}, \qquad \frac{\mu}{\rho U^2}.$$

Each of these combinations omits at least one of the four parameters.

The first time scale relates to the convection process, which can be explained as follows.

The convection process depends essentially upon the main stream velocity. The time taken by a particle moving with speed $U$ to pass the cylinder is $2a/U$. Thus, the time scale $a/U$ derived in the exercise clearly relates to the convection process.

Which of $a^2\rho/\mu$ and $\mu/(\rho U^2)$ gives a time scale for the diffusion process? It helps here to return to the physics of the situation.

Diffusion of vorticity arises because of the presence of viscosity. The vorticity is passed through the fluid by the interaction between parts of the fluid. This type of interaction is more efficient for fluids with high viscosity; it is non-existent for the inviscid fluid model.

## Exercise 4.3

Does an efficient diffusion process imply a short time scale or a long time scale, i.e. does it imply a fast process or a slow process?

It follows from Exercise 4.3 and the text before that the time scale for diffusion will decrease with increasing $\mu$. The appropriate time scale for diffusion is therefore $a^2\rho/\mu$.

By contrast, $\mu/(\rho U^2)$ increases with increasing $\mu$.

For the vorticity to remain close to the cylinder, convection must be a much faster process than diffusion. In terms of time scales, the convection time scale, $a/U$, must be much less than the diffusion time scale, $a^2\rho/\mu$.

## Exercise 4.4

Show that if the vorticity is to remain close to the cylinder, then

$$Re \gg 1,$$

where the Reynolds number is $Re = Ua\rho/\mu$.

Exercise 4.4 shows that the condition for the vorticity to be confined to a thin layer around the cylinder is that the Reynolds number for the motion is much greater than 1. This conclusion is consistent with the behaviour noted in flows (b)–(e) of Figure 4.3 on page 143.

The layer of vorticity around the cylinder is known as the boundary layer, as mentioned earlier. Boundary layer theory is a very important subject in fluid mechanics, because its use enables us to set up simple models of flow situations. Essentially, the theory assumes that the effects of viscosity can be confined to the layer around the cylinder (or other body), and the remainder of the fluid (the main stream) is assumed to be inviscid. The bonus obtained from this approach is appreciable: all of the results relating to an inviscid fluid (Euler's equation of motion, Kelvin's Theorem, persistence of irrotational motion) then apply to the outer or 'main stream' region. The subject of boundary layers is considered briefly in *Unit 8* and more extensively in *Unit 13*.

## End-of-section exercise

### Exercise 4.5

(a) Consider the flow of a liquid past a circular cylinder. Use dimensional analysis to find possible combinations of $\mu$, $\rho$, $U$ and $a$ which have the dimension of length, in the form

$$D = \mu^\alpha \rho^\beta U^\gamma a^\delta \qquad (\alpha, \beta, \gamma, \delta \text{ constants}),$$

where $\mu$, $\rho$, $U$ and $a$ are respectively the coefficient of viscosity, the density, the undisturbed stream speed and the radius of the cylinder.

(b) Identify the two distinct length scales found in part (a) with the convection and diffusion processes.

(c) Derive the result of Exercise 4.4 by investigating length scales.

# 5   The forces on an obstacle in a real fluid

This section continues with the problem first met in Subsection 2.3. There, the streaming two-dimensional flow past a circular cylinder was modelled. It was shown that the presence of circulation around the cylinder gave rise to a lift force, perpendicular to the stream. Also, it was shown that for the (inviscid) fluid model used, there was no drag force on the cylinder parallel to the stream. This last result is known as **d'Alembert's Paradox**, and is at variance with experience.

The circulation was modelled by means of a line vortex. The result was recast in terms of circulation.

In the next two subsections, the predictions arising from the inviscid model are related more precisely to experimental observations of the behaviour of real fluids, and an attempt is made to reconcile the discrepancies between the model and reality.

## 5.1   Drag and separation of the boundary layer

It was pointed out in the last section that the presence of viscosity plays an important role in the flow of fluids in the neighbourhood of a solid boundary, owing to the no-slip condition. Under certain conditions, the effect of viscosity can be considered to be confined to a layer of fluid near the cylinder. In any event, it would appear reasonable to expect that the presence of viscosity in a fluid would result in drag on the body, because such fluids are able to impart stresses that are tangential to the body. That part of the drag directly attributable to the viscosity is called *skin friction drag*.

drag = skin friction drag
      + profile drag.

Viscosity also causes drag in a less obvious way, giving rise to so-called *profile drag*. This type of drag is more a feature of bluff (or blunt) bodies such as cylinders, rather than of streamlined bodies.

Some car advertisements refer to 'drag coefficients', to illustrate efforts made to reduce profile drag.

Consider the flow around the cylinder, starting with the inviscid model. Now, the flow past the cylinder was modelled in Subsection 2.3. It was shown there, in Frame 6A, that the $\theta$-component of the velocity at a point on the cylinder's surface is $u_\theta = -2U \sin \theta$, where for convenience the circulation, $\kappa$, is neglected (see Figure 5.1).

The argument can be modified easily when circulation is present.

From Frame 6A, the pressure distribution on the cylinder (with $\kappa = 0$) is

$$p = M - \tfrac{1}{2}\rho u^2 = M - \tfrac{1}{2}\rho(4U^2 \sin^2 \theta), \qquad \text{where } M \text{ is a constant.}$$

See also Example 2.1 of *Unit 6*.

Here $u = |\mathbf{u}|$ and $\rho$ is the constant density. Far upstream (where $u = U$), let $p = p_0$; then, from Bernoulli's equation, we have

$$p_0 + \tfrac{1}{2}\rho U^2 = M,$$

and so

$$p = p_0 + \tfrac{1}{2}\rho U^2 - \tfrac{1}{2}\rho(4U^2 \sin^2 \theta).$$

Rearranging this equation to obtain a dimensionless form gives

$$\frac{p - p_0}{\tfrac{1}{2}\rho U^2} = 1 - 4\sin^2 \theta = 2\cos(2\theta) - 1.$$

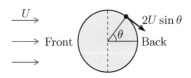

*Figure 5.1*

Figure 5.2 shows this *theoretical* dimensionless pressure distribution around the cylinder (marked by T), proceeding from the front of the cylinder, round the bottom to the back of the cylinder, then returning to the front over the top of the cylinder. Also shown in this figure are *measured* pressure distributions (M) for two values of the Reynolds number.

A dimensionless quantity has dimensions $M^0 L^0 T^0 = 1$.

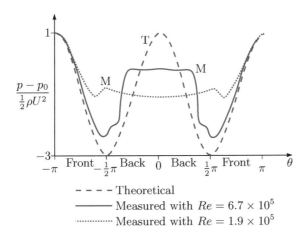

- - - - Theoretical
——— Measured with $Re = 6.7 \times 10^5$
············ Measured with $Re = 1.9 \times 10^5$

*Figure 5.2*    Distribution of dimensionless pressure around the cylinder

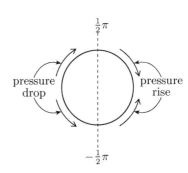

*Figure 5.3*    Pressure changes around the cylinder for the theoretical situation

A feature of the theoretical curve is that the pressure drops over the front of the cylinder (for top and bottom) are balanced exactly by the pressure rises over the back of the cylinder (see Figure 5.3).

This symmetry of the pressure about the $\pm\tfrac{1}{2}\pi$ line results in there being no predicted overall force on the cylinder in the direction of the stream, that is, no predicted drag force.

This line divides the front from the back.

According to the (inviscid) theory, the fluid is accelerated from the higher pressure region to the lower pressure region for $-\pi < \theta < -\tfrac{1}{2}\pi$ and for $\pi > \theta > \tfrac{1}{2}\pi$, and is then decelerated from points of low pressure to high pressure for $-\tfrac{1}{2}\pi < \theta < 0$ and for $\tfrac{1}{2}\pi > \theta > 0$. Thus, the prediction of the inviscid fluid model is that the fluid attains enough energy during flow over the front half of the cylinder to enable it to move against the adverse pressure gradient it encounters over the rear part.

These arguments based on the inviscid fluid model have to be modified when considering the flow of real fluids. The viscosity of a fluid plays a key role near the solid boundary. Specifically, it is responsible for the adherence of the fluid to the boundary. The effect of this no-slipping of fluid at the cylinder surface becomes particularly important during the flow over the rear part of the cylinder.

The inviscid fluid model allows slipping of the fluid at boundaries.

Near the cylinder, the fluid is, of necessity, moving slowly (because of adherence at the boundary). Over the rear half of the cylinder, that slow-moving fluid is moving against an adverse pressure gradient (from a low- to a high-pressure region) and, indeed, may even be pushed backwards. The forward-moving fluid is then forced outwards by the backward flow, causing the boundary layer to separate from the cylinder. There is a region of slow-moving fluid behind the cylinder known as the wake, and this is separated from the outer flow region of fast-moving fluid by a thin layer of vorticity known as a *vortex sheet* (see Figure 5.4).

The streamlining of a body is intended to delay or eliminate separation of the boundary layer.

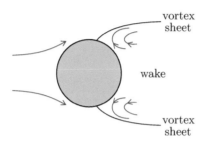

*Figure 5.4*

The discussion in the last section pointed out that, for high Reynolds number, the convection of vorticity was an important process. In that case, the vorticity remains close to the cylinder, and the wake is rather narrow. In contrast, for low-Reynolds-number flows, there should be a good deal of diffusion of vorticity and wide wakes of very weak vorticity.

For flow (a) of Figure 4.3 on page 143, the vorticity in the wake is so weak that its presence is not shown.

Thus, a fluid's viscous properties result in a change of the flow pattern around the cylinder from that predicted by the inviscid model. Associated with the changed flow pattern are also the measured pressure distributions (M in Figure 5.2). In contrast to the situation for the theoretical pressure distribution, the pressure drop over the front half of the cylinder is not recovered over the rear part. The imbalance of the front and rear pressure distributions results in the cylinder being subjected to a force in the direction of the stream.

Also, the measured pressure drop over the front of the cylinder is less than predicted by the inviscid model.

The foregoing considerations provide a resolution to the apparent difficulty in relation to d'Alembert's Paradox.

See also Question (a) on page 130, which is now answered.

## 5.2    Lift and the generation of circulation

In considering the flow past a cylinder in Subsection 2.3, it was shown that the inviscid fluid theory predicts a lift force when there is a circulation of fluid around the cylinder. What has not been considered until now is how this circulation arises in the flow of a real fluid. As a first step in explaining this, recall the discussion in Subsection 4.3. There, the role of a solid boundary in the generation of vorticity was indicated, and the methods of transporting vorticity were described. The occurrence of the various flow regimes outlined in Subsection 4.2 was explained (in Subsection 4.3) in terms of a contest between the convection and diffusion mechanisms. In particular, when convection is dominant, vortices are shed alternately from the rear of the cylinder during the streaming of fluid past it. Consider the situation when a vortex is shed.

The vorticity is created essentially by the shear flow caused by adherence of fluid at the boundary.

See Figure 4.3(c) on page 143.

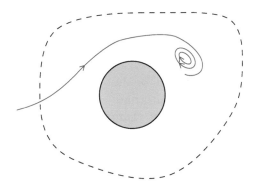

*Figure 5.5*

Let the dashed line in Figure 5.5 denote a large closed curve (containing the cylinder) moving with the fluid. Note that initially there is no vorticity near the curve, as it is far from the region where viscous effects are important, namely, near the cylinder. Then, for the initial stages at least, the conditions for Kelvin's Theorem are valid for any flow region which contains the curve and is well away from the cylinder. Under these conditions, the circulation around the curve does not change during the early stages of the motion, so that since it is initially zero, it remains zero during the early stages.

Suppose that the stream speed $U$ builds up steadily, from $U = 0$ initially.

Kelvin's Theorem was stated in Subsection 3.3.

The vanishing of the velocity at the surface of the cylinder is instrumental in creating a detached vortex behind the cylinder, as shown in Figure 4.3(c) on page 143. So the curve in question contains within it a vortex of strength $-\kappa$, say, and this vortex gives rise to a clockwise circulation $\kappa$ around it. To satisfy the requirement of zero overall circulation around the large curve, it is necessary for a compensating opposite circulation to exist around the cylinder, as shown in Figure 5.6.

Figures 5.5 and 5.6 show a vortex shed from one side of the cylinder. The argument for a vortex shed from the other side is very similar.

Some slight asymmetry in the flow will suffice to ensure that a vortex is shed first from one side of the cylinder rather than the other.

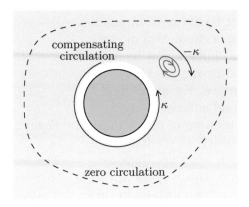

The white collar in Figure 5.6 is a region in which viscosity cannot be ignored, and so Kelvin's Theorem does not apply there. The compensating circulation is calculated by using any curve within the large curve that excludes the shed vortex and encloses the cylinder but does not enter the collar.

*Figure 5.6*

The argument can be summarised as follows.

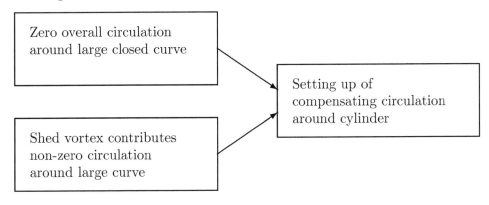

The induced (compensating) circulation, anticlockwise in this case, gives rise to a (downward) 'lift' force on the cylinder.

After a short time, a vortex of a sense opposite to that of the first detaches from the cylinder. A circulation is set up around the body in a sense opposite to the previous one. This then gives rise to a lift force of the opposite sense. This process continues, with the shedding of alternate vortices, so that the sense of the circulation around the cylinder changes repeatedly, and therefore the resulting lift force also alternates in direction.

A comment is appropriate here. The relationship between circulation and lift established in Subsection 2.3 was derived on the assumption that flow conditions were steady, the circulation being assumed to be of constant magnitude and sense. Here, the situation is one in which both the magnitude and sense of the circulation around the cylinder are changing repeatedly; so this is a non-steady situation. Extending the previous result to this case would entail an analysis which is difficult and unprofitable in the present context. You are asked to accept that, while the precise relationship between circulation and lift derived previously may not apply, the result is still true qualitatively: circulation causes lift.

Question (b) on page 130 has now been considered.

The effect of the alternating lift tends to produce a forced sideways vibration of the cylinder. If the frequency of these forced vibrations is close to the natural frequency of the system, then resonance may occur. This can be a serious problem, and must be taken into account in the design of chimneys and bridges, for example. Wind-induced vortices have led to some spectacular disasters for such structures, the collapse of the Tacoma Narrows Bridge (Washington DC, USA) on a windy day in 1940 being a famous example. Less catastrophic, but more familiar, is the 'singing' of overhead power wires, which occurs on windy days when the frequency of the vortex shedding is close to the natural frequency of the wires.

Here 'sideways' means perpendicular to the stream direction.

Resonance is discussed in MST209 *Unit 17*.

The circulation of constant strength and magnitude assumed in the derivation of the lift force in Subsection 2.3 cannot be obtained in practice with a stationary cylinder. A method of setting up a circulation of constant sense around a cylinder is to rotate the cylinder about its axis. If the fluid were inviscid, then it would be unaffected by the rotation of the cylinder, with fluid slipping past the cylinder's surface. For a *real* fluid possessing viscosity, no slipping occurs, and the fluid adheres to the cylindrical surface (see Figure 5.7). The effect of rotation of the cylindrical surface *diffuses* into the fluid by the action of viscosity; so the fluid then rotates with the cylinder, and a non-zero circulation is set up. Such a rotating cylinder is subject to a lift force when fluid streams past it; this is known as the *Magnus force* or *Magnus effect*. It has been utilised in ship propulsion, using devices known as *Flettner Rotors*. These consisted of tall cylinders mounted on a ship's deck (see Figure 5.8). The cylinders were rotated in the wind (not by the wind), with the combination of wind and rotation giving rise to a propulsive force at right angles to the wind.

*Figure 5.7*

This has now dealt with Question (c) on page 130.

The force was explained in 1852 by Gustav Magnus, a German physicist.

These devices were the invention of Anton Flettner, a German engineer.

A similar phenomenon (known as the *Robins effect*) arises from streaming flow past a rotating sphere. This can be used to explain the swerving motion of tennis balls, footballs, etc. to which spin has been imparted.

Benjamin Robins, an English mathematician and engineer, showed in 1742 that a transverse force on a rotating sphere in an air stream could be detected by suspending it as a pendulum.

*Figure 5.8*   *Buckau* (converted to a rotor ship in 1924)

A fuller description of Flettner Rotors is given by Seufert and Seufert in 'Critics in a spin over Flettner's ship', *New Scientist*, 10 March 1983.

The ship shown here was technically successful, and crossed the Atlantic in 1926. However, the system proved to be less efficient than conventional engines.

Another example of the beneficial effect of setting up a controlled circulation of fluid around a body is the flow around an aircraft wing. It is a matter of experience that such a wing undergoes a lift. This lift can be explained in terms of circulation, as was the lift force on a cylinder. How is a lift force of constant direction set up, or equivalently, how is a circulation of constant sense set up?

Consider the flow of air past a wing of constant cross-section and of infinite length, assuming two-dimensional flow. The inviscid model without circulation predicts the flow pattern shown in Figure 5.9, in which $S_1$ and $S_2$ are stagnation points. Now, a real fluid (possessing viscosity) is not able to sustain the flow shown at the trailing edge. The fluid is unable to turn the corner and reach the idealised stagnation point at $S_2$.

Clearly, an alternating circulation (and lift force) would not be useful in aeroplane flight!

The flow pattern past an idealised wing can be deduced from the flow around a cylinder, using *conformal mapping*. This is discussed in M337 *Complex Analysis*.

The exact position of $S_2$ depends on the orientation of the aerofoil.

*Figure 5.9*                    *Figure 5.10*

Figure 5.10 shows the flow pattern for a real fluid. The rear stagnation point, at $S_2$ in the inviscid flow, is now at the trailing edge, labelled $S_2'$, and this shift is achieved by a net clockwise circulation around the wing.

The generation of this clockwise circulation is not possible in an inviscid model. Initially, when the fluid is at rest, there is no circulation, and by Kelvin's Theorem the circulation will always be zero if the fluid is assumed to be inviscid. The generation of the circulation requires viscous action.

To explain the generation of circulation, consider the flow patterns as the stagnation point moves from $S_2$ towards the trailing edge $S_2'$. The initial flow pattern as the motion starts corresponds to the inviscid model shown in Figure 5.9.

This argument was first presented around 1900 by Frederick Lanchester and Ludwig Prandtl, independently of each other.

Almost immediately, there is separation of the fluid at the trailing edge (see Figure 5.11). This causes the fluid above the wing to turn back on itself between $S_2'$ and $S_2$, as shown. This flow is in the opposite direction to the main fluid, and so a vortex is formed. This vortex is quickly shed from the trailing edge as the speed of flow past the wing increases (see Figure 5.12).

Consider the situation when a vortex is shed.

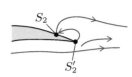

*Figure 5.11*   Near the trailing edge a vortex is formed ...

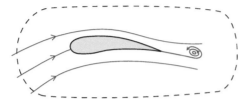

*Figure 5.13*

*Figure 5.12*   ... and shed.

Let the dashed line in Figure 5.13 denote a large closed curve (containing the aerofoil) moving with the fluid. Initially there is no vorticity near the curve, as it is far from the region where viscous effects are important, namely, near the aerofoil. Then, for the initial stages at least, the conditions for Kelvin's Theorem are valid for any flow region which contains the curve and is well away from the aerofoil. Under these conditions, the circulation around the curve does not change during the early stages of motion, so that since it is initially zero, it remains zero during these early stages. The curve eventually contains within it a shed vortex, giving rise to an anticlockwise circulation $\kappa$, say, around it. To satisfy the requirement of zero overall circulation around the large curve, it is necessary for a compensating clockwise circulation to exist around the aerofoil (see Figure 5.14).

This repeats the argument for the cylinder.

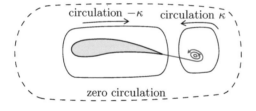

*Figure 5.14*

This compensating circulation moves the stagnation point back to the trailing edge. The process is then repeated with a second vortex of the same sense as the first being formed and shed, and the circulation around the aerofoil is increased, moving the stagnation point nearer to the trailing edge. Similar vortices are formed and shed, each time increasing the circulation, until it is sufficient to maintain the stagnation point at the trailing edge.

See the *Media Guide* for more about the topics in Section 5.

This has answered Question (d) on page 130.

The induced circulation around the aerofoil gives rise to a lift force on the aerofoil. However, although the viscosity is required to explain the generation of the circulation, the magnitude of the lift force is not affected very much by the magnitude of the viscosity.

In fact, as in Frame 7A of Subsection 2.3 for the cylinder, the lift force on the aerofoil has magnitude $\rho U \kappa$, where $\rho$ is the air density, $U$ is the relative air speed, and $\kappa$ is the circulation around the wing. This assumes that the flow remains attached to the wing, so that 'stalling' is avoided.

This result is known as the Kutta–Joukowski Lift Theorem.

# End-of-section exercise

### Exercise 5.1

Decide whether the following statements are true or false.

(a)  The effect of streamlining is to reduce the skin friction drag.

(b)  Streamlining a body is, in effect, delaying or avoiding the separation of the boundary layer.

(c)  To explain the setting up of circulation around a cylinder in a real fluid, the viscous model for a fluid must be used everywhere.

(d)  For streaming flow past a cylinder, the viscosity of the fluid is important only at large distances from the cylinder.

(e)  For the flow situation of statement (d), the vortex sheet set up at the rear of the cylinder is a consequence of the viscous properties of the fluid.

(f)  When a vortex is shed from a cylinder, a circulation of the same sense is set up around the cylinder.

(g)  The setting up of circulation around a cylinder is explained by the persistence of irrotational motion rather than by Kelvin's Theorem.

(h)  For the flow situation of statement (d), Kelvin's Theorem is applicable to those regions of fluid near the cylinder.

(i)  Low-Reynolds-number streaming flows past bodies are associated with narrow wakes.

(j)  Flettner Rotors generate a lift force of alternating direction.

(k)  An essential requirement for vortex shedding to set up vibrations in structures is that the prevailing wind be of variable magnitude.

Only two-dimensional flow situations are referred to.

# Outcomes

After studying this unit you should be able to:

- explain how to develop a model for a tornado;
- apply the line vortex model where appropriate;
- explain and apply the relationship between vorticity and circulation;
- explain and apply the effect of combining line vortices to model flow with a planar boundary;
- explain why the combination of a line vortex (or circulation) with a streaming flow past an obstacle produces lift but no drag for an inviscid fluid;
- explain the concepts of vortex line and vortex tube;
- use Kelvin's Theorem and the persistence of irrotational motion to deduce the circulation in various flow patterns;
- describe how real fluids can be modelled;
- explain how the Reynolds number can be used to classify flow behaviour;
- explain how vorticity is generated and transported;
- explain how the time scales associated with convection and diffusion of vorticity can be compared for a given flow;
- explain d'Alembert's Paradox and its resolution in simple terms;
- explain the difference between skin friction drag and profile drag;
- explain how circulation (causing lift) can be generated around cylinders and aerofoils.

# Acknowledgements

Grateful acknowledgement is made to the following sources:

Figure 1.1: © Dr J.H. Golden/NOAA; large cyclonic waterspout photographed from a research aircraft by Dr J.H. Golden, NOAA, 14 nautical miles north of Key West, Florida on 10 September 1969;

Figures 1.3 and 1.4: From Goldstein (ed) (1938), *Modern Developments in Fluid Mechanics*, vol. 1, Dover Publications Ltd;

Figure 1.5: Courtesy of The Royal Aeronautical Society;

Figure 3.5: © Lawrence Lawry/Science Photo Library;

Figure 3.16: © Jeremy Walker/Science Photo Library;

Figure 4.3: Feynman, R.P., Leighton, R.B. and Sands, M. (1964), *Lectures on Physics*, vol. 2 © Addison-Wesley Publishing Company Inc;

Figure 4.4: Scorer, R.S. (1978) *Environmental Aerodynamics*, Ellis Horwood;

Figure 5.8: Taken from www.wikipedia.org.

# Solutions to the exercises

## Section 1

### Solution 1.1

In SI units,
$$a = 100 \quad \text{and} \quad \Omega_1 a = 50,$$
so that $\Omega_1 = 0.5$ and
$$\Omega_2 = \Omega_1 a^2 = 0.5 \times (100)^2 = 5000.$$
Hence the velocity field is
$$\mathbf{u} = \begin{cases} 0.5r\,\mathbf{e}_\theta & (r \leq 100), \\ \dfrac{5000}{r}\,\mathbf{e}_\theta & (r > 100). \end{cases}$$

### Solution 1.2

In cylindrical polar coordinates, for any vector field $\mathbf{F}$,
$$\mathbf{curl\,F} = \left(\frac{1}{r}\frac{\partial F_z}{\partial \theta} - \frac{\partial F_\theta}{\partial z}\right)\mathbf{e}_r + \left(\frac{\partial F_r}{\partial z} - \frac{\partial F_z}{\partial r}\right)\mathbf{e}_\theta$$
$$+ \left(\frac{1}{r}\frac{\partial}{\partial r}(rF_\theta) - \frac{1}{r}\frac{\partial F_r}{\partial \theta}\right)\mathbf{e}_z \quad (r \neq 0).$$
For $0 < r < a$ : $u_r = u_z = 0$, $u_\theta = \Omega r$. Thus
$$\mathbf{curl\,u} = \frac{1}{r}\frac{\partial}{\partial r}(\Omega r^2)\,\mathbf{e}_z = 2\Omega\,\mathbf{e}_z.$$
For $r > a$ : $u_r = u_z = 0$, $u_\theta = \Omega a^2/r$. Thus
$$\mathbf{curl\,u} = \frac{1}{r}\frac{\partial}{\partial r}\left(r\frac{\Omega a^2}{r}\right)\mathbf{e}_z = \mathbf{0}.$$

### Solution 1.3

On $C_1$, $\delta\mathbf{r} = a\,\delta\theta\,\mathbf{e}_\theta$; thus
$$\oint_{C_1} \mathbf{u}\cdot d\mathbf{r} = \int_{-\pi}^{\pi} (\Omega a\,\mathbf{e}_\theta)\cdot(a\,\mathbf{e}_\theta)\,d\theta$$
$$= \int_{-\pi}^{\pi} \Omega a^2 d\theta = 2\pi\Omega a^2.$$

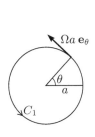
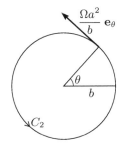

On $C_2$, $\delta\mathbf{r} = b\,\delta\theta\,\mathbf{e}_\theta$; thus
$$\oint_{C_2} \mathbf{u}\cdot d\mathbf{r} = \int_{-\pi}^{\pi} \left(\frac{\Omega a^2}{b}\,\mathbf{e}_\theta\right)\cdot(b\,\mathbf{e}_\theta)\,d\theta$$
$$= \int_{-\pi}^{\pi} \Omega a^2 d\theta = 2\pi\Omega a^2$$
$$= \oint_{C_1} \mathbf{u}\cdot d\mathbf{r}, \quad \text{as required.}$$

### Solution 1.4

The circulation around a circle $C$ of radius $R$, in a plane perpendicular to the $z$-axis and with centre on that axis, traversed anticlockwise, is given by the integral
$$\oint_C \mathbf{u}\cdot d\mathbf{r}, \quad \text{and here,} \quad \mathbf{u} = \frac{\kappa}{2\pi r}\,\mathbf{e}_\theta.$$
Also, $\delta\mathbf{r} = R\,\delta\theta\,\mathbf{e}_\theta$. Hence
$$\oint_C \mathbf{u}\cdot d\mathbf{r} = \int_{-\pi}^{\pi} \left(\frac{\kappa}{2\pi R}\,\mathbf{e}_\theta\right)\cdot(R\,\mathbf{e}_\theta)\,d\theta$$
$$= \int_{-\pi}^{\pi} \frac{\kappa}{2\pi}\,d\theta = 2\pi\left(\frac{\kappa}{2\pi}\right) = \kappa,$$
which is independent of the radius, $R$.

### Solution 1.5

**(a)** Here $\mathbf{curl\,u}$ is defined at every point in the region $S$, since $S$ is chosen not to intersect the $z$-axis. Then
$$\mathbf{curl\,u} = \frac{1}{r}\frac{\partial}{\partial r}\left(r\frac{\kappa}{2\pi r}\right)\mathbf{e}_z = \mathbf{0}.$$
**(b)** Stokes' Theorem states that
$$\int_S (\mathbf{curl\,u})\cdot\mathbf{n}\,dA = \oint_C \mathbf{u}\cdot d\mathbf{r}.$$
Since $\mathbf{curl\,u} = \mathbf{0}$ everywhere on $S$, it follows that
$$\oint_C \mathbf{u}\cdot d\mathbf{r} = 0.$$
**(c)**
$$\oint_C \mathbf{u}\cdot d\mathbf{r} = \int_{A_1 A_2} \mathbf{u}\cdot d\mathbf{r} + \int_{A_2 D_2 B_2} \mathbf{u}\cdot d\mathbf{r}$$
$$+ \int_{B_2 B_1} \mathbf{u}\cdot d\mathbf{r} + \int_{B_1 D_1 A_1} \mathbf{u}\cdot d\mathbf{r}.$$
**(d)** Now, if $B_1 \to A_1$ and $B_2 \to A_2$, then
$$\int_{A_1 A_2} \mathbf{u}\cdot d\mathbf{r} + \int_{B_2 B_1} \mathbf{u}\cdot d\mathbf{r}$$
$$\to \int_{A_1 A_2} \mathbf{u}\cdot d\mathbf{r} + \int_{A_2 A_1} \mathbf{u}\cdot d\mathbf{r} = 0.$$
Thus, from parts (b) and (c),
$$\int_{A_2 D_2 A_2} \mathbf{u}\cdot d\mathbf{r} + \int_{A_1 D_1 A_1} \mathbf{u}\cdot d\mathbf{r} = 0,$$
$$\text{(clockwise)} \qquad \text{(anticlockwise)}$$
or
$$\oint_{C_1} \mathbf{u}\cdot d\mathbf{r} = \oint_{C_2} \mathbf{u}\cdot d\mathbf{r} \quad \text{(in the same sense).}$$

## Solution 1.6

For the stream function
$$\psi = -\frac{\kappa}{4\pi}\ln(x^2 + y^2),$$

the velocity components are
$$u_1 = \frac{\partial \psi}{\partial y} = -\frac{\kappa y}{2\pi(x^2 + y^2)},$$

$$u_2 = -\frac{\partial \psi}{\partial x} = \frac{\kappa x}{2\pi(x^2 + y^2)}.$$

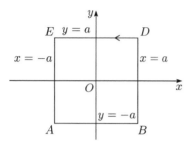

On $DE$, we have $y = a$, $\delta y = 0$, $\delta \mathbf{r} = \delta x\,\mathbf{i}$. Then
$$\int_{DE} \mathbf{u}\cdot d\mathbf{r} = \int_{a}^{-a}\left(-\frac{\kappa a}{2\pi(x^2+a^2)}\mathbf{i} + \frac{\kappa x}{2\pi(x^2+a^2)}\mathbf{j}\right)\cdot\mathbf{i}\,dx$$

$$= \int_{-a}^{a}\frac{\kappa a}{2\pi(x^2+a^2)}\,dx$$

$$= \frac{\kappa}{2\pi}\left[\arctan\left(\frac{x}{a}\right)\right]_{-a}^{a}$$

$$= \frac{\kappa}{2\pi}[\arctan 1 - \arctan(-1)]$$

$$= \frac{\kappa}{2\pi}\left[\tfrac{1}{4}\pi - \left(-\tfrac{1}{4}\pi\right)\right] = \tfrac{1}{4}\kappa.$$

On $BD$, we have $x = a$, $\delta x = 0$, $\delta \mathbf{r} = \delta y\,\mathbf{j}$. Then
$$\int_{BD} \mathbf{u}\cdot d\mathbf{r} = \int_{-a}^{a}\left(-\frac{\kappa y}{2\pi(a^2+y^2)}\mathbf{i} + \frac{\kappa a}{2\pi(a^2+y^2)}\mathbf{j}\right)\cdot\mathbf{j}\,dy$$

$$= \frac{\kappa}{2\pi}\int_{-a}^{a}\frac{a}{a^2+y^2}\,dy$$

$$= \frac{\kappa}{2\pi}\left[\arctan\left(\frac{y}{a}\right)\right]_{-a}^{a} = \tfrac{1}{4}\kappa,$$

as before. A similar calculation applies for the integrals over paths $AB$ and $EA$. Then the total circulation is
$$\tfrac{1}{4}\kappa + \tfrac{1}{4}\kappa + \tfrac{1}{4}\kappa + \tfrac{1}{4}\kappa = \kappa.$$

# Section 2

## Solution 2.1

The given stream function is
$$\psi = -\frac{\kappa}{2\pi}\ln r.$$

Using polar coordinates,
$$u_r = \frac{1}{r}\frac{\partial \psi}{\partial \theta} = 0 \quad \text{and} \quad u_\theta = -\frac{\partial \psi}{\partial r} = \frac{\kappa}{2\pi r},$$

so that $\mathbf{u} = \frac{\kappa}{2\pi r}\mathbf{e}_\theta$.

## Solution 2.2

Using the model in Example 2.1, the flow above the wall due to the given line vortex is equivalent to the flow due to the two line vortices shown in the figure.

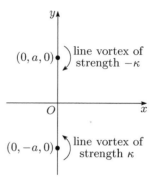

The line vortex at $(0, a, 0)$ moves under the influence of the line vortex at $(0, -a, 0)$. The velocity at $(0, a, 0)$ due to the lower line vortex is in the direction of $\mathbf{e}_\theta$ at this point (i.e. $-\mathbf{i}$), and its magnitude is
$$\left|\frac{\kappa}{2\pi(2a)}\right| = \frac{\kappa}{4\pi a}.$$

This is illustrated below.

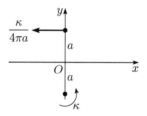

## Solution 2.3

Since the streamlines due to two vortices of strengths $\pm\kappa$ are circles (see Figure 2.7), the solid cylindrical boundary can replace a streamline. No circular streamline has its centre at the position of the line vortex, so by an appropriate choice of $a$ (in the solution to Example 2.1), any off-centre position can be modelled. The cylindrical boundary will correspond to one particular value of the parameter $M$.

(In fact, it can be shown that if the cylinder has radius $R$ and the line vortex is at distance $d$ from the axis, then $a = (R^2 - d^2)/(2d)$ and $M = d/R$ at the boundary.)

## Solution 2.4

(a) The equivalent system of two line vortices is shown in the figure below.

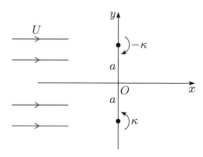

The velocity of the original line vortex due to the one of equal and opposite strength at $(0, -a, 0)$ is

$$-\frac{\kappa}{4\pi a}\,\mathbf{i} \qquad \text{(from Solution 2.2)}.$$

Since the original line vortex is in the uniform stream given by $\mathbf{u} = U\,\mathbf{i}$, its resultant velocity is

$$U\,\mathbf{i} - \frac{\kappa}{4\pi a}\,\mathbf{i}.$$

Since the line vortex is stated to be at rest, $\kappa = 4\pi a U$.

**(b)** At any point on $y = 0$, the resultant velocity is the sum of the uniform stream velocity and the **i**-component vectors of the velocities due to the two vortices. (The **j**-component vectors cancel each other.) Hence the speed at $(x, 0, 0)$ is

$$\left| U - 2 \times \frac{\kappa}{2\pi\sqrt{a^2 + x^2}}\cos\alpha \right| = \left| U - \frac{\kappa a}{\pi(a^2 + x^2)} \right|,$$

since $\cos\alpha = a/\sqrt{a^2 + x^2}$, where $\alpha$ is shown below.

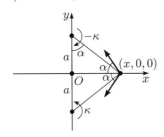

Bernoulli's equation for the boundary $y = 0$ is

$$p + \tfrac{1}{2}\rho\left( U - \frac{\kappa a}{\pi(a^2 + x^2)} \right)^2 = M \text{ (constant)},$$

that is,

$$p + \tfrac{1}{2}\rho U^2 - \frac{\rho U \kappa a}{\pi(a^2 + x^2)} + \frac{\rho \kappa^2 a^2}{2\pi^2(a^2 + x^2)^2} = M.$$

As $x \to \pm\infty$, $1/(a^2 + x^2) \to 0$ and $p \to p_0$. Then $M = p_0 + \tfrac{1}{2}\rho U^2$ and

$$p + \tfrac{1}{2}\rho U^2 - \frac{\rho U \kappa a}{\pi(a^2 + x^2)} + \frac{\rho \kappa^2 a^2}{2\pi^2(a^2 + x^2)^2} = p_0 + \tfrac{1}{2}\rho U^2,$$

so that

$$p = p_0 + \frac{\rho U \kappa a}{\pi(a^2 + x^2)} - \frac{\rho \kappa^2 a^2}{2\pi^2(a^2 + x^2)^2}.$$

The magnitude of the net force on the boundary $y = 0$, per unit length in the $z$-direction, is

$$\int_{-\infty}^{\infty} (p - p_0)\,dx$$

$$= \int_{-\infty}^{\infty} \frac{\rho U \kappa a}{\pi(a^2 + x^2)}\,dx - \int_{-\infty}^{\infty} \frac{\rho \kappa^2 a^2}{2\pi^2(a^2 + x^2)^2}\,dx$$

$$= \frac{\rho U \kappa}{\pi}\left[ \arctan\left(\frac{x}{a}\right) \right]_{-\infty}^{\infty}$$

$$\quad - \frac{\rho \kappa^2}{2\pi^2}\left[ \frac{1}{2a}\arctan\left(\frac{x}{a}\right) + \frac{x}{2(a^2 + x^2)} \right]_{-\infty}^{\infty}$$

$$= \frac{\rho U \kappa}{\pi}(\pi) - \frac{\rho \kappa^2}{2\pi^2}\left( \frac{\pi}{2a} + 0 \right)$$

$$= \rho U \kappa - \frac{\rho \kappa^2}{4\pi a} = \rho\kappa\left( U - \frac{\kappa}{4\pi a} \right).$$

But $\kappa = 4\pi a U$ (from part (a)), and so

$$\int_{-\infty}^{\infty} (p - p_0)\,dx = 0.$$

The net force on the plate is therefore zero.

# Section 3

## Solution 3.1

In cylindrical polar coordinates,

$$\mathbf{curl}\,\mathbf{u} = \left( \frac{1}{r}\frac{\partial u_z}{\partial \theta} - \frac{\partial u_\theta}{\partial z} \right)\mathbf{e}_r + \left( \frac{\partial u_r}{\partial z} - \frac{\partial u_z}{\partial r} \right)\mathbf{e}_\theta$$

$$\quad + \left( \frac{1}{r}\frac{\partial}{\partial r}(r u_\theta) - \frac{1}{r}\frac{\partial u_r}{\partial \theta} \right)\mathbf{e}_z \qquad (r \neq 0).$$

Here, $u_r = u_\theta = 0$ and $u_z = u_z(r)$; hence

$$\mathbf{curl}\,\mathbf{u} = -\frac{du_z}{dr}\,\mathbf{e}_\theta.$$

The vortex lines are circles centred on the $z$-axis and in planes perpendicular to it, as shown in the figure below (for the case $du_z/dr < 0$).

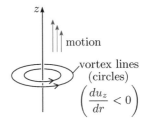

## Solution 3.2

In Exercise 3.1, you showed that the vortex lines for this flow are circles around the $z$-axis. The set of all vortex lines which pass through a circle in the $(y, z)$-plane is a torus (as shown in the figure below) with the axis of symmetry along the $z$-axis.

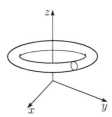

## Solution 3.3

Let $\mathbf{n}$ be the outward-pointing unit normal to the surface of the region $B$.

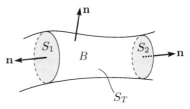

Then, by Gauss' Theorem, we have

$$\int_B \operatorname{div}\boldsymbol{\omega}\,dV = \int_{S_1} \boldsymbol{\omega}\cdot\mathbf{n}\,dA + \int_{S_2} \boldsymbol{\omega}\cdot\mathbf{n}\,dA + \int_{S_T} \boldsymbol{\omega}\cdot\mathbf{n}\,dA.$$

## Solution 3.4

Since $\boldsymbol{\omega} = \mathbf{curl\,u}$, we have

$$\operatorname{div}\boldsymbol{\omega} = \operatorname{div}(\mathbf{curl\,u})$$
$$= 0 \quad \text{(see the back of the \emph{Handbook}).}$$

Hence $\int_B \operatorname{div}\boldsymbol{\omega}\,dV = 0$.

## Solution 3.5

The vortex tube is made up of vortex lines, and each vortex line has the same direction as $\boldsymbol{\omega}$ at each point. On the surface $S_T$ of the vortex tube, the unit vector $\mathbf{n}$ at a point is normal to $S_T$ (by definition). Hence $\mathbf{n}$ is perpendicular to $\boldsymbol{\omega}$, the vorticity vector at that point (see the figure below). Thus $\boldsymbol{\omega}\cdot\mathbf{n} = 0$ at each point of $S_T$, and so

$$\int_{S_T}\boldsymbol{\omega}\cdot\mathbf{n}\,dA = 0.$$

## Solution 3.6

The strength of the vortex tube is

$$\int_S \boldsymbol{\omega}\cdot\mathbf{n}\,dA = \int_S (\mathbf{curl\,u})\cdot\mathbf{n}\,dA$$
$$= \oint_C \mathbf{u}\cdot d\mathbf{r} \quad \text{(by Stokes' Theorem),}$$

which is the circulation of $\mathbf{u}$ around $C$.

## Solution 3.7

The strength of the vortex tube is $\oint_{C_1}\mathbf{u}\cdot d\mathbf{r}$. Kelvin's Theorem says that this integral is constant, and therefore vortex tubes passing through $C_1(t)$ at various times have the same strength.

## Solution 3.8

(a)  If $S_2$ is that part of the surface of the vortex tube enclosed by $C_2$ then, by Stokes' Theorem,

$$\oint_{C_2}\mathbf{u}\cdot d\mathbf{r} = \int_{S_2}(\mathbf{curl\,u})\cdot\mathbf{n}\,dA$$
$$= \int_{S_2}\boldsymbol{\omega}\cdot\mathbf{n}\,dA.$$

(b)  The unit normal to the surface at a point is perpendicular to the vorticity vector at that point, by definition of 'unit normal' and 'vortex tube'.

(c)  From part (b), $\boldsymbol{\omega}\cdot\mathbf{n} = 0$ on the surface, so that

$$\int_{S_2}\boldsymbol{\omega}\cdot\mathbf{n}\,dA = 0.$$

Hence, from part (a),

$$\oint_{C_2}\mathbf{u}\cdot d\mathbf{r} = 0.$$

By Kelvin's Theorem, the circulation around $C_2(t)$ is zero at all times.

## Solution 3.9

(a)  No. Vortex tubes do not exist if there is no vorticity.

(b)  The mechanisms are those of convection, that is, the translation, rotation and stretching (or compressing) of vortex tubes.

(c)  If there are no vortex tubes, then the mechanisms of part (b) are not at work and so the motion continues to be vorticity-free, i.e. the irrotational motion persists.

## Solution 3.10

(a)  False. (Kelvin's Theorem does not apply if the fluid is viscous, as all real fluids are. Although, strictly speaking, the falsity of the statement has yet to be established, since only the inviscid model has been considered so far.)

(b)  True. (The strength of a vortex tube can be written as a circulation, and, by Kelvin's Theorem, this remains constant in an inviscid fluid.)

(c)  False. (It is 'true' only for such curves which encompass the tube.)

## Solution 3.11

(a)  False. (Diffusion is also present, because a real fluid is viscous.)

(b)  True. (For two-dimensional flow, the vorticity is always perpendicular to the planes of motion. Hence vortex tubes cannot be extended or compressed, and the intensity of vorticity cannot change.)

(c)  False (owing to the presence of viscosity).

## Solution 3.12

If the fluid is assumed inviscid, then since the motion is initially irrotational, the motion will always be irrotational, i.e. vorticity-free. The appearance of the two vortices cannot be explained by this model; in the real fluid, they owe their existence to the presence of viscosity (which cannot be ignored near boundaries, such as the hand).

# Section 4

## Solution 4.1

The dimensions of $\mu$, $U$, $\rho$, $a$ are

$$[\mu] = \mathrm{M\,L^{-1}T^{-1}}, \ [U] = \mathrm{L\,T^{-1}}, \ [\rho] = \mathrm{M\,L^{-3}}, \ [a] = \mathrm{L}.$$

Then

$$[Re] = \left[\frac{\rho U a}{\mu}\right] = \frac{(\mathrm{M\,L^{-3}})(\mathrm{L\,T^{-1}})\,\mathrm{L}}{\mathrm{M\,L^{-1}T^{-1}}}$$
$$= \frac{\mathrm{M\,L^{-1}T^{-1}}}{\mathrm{M\,L^{-1}T^{-1}}} = 1.$$

Thus $Re$ is dimensionless.

## Solution 4.2

If $t = \mu^\alpha \rho^\beta U^\gamma a^\delta$, then $[t] = [\mu]^\alpha [\rho]^\beta [U]^\gamma [a]^\delta$, so

$$\text{T} = (\text{M}^\alpha \text{L}^{-\alpha} \text{T}^{-\alpha})(\text{M}^\beta \text{L}^{-3\beta})(\text{L}^\gamma \text{T}^{-\gamma})\,\text{L}^\delta.$$

Equating dimensions, we have

T: $\quad 1 = -\alpha - \gamma;$
L: $\quad 0 = -\alpha - 3\beta + \gamma + \delta;$
M: $\quad 0 = \alpha + \beta.$

• If the choice is to express $\beta$, $\gamma$ and $\delta$ in terms of $\alpha$, then

$$\beta = -\alpha, \qquad \gamma = -\alpha - 1, \qquad \text{and}$$
$$\delta = \alpha + 3\beta - \gamma = \alpha + 3(-\alpha) - (-\alpha - 1) = 1 - \alpha.$$

Hence

$$t = \mu^\alpha \rho^{-\alpha} U^{-\alpha-1} a^{1-\alpha}$$
$$= \frac{a}{U}\left(\frac{\mu}{\rho a U}\right)^\alpha \quad \text{with } \alpha \text{ undetermined.}$$

The term $\mu/(\rho a U)$ is dimensionless $(= 1/Re)$ and $a/U$ has dimension T. The associated time scale is $a/U$.

• If the choice is to express $\alpha$, $\gamma$ and $\delta$ in terms of $\beta$, then

$$\alpha = -\beta, \qquad \gamma = -\alpha - 1 = \beta - 1, \qquad \text{and}$$
$$\delta = \alpha + 3\beta - \gamma = -\beta + 3\beta - (\beta - 1) = \beta + 1.$$

Hence

$$t = \mu^{-\beta} \rho^\beta U^{\beta-1} a^{\beta+1}$$
$$= \frac{a}{U}\left(\frac{a\rho U}{\mu}\right)^\beta \quad \text{with } \beta \text{ undetermined.}$$

The associated time scale is $a/U$, as before.

• If the choice is to express $\alpha$, $\beta$ and $\delta$ in terms of $\gamma$, then

$$\alpha = -\gamma - 1, \qquad \beta = -\alpha = \gamma + 1, \qquad \text{and}$$
$$\delta = \alpha + 3\beta - \gamma = (-\gamma - 1) + 3(\gamma + 1) - \gamma = \gamma + 2.$$

Hence

$$t = \mu^{-\gamma-1} \rho^{\gamma+1} U^\gamma a^{\gamma+2}$$
$$= \frac{a^2 \rho}{\mu}\left(\frac{\rho U a}{\mu}\right)^\gamma \quad \text{with } \gamma \text{ undetermined.}$$

The associated time scale is $a^2\rho/\mu$.

• If the choice is to express $\alpha$, $\beta$ and $\gamma$ in terms of $\delta$, the calculations are a little more complicated than those given previously. The equations become

$$\alpha + \gamma = -1,$$
$$\alpha + 3\beta - \gamma = \delta,$$
$$\alpha + \beta = 0.$$

Substituting for $\gamma$ and $\beta$ from the first and third equations into the second gives

$$\alpha - 3\alpha - (-1 - \alpha) = \delta, \qquad \text{so} \qquad \alpha = 1 - \delta.$$

Then $\beta = -\alpha = \delta - 1$, and

$$\gamma = -1 - \alpha = -1 - (1 - \delta) = \delta - 2.$$

Thus

$$t = \mu^{1-\delta} \rho^{\delta-1} U^{\delta-2} a^\delta$$
$$= \frac{\mu}{U^2 \rho}\left(\frac{aU\rho}{\mu}\right)^\delta \quad \text{with } \delta \text{ undetermined.}$$

The associated time scale is $\mu/(U^2\rho)$.

## Solution 4.3

An efficient diffusion process implies a fast process, i.e. a short time scale.

## Solution 4.4

If the vorticity remains close to the cylinder, then

$$\frac{a}{U} \ll \frac{a^2\rho}{\mu}, \qquad \text{or} \qquad 1 \ll \frac{Ua\rho}{\mu},$$

which is equivalent to $Re \gg 1$.

## Solution 4.5

(a) If $D = \mu^\alpha \rho^\beta U^\gamma a^\delta$, then $[D] = [\mu]^\alpha [\rho]^\beta [U]^\gamma [a]^\delta$, so

$$\text{L} = (\text{M}^\alpha \text{L}^{-\alpha} \text{T}^{-\alpha})(\text{M}^\beta \text{L}^{-3\beta})(\text{L}^\gamma \text{T}^{-\gamma})\,\text{L}^\delta.$$

Equating dimensions, we have

L: $\quad 1 = -\alpha - 3\beta + \gamma + \delta;$
M: $\quad 0 = \alpha + \beta;$
T: $\quad 0 = -\alpha - \gamma.$

• If the choice is to express $\beta$, $\gamma$ and $\delta$ in terms of $\alpha$, then

$$\beta = -\alpha, \qquad \gamma = -\alpha, \qquad \text{and}$$
$$\delta = 1 + \alpha + 3\beta - \gamma = 1 + \alpha + 3(-\alpha) - (-\alpha) = 1 - \alpha.$$

Hence

$$D = \mu^\alpha \rho^{-\alpha} U^{-\alpha} a^{1-\alpha}$$
$$= a\left(\frac{\mu}{\rho U a}\right)^\alpha \quad \text{with } \alpha \text{ undetermined.}$$

The associated length scale is $a$.

• If the choice is to express $\alpha$, $\gamma$ and $\delta$ in terms of $\beta$, then

$$\alpha = -\beta, \qquad \gamma = -\alpha = \beta, \qquad \text{and}$$
$$\delta = 1 + \alpha + 3\beta - \gamma = 1 - \beta + 3\beta - \beta = 1 + \beta.$$

Hence

$$D = \mu^{-\beta} \rho^\beta U^\beta a^{1+\beta}$$
$$= a\left(\frac{\rho U a}{\mu}\right)^\beta \quad \text{with } \beta \text{ undetermined.}$$

The associated length scale is again $a$.

• If the choice is to express $\alpha$, $\beta$ and $\delta$ in terms of $\gamma$, then

$$\alpha = -\gamma, \qquad \beta = -\alpha = \gamma, \qquad \text{and}$$
$$\delta = 1 + \alpha + 3\beta - \gamma = 1 - \gamma + 3\gamma - \gamma = 1 + \gamma.$$

Hence

$$D = \mu^{-\gamma} \rho^\gamma U^\gamma a^{1+\gamma}$$
$$= a\left(\frac{\rho U a}{\mu}\right)^\gamma \quad \text{with } \gamma \text{ undetermined.}$$

The length scale is again $a$. (Note that, since $\beta = \gamma$, it can immediately be deduced that the length scale is $a$, as found before.)

• If the choice is to express $\alpha$, $\beta$ and $\gamma$ in terms of $\delta$, then the equations become

$$-\alpha - 3\beta + \gamma = 1 - \delta,$$
$$\alpha + \beta = 0,$$
$$-\alpha - \gamma = 0.$$

Substituting for $\beta$ and $\gamma$ from the second and third equations into the first gives

$$-\alpha + 3\alpha - \alpha = 1 - \delta, \qquad \text{so} \qquad \alpha = 1 - \delta.$$

Then $\beta = \gamma = \delta - 1$. Thus

$$D = \mu^{1-\delta}\rho^{\delta-1}U^{\delta-1}a^{\delta}$$

$$= \frac{\mu}{\rho U}\left(\frac{aU\rho}{\mu}\right)^{\delta} \qquad \text{with } \delta \text{ undetermined.}$$

The length scale in this case is $\mu/(\rho U)$.

**(b)** Note that this last length scale increases with $\mu$. The diffusion process also becomes more important as $\mu$ increases, so $\mu/(\rho U)$ is interpreted as the diffusion length scale. The length scale $a$ is associated with the convection process.

**(c)** An inefficient diffusion process implies a smaller diffusion length scale. Then if the vorticity remains close to the cylinder, the convection length scale is much greater than the diffusion length scale.

(Compare with time scales, for which an inefficient diffusion process implies a larger time scale.)

Then

$$a \gg \frac{\mu}{\rho U}, \qquad \text{or} \qquad \frac{\rho U a}{\mu} \gg 1,$$

giving $Re \gg 1$ as before.

# Section 5

## Solution 5.1

**(a)** False. (Streamlining is designed to reduce profile drag.)

**(b)** True.

**(c)** False. (Model the flow near the cylinder by a viscous fluid, but assume that Kelvin's Theorem applies in the fluid at some distance from the cylinder.)

**(d)** False. (Viscous properties are important near the cylinder.)

**(e)** True.

**(f)** False. (The circulation set up around the cylinder is of the opposite sense.)

**(g)** False. (The explanation involves the use of Kelvin's Theorem and the fact that the motion is not irrotational.)

**(h)** False. (Kelvin's Theorem is taken to apply in regions at some distance from the cylinder.)

**(i)** False. (Narrow wakes are associated with high-Reynolds-number flows.)

**(j)** False. (Flettner Rotors generate a lift force of constant direction.)

**(k)** False. (The alternate shedding of vortices for the flow past a cylinder at *constant* speed — as in Figure 4.3(c) on page 143 — produces vibrations of the cylinder.)

# UNIT 8    The flow of a viscous fluid

## Study guide

This unit, bringing Block 2 to a conclusion, builds on what you have seen in *Units 5* and *7*.

The five sections should mostly require similar study times, though Section 4 will probably take longer than the others.

Section 1 is where the main theory of the unit is developed. You will not be expected to reproduce this theory, but you will need to understand, and be able to use, the results from Section 1 which appear in the *Handbook*.

There is an audio session associated with Section 5, which should provide a useful review of the unit.

## Introduction

This last unit of Block 2 develops an improved model of fluid flows. The first encounter with fluid flow problems (in *Unit 5*) involved working with an inviscid model, but experience of several flow situations and the emergence of some apparent paradoxes show that viscous effects need to be included in the model.

For example, *Unit 7* Section 4 considered the effects of viscosity.

The revision of the model to include viscosity takes place mainly in Section 1. Once this revised model is established, Section 2 shows that the solutions from earlier units can be considered as special cases (with no viscosity) of the new flow model.

However, imagining the viscosity as tending to zero does not always recapture the situations described in earlier units. Sections 3 and 4 show that these limiting procedures present a quite different way of looking at fluid flow problems and at the equations modelling them.

In order to embark on the discussion of viscous fluid flows, the appropriate equations must be established. The equation of motion in this case is the *Navier–Stokes equation* of fluid flow which, except for an added viscous term, is just Euler's equation of motion. However, to establish this equation rigorously is beyond the scope of the course. Instead a simple case is considered first, in Section 1, and it is then shown how this can be generalised and combined with the appropriate boundary conditions, and the continuity equation, to describe a viscous fluid flow.

Section 4 is devoted to analysis of a slider bearing and discussion of industrial coating processes, and Section 5 shows how the viscous fluid theory can be used to model a coating process.

# 1  First steps in modelling a viscous fluid

## 1.1  Forces and flow rates in a viscous fluid

The forces acting on a fluid element were first discussed in *Unit 1*
Subsection 3.4, where body forces (forces per unit mass) and surface forces
(forces per unit area) were introduced. It was stated there that, although
the body forces are assumed to be constant within a fluid element, changes
in the surface forces must be considered carefully since these will, in
general, vary considerably with position on the surface of the fluid element.
In the formulation of Euler's equation (*Unit 5* Section 5), the equation of
motion for an inviscid fluid, we only considered surface forces which were
normal to the surface of the fluid element, identifying these as pressure
forces and ignoring any tangential forces which were expected to arise from
viscous effects within the fluid.

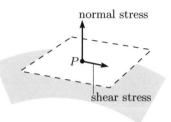

*Figure 1.1*

Here 'stress' means force per
unit area.

Now the model of a real fluid is to be reformulated to include viscous
forces. In general, at a given point $P$, the surface force can be resolved into
components normal and tangential to the surface at $P$. These surface
forces (per unit area) are known as *normal* and *shear stresses*, respectively
(see Figure 1.1). The normal stress acts perpendicularly to the surface
at $P$, and the shear stress acts in the plane tangential to the surface at $P$.
For example, consider a fluid element in the shape of a rectangular block,
orientated so that its edges are parallel to the Cartesian axes. The surface
forces acting at an arbitrary point $P$ on the top face are as shown in
Figure 1.2.

For such a fluid element, the
tangent plane at $P$ coincides
with the top face.

The surface force on this face
is the area of the face times
the resultant of the normal
and shear stress vectors. In
other words, the surface force
is the resultant of the normal
and shear forces.

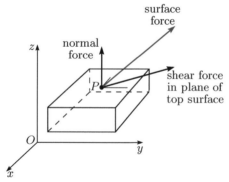

*Figure 1.2*

Why complicate the mathematical model at this stage? *Unit 7* showed the
need for viscous effects to be considered for flow around a cylinder. But
what about the simple example, from *Unit 6*, of flow through a pipe or
tube? Can viscosity be important there?

See *Unit 7* Subsection 4.3.

See *Unit 6* Subsection 2.2.

You may recall that if an *incompressible* fluid flows steadily with velocity **u**
through a pipe of constant cross-section, then the volume flow rate, $Q$, is
constant along the pipe; that is,

See *Unit 4* Subsection 2.1.

$$Q = \int_S \mathbf{u} \cdot \mathbf{n} \, dA = \text{constant},$$

where $S$ is a surface that spans the pipe and **n** is a unit normal to it. If the
fluid is also inviscid and the pipe has circular cross-section, then the
volume flow rate is the product of the (uniform) speed and the
cross-sectional area; that is,

$$Q = \text{speed} \times \pi a^2,$$

where $a$ is the radius of the pipe. So $Q$ varies in proportion to $a^2$.

However, this prediction from the inviscid model does not accord with experiment. In the mid nineteenth century, two independent sets of experiments established that the volume flow rate for laminar flow in circular pipes varies as the *fourth power* of the radius, not the second. The inviscid theory does not account for this experimental result. (In addition, these experiments established that the volume flow rate is proportional to the pressure drop along the pipe.)

The experiments referred to were performed (in 1839) by Hagen, a German hydraulic engineer, who was investigating the flow of water through cylindrical pipes, and (in 1840) by Poiseuille, a French physician, who spent 11 years of his life observing the flow in blood vessels and contributed much to the study of fluid dynamics as a result.

Gotthilf Heinrich Ludwig Hagen (1797–1884)

Jean Louis Marie Poiseuille (1799–1869)

Figure 1.3 shows schematically the outcome of another experiment. Viscous fluid is streaming steadily from left to right along a horizontal tank of constant cross-section, one side of which lies along the $x$-axis. At time $t = 0$, particles which do not interfere with the fluid flow are sprinkled on the fluid's surface along a straight line (the $y$-axis) that is perpendicular to the sides of the tank. Now, if the theory from *Unit 6* were to hold for this viscous fluid, the line of particles would remain straight since, for an incompressible fluid, the volume flow rate is constant, and therefore for a tank of constant cross-section, the velocity is uniform. However, as indicated by Figure 1.3(b), the actual outcome of such an experiment for a laminar flow shows clearly that the velocity

(i) is not uniform across the tank;

(ii) exhibits a parabolic variation with $y$;

(iii) is zero along both edges of the tank.

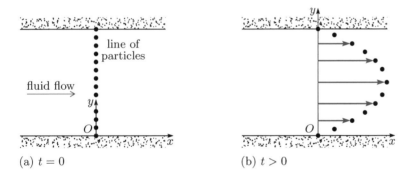

(a) $t = 0$                    (b) $t > 0$

*Figure 1.3*

Such a picture or plot of velocity against transverse position is called a **velocity profile**. For this particular flow, the profile is parabolic, a situation which is not predicted by the inviscid model.

To summarise, the previous mathematical model for inviscid, incompressible fluids, in which tangential (shear) stresses are neglected, results in

(i) a predicted velocity profile for flow through a tank which is uniform rather than parabolic;

(ii) a predicted volume flow rate for a circular pipe which varies as the radius squared rather than as the radius to the fourth power;

(iii) an inadequate description for flow past a cylinder (see *Unit 7*).

165

The model therefore needs to be revised so as to reconcile the differences between observation and theory. This section sets out to explain Stokes' theory of viscous fluids. Section 2 shows that Hagen's and Poiseuille's result,

$$Q \propto a^4,$$

for the volume flow rate $Q$ of a viscous fluid flowing along a circular pipe of radius $a$, can be derived as a consequence of Stokes' theory.

Incidentally, Stokes also compared experimental data with the formula for the volume flow rate (deduced by Hagen and Poiseuille), which he had derived theoretically. He found no agreement whatever between the data and his formula, but it is now known that the data available to Stokes were for turbulent, not laminar, flows. Turbulent flows are considered in *Unit 13*.

### Exercise 1.1

(a) Referring to *Unit 5*, if necessary, write down in vector form Euler's equation of motion for an inviscid fluid. Identify the terms in the equation.

(b) Give an example of a typical body force.

## 1.2 Newtonian fluids

When viscosity was first mentioned in *Unit 1*, it was described qualitatively as a measure of the fluid's resistance to the shearing forces acting on the fluid. An analogy was drawn between a pack of cards, sliding over one another, and a viscous fluid placed between parallel plates, the upper plate moving in its own plane and causing shearing forces which 'deformed' the fluid (see Figure 1.4). Some fluids — the more viscous ones — will offer more resistance to the shearing forces than others; so there is an expectation that, on a small scale, a fluid element in a more viscous fluid will deform more slowly than one in a fluid of lower viscosity subject to the same shearing force. The formulation of Euler's equation of motion in *Unit 5* ignored the shearing (tangential) stresses, and so also implicitly ignored the fluid's deformation.

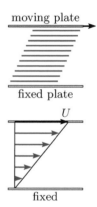

*Figure 1.4*

In considering all fluids, there are several possible models to describe the relationship between the shear stresses and the fluid's deformation. In this course, just one of these models is used; it is found to hold experimentally to a good approximation for many fluids (e.g. water, oil, air). It is that

shear stress is proportional to the rate of deformation.     (1.1)

This means that the shear stresses in fluids are related linearly to the spatial derivatives of the velocity components. This is exactly what Newton stated in his discussion of viscous fluids, and for this reason fluids which obey the stress–deformation relationship (1.1) are called *Newtonian fluids*. Only such fluids are considered in this course.

This discussion is given in Newton's thesis *Mathematical Principles of Natural Philosophy* (Section IX, Book II).

The relationship (1.1) needs to be turned into mathematical symbols. To do this, we consider the special case of a simple steady shearing flow, as mentioned briefly in *Unit 1*, and interpret relationship (1.1) for this case.

A fluid of constant density is confined between parallel plates, infinite in the $x$- and $y$-directions, and the flow is two-dimensional, being independent of $y$. The lower plate is held fixed while the upper plate moves in the $x$-direction with constant speed $U$. Figure 1.5 shows this situation in any plane $y = $ constant. The $z$-axis is perpendicular to the plates.

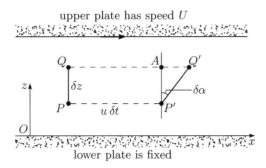

*Figure 1.5*

For this particular flow, assume that the velocity of the fluid is in the $x$-direction only, which seems reasonable given the confining influence of the plates, symmetry and the fact that (if body forces are negligible) there are no forces acting perpendicular to the plates and causing the fluid to move in that direction. Thus $u_2 = u_3 = 0$, and the continuity equation, $\nabla \cdot \mathbf{u} = 0$, reduces to $\partial u_1 / \partial x = 0$, showing that $u_1$ does not depend on $x$. Since it is assumed also that there is no $y$-dependence, it follows that

$$\mathbf{u} = u_1(z)\,\mathbf{i},$$

which means that the velocity is in the $x$-direction and is a function of the transverse dimension, $z$, of the channel formed by the two plates.

Let $P$ and $Q$ have coordinates $(x, z)$ and $(x, z + \delta z)$, respectively, and let the velocity at $P$ be $u\,\mathbf{i}$ and that at $Q$ be $(u + \delta u)\,\mathbf{i}$. In a time $\delta t$, the fluid particles at the points $P$ and $Q$ have moved to the positions $P'$ and $Q'$, respectively, so that $P'Q'$ is the *deformed* position of $PQ$, and the angle $\delta\alpha$ through which $PQ$ has turned measures the *deformation* for this shearing flow (see Figure 1.5).

The subscript 1 on $u$ is omitted from here on.

To a first approximation, the angle $\delta\alpha$ is given by

$$\delta\alpha \simeq \tan(\delta\alpha) = \frac{AQ'}{AP'} = \frac{AQ'}{PQ}.$$

Now $QQ'$ has length $(u + \delta u)\,\delta t$, since this is the distance travelled by a particle moving with speed $u + \delta u$ in time $\delta t$; similarly, $PP'$ has length $u\,\delta t$. Thus the deformation, $\delta\alpha$, is given by

$$\delta\alpha \simeq \frac{AQ'}{PQ} = \frac{QQ' - PP'}{PQ} = \frac{(u + \delta u)\,\delta t - u\,\delta t}{\delta z} = \frac{\delta u\,\delta t}{\delta z}. \tag{1.2}$$

The *rate of deformation*, $d\alpha/dt$, is required in order to apply the relationship (1.1) to this fluid flow. This is the limit of the incremental deformation, $\delta\alpha$, divided by the incremental time, $\delta t$. Thus the rate of deformation at $P$ is the limit as $\delta t \to 0$ and $\delta z \to 0$ of

$$\frac{\delta\alpha}{\delta t} = \frac{\delta u\,\delta t}{\delta z}\bigg/ \delta t \quad \text{(using Equation (1.2))}$$

$$= \frac{\delta u}{\delta z}.$$

The continuum model requires the rate of deformation *at* the point $P$, and this is the limit of $\delta\alpha/\delta t$ as $\delta t \to 0$ (so that $P'$ tends to $P$) and $\delta z \to 0$ (so that the line segment $PQ$ tends to the point $P$).

Taking limits gives the rate of deformation at $P$ as

$$\frac{d\alpha}{dt} = \lim_{\substack{\delta t \to 0 \\ \delta z \to 0}} \left( \frac{\delta\alpha}{\delta t} \right) = \lim_{\substack{\delta t \to 0 \\ \delta z \to 0}} \left( \frac{\delta u}{\delta z} \right) = \frac{du}{dz}. \tag{1.3}$$

If the shear stress is denoted by $\tau$, then statement (1.1), which says that shear stress is proportional to rate of deformation, becomes

$$\tau \propto \frac{d\alpha}{dt} \quad \text{or} \quad \tau = \mu \frac{d\alpha}{dt},$$

where the constant of proportionality, $\mu$, is called the **coefficient of viscosity**. From Equation (1.3), the shear stress at $P$ is also given by

$$\tau = \mu \frac{du}{dz}.$$

Further, if the flow is not steady, it can be shown that

$$\tau = \mu \frac{\partial u}{\partial z}. \tag{1.4}$$

This is *Newton's model of viscosity*, first encountered in *Unit 1* Subsection 1.3, but this time it applies quite generally at points of a viscous fluid subject to a shear stress in the $x$-direction, where the velocity, $\mathbf{u}$, is a function of $z$ and $t$ only.

The coefficient of viscosity is a constant, since it arose from a proportionality relation.

The shear stress $\tau$, as given by Equation (1.4), provides a force on any surface parallel to the $(x, y)$-plane. For such a surface $S$, with area $A$, it can be seen from Figure 1.5 that the force on $S$ due to the motion of fluid above it is $\tau A \mathbf{i}$, since the fluid above, moving faster than $S$ in the $\mathbf{i}$-direction, pulls $S$ along with it. By the same token, however, the force on $S$ due to the fluid below it is $-\tau A \mathbf{i}$, since the lower fluid moves more slowly and so drags $S$ back.

### Exercise 1.2

Consider the steady flow of a Newtonian fluid, with velocity $\mathbf{u} = u(x)\,\mathbf{k}$, confined between parallel plates infinite in the $y$- and $z$-directions (see Figure 1.6). The left-hand plate is held fixed and the right-hand plate moves in the $z$-direction with constant speed $U$. Write down an expression for the shear stress on a surface parallel to the $(y, z)$-plane. In what direction does this stress act? (Ignore body forces.)

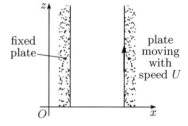

*Figure 1.6*

### Exercise 1.3

What are the dimensions of the coefficient of viscosity, $\mu$? (Remember that stress is a force per unit area.)

## 1.3   Flow between parallel plates

Subsection 1.2 arrived at Equation (1.4) for the shear (tangential) stress in the direction of shear, for a simple shear flow of a Newtonian fluid. We now consider again a flow between parallel plates. The fluid is assumed to be of constant density (no volume changes), Newtonian and of constant viscosity. The flow takes place between two infinite, horizontal plates that are a distance $h$ apart. Take the plates to be in the $(x, y)$-plane and in a plane parallel to it, as indicated by the cross-section for $y = $ constant in Figure 1.7.

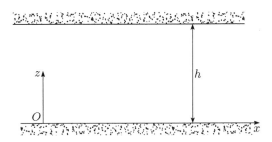

*Figure 1.7*

The aim is to determine the equation of motion for such a flow, starting from the following assumptions.

(i) *The velocity and pressure are independent of y.* The plates have infinite extent perpendicular to the plane of the paper, and so the motion is two-dimensional, in the $(x, z)$-plane, and nothing depends on $y$.

(ii) *The velocity is in the x-direction only.* This seems reasonable enough, given the confining influence of the plates and their infinite dimensions. Thus $u_2 = u_3 = 0$ everywhere. The continuity equation, $\nabla \cdot \mathbf{u} = 0$, then gives $\partial u_1 / \partial x = 0$, so that $u_1$ is a function of $z$ and $t$ only.

> Assumption (i) says that $u_1$ does not depend on $y$.

The velocity field is therefore $\mathbf{u} = u_1(z, t)\, \mathbf{i}$, which means that the flow at any instant of time is the same at each $x$-value. This condition is described by saying that the flow is **fully developed** in the $x$-direction. At *any instant of time*, the flow looks the same at whatever point $x$ along the channel is chosen. So if two snapshots were taken, at the *same time* but at *different points* along the channel, the pictures would be identical. However, two snapshots taken at *different times* at the *same point* along the channel would not necessarily be the same, since the flow need not be steady. (Figure 1.8 shows possible velocity profiles, at positions $x_1$ and $x_2$, for two instants of time, $t_1$ and $t_2$, for a non-steady flow.)

> In other words, the flow is fully developed in the $x$-direction if $\partial \mathbf{u} / \partial x = \mathbf{0}$.

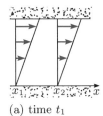
(a) time $t_1$

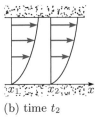
(b) time $t_2$

*Figure 1.8*

(iii) *Body forces are negligible.* This assumption is made only to simplify the argument. They will be included later.

We now set out to determine the equation of motion for this flow.

Consider a fluid element in the shape of a rectangular block (as shown in Figure 1.9), orientated so that the edges $AB$, $AD$ and $AE$ are parallel to the Cartesian coordinate axes $Ox$, $Oy$ and $Oz$, respectively. Suppose that the edges of the block have lengths $\delta x$, $\delta y$ and $\delta z$, and that the centre of the block, $Q$, has coordinates $(x, y, z)$.

The flow is (by assumptions (i) and (ii)) considered as two-dimensional, moving in the $x$-direction between two plates, each of which is parallel to the $(x, y)$-plane. The fluid element will therefore travel along a path such that the pathline of the point $Q$ is a straight line parallel to the $x$-axis. To obtain an equation of motion for the flow, we need to apply Newton's Second Law and the Torque Law to this fluid element.

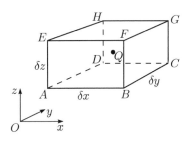

*Figure 1.9*

There are no body forces acting on the fluid element, by assumption (iii); that is, the body force is

$$\mathbf{F}_B = \mathbf{0}.$$

The surface forces acting on the block are of two types:

(a) normal forces, due to the pressure in the fluid;

(b) tangential (shear) forces, due to viscosity in the fluid.

Figure 1.10 shows a cross-section of the block through $Q$ and parallel to the $(x, z)$-plane, indicating the stresses on each face that cause the surface forces. Compared with Figure 1.9, the faces are now labelled $A_1$ (for $BCGF$), $A_2$ (for $EFGH$), etc. Since there is no variation in the $y$-direction, the $y$-coordinates have been suppressed.

> Another way of putting this is that the surface force on each face can be regarded as the sum of a normal and a tangential component.

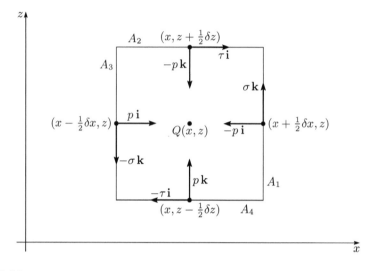

*Figure 1.10*

On each face, the force component due to the pressure acts inwards, as shown. The shear stress $\tau$ on the upper face, $A_2$, due to the fluid above, is shown as causing a force in the positive $x$-direction, in which case the shear force on the bottom face, $A_4$, may be regarded as acting in the negative $x$-direction (see the paragraph before Exercise 1.2). Similarly, the shear stress $\sigma$ on the right-hand face, $A_1$, due to fluid to the right of the block, is shown as causing a force in the positive $z$-direction; so the shear force on the left-hand face, $A_3$, is taken as acting in the negative $z$-direction.

In each case, the stress must be multiplied by the area of the corresponding face of the block, to give the force that acts. Hence the surface forces acting on these four block faces are:

> Variations of $p$, $\sigma$ and $\tau$ over each face may be ignored, for the level of approximation taken here.

$$\left.\begin{array}{ll} \text{on } A_1: & \mathbf{F}_1 = \left[-p(x + \tfrac{1}{2}\delta x, z)\,\mathbf{i} + \sigma(x + \tfrac{1}{2}\delta x, z)\,\mathbf{k}\right]\delta y\,\delta z; \\[4pt] \text{on } A_2: & \mathbf{F}_2 = \left[\tau(x, z + \tfrac{1}{2}\delta z)\,\mathbf{i} - p(x, z + \tfrac{1}{2}\delta z)\,\mathbf{k}\right]\delta x\,\delta y; \\[4pt] \text{on } A_3: & \mathbf{F}_3 = \left[p(x - \tfrac{1}{2}\delta x, z)\,\mathbf{i} - \sigma(x - \tfrac{1}{2}\delta x, z)\,\mathbf{k}\right]\delta y\,\delta z; \\[4pt] \text{on } A_4: & \mathbf{F}_4 = \left[-\tau(x, z - \tfrac{1}{2}\delta z)\,\mathbf{i} + p(x, z - \tfrac{1}{2}\delta z)\,\mathbf{k}\right]\delta x\,\delta y. \end{array}\right\} \quad (1.5)$$

The total surface force acting on the block is

$$\mathbf{F}_S = \mathbf{F}_1 + \mathbf{F}_2 + \mathbf{F}_3 + \mathbf{F}_4.$$

Also, from assumption (ii), the acceleration of the block is

$$\frac{d\mathbf{u}}{dt} = \frac{du_1}{dt}\,\mathbf{i}.$$

> Here $d/dt$ is the total rate of change.

Since $\mathbf{F}_B = \mathbf{0}$ (no body forces), Newton's Second Law then gives

$$\rho\,\delta x\,\delta y\,\delta z\,\frac{du_1}{dt}\,\mathbf{i} = \mathbf{F}_S = \mathbf{F}_1 + \mathbf{F}_2 + \mathbf{F}_3 + \mathbf{F}_4. \quad (1.6)$$

> The fluid has density $\rho$, so the mass of the block is
> $$\rho\,\delta x\,\delta y\,\delta z.$$

Taking the **i**-component of Equation (1.6) we have, from Equations (1.5) and after division by $\delta x \, \delta y \, \delta z$, that

$$\rho \frac{du_1}{dt} = -\frac{p(x+\frac{1}{2}\delta x, z) - p(x-\frac{1}{2}\delta x, z)}{\delta x} + \frac{\tau(x, z+\frac{1}{2}\delta z) - \tau(x, z-\frac{1}{2}\delta z)}{\delta z}.$$

Taking the limit here as $\delta x \to 0$ and $\delta z \to 0$ gives

$$\rho \frac{du_1}{dt} = -\frac{\partial p}{\partial x} + \frac{\partial \tau}{\partial z}.$$

Incorporating Equation (1.4), which says that in this case $\tau = \mu \, \partial u_1/\partial z$, gives the equation of motion

$$\rho \frac{du_1}{dt} = -\frac{\partial p}{\partial x} + \mu \frac{\partial^2 u_1}{\partial z^2}. \tag{1.7}$$

This was obtained from the **i**-component of Equation (1.6). Taking the **k**-component of that equation, and proceeding in a similar way, leads to

$$0 = \frac{\sigma(x+\frac{1}{2}\delta x, z) - \sigma(x-\frac{1}{2}\delta x, z)}{\delta x} - \frac{p(x, z+\frac{1}{2}\delta z) - p(x, z-\frac{1}{2}\delta z)}{\delta z}.$$

Taking the limit here as $\delta x \to 0$ and $\delta z \to 0$ gives

$$0 = \frac{\partial \sigma}{\partial x} - \frac{\partial p}{\partial z}. \tag{1.8}$$

Equations (1.7) and (1.8) are the outcome of applying Newton's Second Law and (in the case of Equation (1.7)) the viscosity model for Newtonian fluids. It remains to model the rotational motion of the block, by applying the Torque Law relative to the centre of mass, $Q$.

*This law was introduced in MST209 Unit 27.*

Referring once more to Figure 1.10, the line of action of the pressure force on each face passes through $Q$, and therefore leads to no torque about $Q$. The torques due to the shear stresses are:

$$\left.\begin{aligned}
\text{on } A_1: \quad \mathbf{\Gamma}_1 &= \tfrac{1}{2}\delta x \, \mathbf{i} \times \sigma(x+\tfrac{1}{2}\delta x, z)\delta y \, \delta z \, \mathbf{k} \\
&= -\tfrac{1}{2}\delta x \, \delta y \, \delta z \, \sigma(x+\tfrac{1}{2}\delta x, z)\,\mathbf{j}; \\
\text{on } A_2: \quad \mathbf{\Gamma}_2 &= \tfrac{1}{2}\delta z \, \mathbf{k} \times \tau(x, z+\tfrac{1}{2}\delta z)\delta x \, \delta y \, \mathbf{i} \\
&= \tfrac{1}{2}\delta x \, \delta y \, \delta z \, \tau(x, z+\tfrac{1}{2}\delta z)\,\mathbf{j}; \\
\text{on } A_3: \quad \mathbf{\Gamma}_3 &= -\tfrac{1}{2}\delta x \, \mathbf{i} \times \left(-\sigma(x-\tfrac{1}{2}\delta x, z)\right)\delta y \, \delta z \, \mathbf{k} \\
&= -\tfrac{1}{2}\delta x \, \delta y \, \delta z \, \sigma(x-\tfrac{1}{2}\delta x, z)\,\mathbf{j}; \\
\text{on } A_4: \quad \mathbf{\Gamma}_4 &= -\tfrac{1}{2}\delta z \, \mathbf{k} \times \left(-\tau(x, z-\tfrac{1}{2}\delta z)\right)\delta x \, \delta y \, \mathbf{i} \\
&= \tfrac{1}{2}\delta x \, \delta y \, \delta z \, \tau(x, z-\tfrac{1}{2}\delta z)\,\mathbf{j}
\end{aligned}\right\} \tag{1.9}$$

The Torque Law relative to $Q$ states that

$$I\dot{\boldsymbol{\omega}} = \mathbf{\Gamma}_1 + \mathbf{\Gamma}_2 + \mathbf{\Gamma}_3 + \mathbf{\Gamma}_4,$$

where $I = \frac{1}{12}\rho \, \delta x \, \delta y \, \delta z \left((\delta x)^2 + (\delta z)^2\right)$ is the moment of inertia of the block about the axis of rotation, and $\boldsymbol{\omega} = \omega_2 \mathbf{j}$ is the angular velocity. Applying Equations (1.9), taking the **j**-component and dividing through by $\delta x \, \delta y \, \delta z$, gives $\frac{1}{12}\rho\left((\delta x)^2 + (\delta z)^2\right)\dot{\omega}_2$ equal to

*This moment of inertia follows from that for a solid cuboid given in MST209 Unit 27.*

$$-\tfrac{1}{2}\left(\sigma(x+\tfrac{1}{2}\delta x, z) + \sigma(x-\tfrac{1}{2}\delta x, z)\right) + \tfrac{1}{2}\left(\tau(x, z+\tfrac{1}{2}\delta z) + \tau(x, z-\tfrac{1}{2}\delta z)\right).$$

On taking the limit here as $\delta x \to 0$ and $\delta z \to 0$, we obtain

$$\sigma(x, z) = \tau(x, z).$$

Now, since $\tau = \mu \, \partial u_1/\partial z$ (Equation (1.4)) and $u_1 = u_1(z)$, it follows that

$$\frac{\partial \sigma}{\partial x} = \frac{\partial \tau}{\partial x} = 0,$$

showing that $\sigma$ does not vary in the $x$-direction.

*The dependence of quantities on $t$ has been kept implicit throughout, since this analysis takes place at one instant of time.*

Also, from Equation (1.8), we now have

$$\frac{\partial p}{\partial z} = 0,$$

showing that there is no pressure variation with $z$.

On the basis of three assumptions, we have established that the pressure can vary only in the $x$-direction and that the equation of motion is

$$\rho \frac{du_1}{dt} = -\frac{\partial p}{\partial x} + \mu \frac{\partial^2 u_1}{\partial z^2}. \tag{1.7}$$

Now $du_1/dt$ is a *total* derivative, and can be expanded to

$$\frac{du_1}{dt} = \frac{\partial u_1}{\partial t} + u_1 \frac{\partial u_1}{\partial x} + u_2 \frac{\partial u_1}{\partial y} + u_3 \frac{\partial u_1}{\partial z} = \frac{\partial u_1}{\partial t},$$

since $u_2 = u_3 = 0$ and $u_1$ is not a function of $x$. Hence the equation of motion for the flow between parallel plates becomes

$$\rho \frac{\partial u_1}{\partial t} = -\frac{\partial p}{\partial x} + \mu \frac{\partial^2 u_1}{\partial z^2}. \tag{1.10}$$

### Exercise 1.4

Find the general solution of the equation of motion (1.10) for the case in which

- the flow is steady (that is, it does not vary with time);
- the pressure gradient in the $x$-direction is constant (take $\partial p/\partial x = -C$, where $C$ is a positive constant).

The solution to Exercise 1.4,

$$u_1 = -\frac{Cz^2}{2\mu} + Az + B, \qquad \text{where } A, B \text{ are arbitrary constants,}$$

shows that if the magnitude $C$ of the pressure gradient is non-zero, the resulting velocity profile is described by a parabola. What is more, by choosing the constants of integration suitably (to be done in Section 2) it is possible for the velocity in the $x$-direction to be zero on the boundaries.

Because the force due to gravity was ignored, the analysis above, with $z$ replaced by $y$, is valid for the case of two vertical plates parallel to the $(x, z)$-plane. Thus the solution to Exercise 1.4 agrees with the velocity profile shown in Figure 1.3(b).

In Exercise 1.4, you were asked to assume that the pressure gradient $\partial p/\partial x$ was a constant. It can in fact be shown, from Equation (1.10), that this pressure gradient depends at most on time.

Rearranging Equation (1.10) gives

$$\rho \frac{\partial u_1}{\partial t} - \mu \frac{\partial^2 u_1}{\partial z^2} = -\frac{\partial p}{\partial x}.$$

Now, the left-hand side of the above equation is a function only of $z$ and $t$, and the right-hand side is a function only of $x$ and $t$, since $\partial p/\partial y = \partial p/\partial z = 0$. Each side of the equation must then be a function $C$ of $t$, that is,

$$\frac{\partial p}{\partial x} = -C(t), \qquad \text{as required.} \tag{1.11}$$

In the absence of any body force and given no motion in the $z$-direction, this was to be expected.

The total derivative was introduced in *Unit 5* Subsection 4.2.

The 'pressure gradient in the $x$-direction' is another way of saying 'the $x$-component of the pressure gradient', although in this case the other two components are zero.

It follows on integrating with respect to $x$ that

$$p(x,t) = -C(t)\,x + F(t), \tag{1.12}$$

where $F$ is an arbitrary function.

Suppose that, at time $t$, the pressure is measured at two locations, $x_1$ and $x_2$, that are a distance $L$ apart (that is, $L = x_2 - x_1$). Denoting the difference between these two pressures by $\Delta p(t)$, we have

$$\begin{aligned}
\Delta p(t) &= p(x_2, t) - p(x_1, t) \\
&= -C(t)(x_2 - x_1), \qquad \text{from Equation (1.12)}, \\
&= -C(t)L,
\end{aligned}$$

and so the pressure gradient, $-C(t)$, can be estimated at any time $t$ from the measured pressure difference $\Delta p(t)$ and the distance $L$.

For the formulation of the model for a real fluid, an understanding of a 'real' fluid is required. The aim of the unit is to introduce viscous effects into the model, but in the above discussion, constant viscosity and density are already assumed. These assumptions continue throughout the unit. It is also assumed that the fluid is Newtonian (stress is proportional to rate of deformation), and implicitly it is assumed that the flow is non-turbulent. This may seem to be a long list of restrictions on a 'real' fluid, but the model which is developed will be reasonable for many liquids.

The assumption of non-turbulent flows for most of the course was stated in *Unit 1* Subsection 1.4.

In the rest of the unit, a reference to a **viscous fluid** means that it is:

(a) of constant density—holds for liquids, and for gases at flow speeds low compared to that of sound;

(b) Newtonian—holds for many liquids but excludes, for example, polymers, paints, raw egg and blood in *small* capillaries;

(c) of constant viscosity—is reasonable for many fluids if only small temperature variations are present.

As an example of the variation of viscosity with temperature, the coefficient of viscosity $\mu$ for air is, in $\mathrm{kg\,m^{-1}s^{-1}}$,

$$1.76 \times 10^{-5} \text{ at } 10°C, \qquad 2.18 \times 10^{-5} \text{ at } 100°C.$$

For water, the corresponding values are

$$13.0 \times 10^{-4} \text{ at } 10°C, \qquad 2.83 \times 10^{-4} \text{ at } 100°C.$$

You showed in Exercise 1.3 that the dimensions of $\mu$ are $\mathrm{M\,L^{-1}T^{-1}}$. The corresponding SI unit, $\mathrm{kg\,m^{-1}s^{-1}}$, can also be given as pascal seconds (Pa s).

### Exercise 1.5

Suppose that the assumptions in this subsection still hold (that is, $\mathbf{u} = u_1(z,t)\,\mathbf{i}$), but that the flow is no longer horizontal (see Figure 1.11), so that gravity must be taken into account in applying Newton's Second Law. By considering a constant body force per unit mass $\mathbf{F} = F_1\,\mathbf{i} + F_3\,\mathbf{k}$, derive the $x$- and $z$-components of the equation of motion. What is your conclusion about the pressure gradient in the direction of flow in this case?

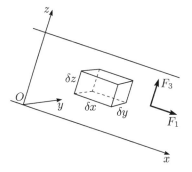

*Figure 1.11*

## *End-of-section exercise*

### *Exercise 1.6*

Consider the fully developed flow of a Newtonian fluid contained in a channel formed by infinite plates lying in the planes $x = 0$, $x = d$ (see Figure 1.6). The plate at $x = d$ moves parallel to the $z$-axis with constant speed $U$, while the plate at $x = 0$ is fixed. Assume that there are no body forces. Are the following statements true or false?

(a) There is no pressure gradient in the $x$-direction.

(b) The pressure gradient in the $z$-direction must be zero.

(c) The shear stresses in the $x$-direction are zero.

(d) The shear stresses in the $z$-direction are zero.

(e) The pressure gradient in the $z$-direction is at most a function of $t$.

Would your conclusions be the same if there were a constant body force (gravity) acting in the negative $z$-direction?

# 2   The Navier–Stokes equations

## 2.1   The Navier–Stokes equations

In Subsection 1.3 the equation of motion was formulated for a special case of viscous fluid flow, namely, the fully developed flow with $\mathbf{u} = u_1(z,t)\,\mathbf{i}$ between parallel plates. The equation which described this flow,

$$\rho\frac{\partial u_1}{\partial t} = -\frac{\partial p}{\partial x} + \rho F_1 + \mu\frac{\partial^2 u_1}{\partial z^2},$$  (2.1)

is a special case of the $x$-component of the *Navier–Stokes equation*,

$$\rho\frac{du_1}{dt} = -\frac{\partial p}{\partial x} + \rho F_1 + \mu\left(\frac{\partial^2 u_1}{\partial x^2} + \frac{\partial^2 u_1}{\partial y^2} + \frac{\partial^2 u_1}{\partial z^2}\right).$$

This is Equation (1.10), with the addition of the $\rho F_1$ term as in the solution to Exercise 1.5. Here $\partial p/\partial x$ is a function of time only; see Equation (1.11).

---

The **Navier–Stokes equation**, for the flow of a fluid with velocity $\mathbf{u}$, constant density $\rho$, pressure $p$, body force $\mathbf{F}$ per unit mass and coefficient of viscosity $\mu$, is

$$\rho\frac{d\mathbf{u}}{dt} = -\boldsymbol{\nabla}p + \rho\mathbf{F} + \mu\nabla^2\mathbf{u},$$  (2.2)

where

$$\frac{d}{dt} = \frac{\partial}{\partial t} + \mathbf{u}\cdot\boldsymbol{\nabla}, \qquad \boldsymbol{\nabla} = \mathbf{i}\frac{\partial}{\partial x} + \mathbf{j}\frac{\partial}{\partial y} + \mathbf{k}\frac{\partial}{\partial z},$$

$$\nabla^2\mathbf{u} = \left(\nabla^2 u_1\right)\mathbf{i} + \left(\nabla^2 u_2\right)\mathbf{j} + \left(\nabla^2 u_3\right)\mathbf{k}.$$

It is common to speak either of the Navier–Stokes *equation*, meaning the single vector equation, or *equations*, meaning the three scalar component equations.

For the total derivative, $d/dt$, see *Unit 5* Subsection 4.2.

For $\boldsymbol{\nabla}$ and $\nabla^2$, see *Unit 4* Subsection 5.2.

With the aid of the identities

$$(\mathbf{u} \cdot \boldsymbol{\nabla})\mathbf{u} = \boldsymbol{\nabla}(\tfrac{1}{2}u^2) - \mathbf{u} \times (\boldsymbol{\nabla} \times \mathbf{u})$$

and

$$\nabla^2\mathbf{u} = \boldsymbol{\nabla}(\boldsymbol{\nabla} \cdot \mathbf{u}) - \boldsymbol{\nabla} \times (\boldsymbol{\nabla} \times \mathbf{u}),$$

Equation (2.2) can also be written as

$$\rho\left(\frac{\partial \mathbf{u}}{\partial t} + \boldsymbol{\nabla}(\tfrac{1}{2}u^2) - \mathbf{u} \times (\boldsymbol{\nabla} \times \mathbf{u})\right)$$
$$= -\boldsymbol{\nabla}p + \rho\mathbf{F} - \mu\left(\boldsymbol{\nabla} \times (\boldsymbol{\nabla} \times \mathbf{u})\right). \tag{2.3}$$

This apparently more complicated version of the Navier–Stokes equation is sometimes more convenient to apply than Equation (2.2).

To establish Equation (2.2) from first principles requires mathematical techniques (of tensor calculus) which are not included in this course. You will shortly be asked to show that Equation (2.1) is a special case of the Navier–Stokes equation, giving some confidence in the validity of the latter. You will see in Subsection 2.3 that the Navier–Stokes equation leads to a prediction for the viscous flow through a pipe which is validated by the experimental results of Hagen and Poiseuille, described in Subsection 1.1.

### Exercise 2.1

Assuming that the body force $\mathbf{F}$ per unit mass has Cartesian components $(F_1, F_2, F_3)$, write out the Cartesian $z$-component of Equation (2.2).

### Exercise 2.2

Use the result of Exercise 2.1 (and the analogous result for the $x$-component) to write down the $x$- and $z$-components of Equation (2.2) for two-dimensional, fully developed, viscous flow with velocity field $\mathbf{u} = u_1(z,t)\,\mathbf{i}$. Taking the body force to be constant, show that the equations of motion found in Exercise 1.5 are a special case of the Navier–Stokes equations.

---

If the Navier–Stokes equation is to be used as a model for various fluid flows, then this equation needs to be expressed in any of Cartesian, cylindrical or spherical polar coordinates, depending upon the fluid flow situation under consideration. For example, in order to model the flow in a blood vessel, as in Poiseuille's experiments, a mathematical model using cylindrical polar coordinates would be best.

This unit will require the Navier–Stokes equation only in Cartesian and cylindrical polar coordinates. The latter can be obtained from Equation (2.3) and then expressed in terms of $\boldsymbol{\nabla}$ and $\nabla^2$, as follows.

See Exercise 5.5 and Equation (5.10) in *Unit 4*.

The flow is incompressible, and so the continuity equation is
$$\boldsymbol{\nabla} \cdot \mathbf{u} = 0.$$

This form can be compared with the form of Euler's equation in Equation (1.1) of *Unit 6*.

In *cylindrical polar coordinates*, the three components of the Navier–Stokes equation (2.2) or (2.3) are

$$\left.\begin{aligned}\rho\left(\frac{du_r}{dt}-\frac{u_\theta^2}{r}\right) &= -\frac{\partial p}{\partial r}+\rho F_r+\mu\left(\nabla^2 u_r-\frac{u_r}{r^2}-\frac{2}{r^2}\frac{\partial u_\theta}{\partial\theta}\right),\\ \rho\left(\frac{du_\theta}{dt}+\frac{u_r u_\theta}{r}\right) &= -\frac{1}{r}\frac{\partial p}{\partial\theta}+\rho F_\theta+\mu\left(\nabla^2 u_\theta-\frac{u_\theta}{r^2}+\frac{2}{r^2}\frac{\partial u_r}{\partial\theta}\right),\\ \rho\frac{du_z}{dt} &= -\frac{\partial p}{\partial z}+\rho F_z+\mu\nabla^2 u_z,\end{aligned}\right\} \quad (2.4)$$

Do not concern yourself with the derivation of these equations.

where

$$\frac{d}{dt}=\frac{\partial}{\partial t}+\mathbf{u}\cdot\boldsymbol{\nabla}, \qquad \boldsymbol{\nabla}=\mathbf{e}_r\frac{\partial}{\partial r}+\mathbf{e}_\theta\frac{1}{r}\frac{\partial}{\partial\theta}+\mathbf{e}_z\frac{\partial}{\partial z},$$

$$\nabla^2=\frac{1}{r}\frac{\partial}{\partial r}\left(r\frac{\partial}{\partial r}\right)+\frac{1}{r^2}\frac{\partial^2}{\partial\theta^2}+\frac{\partial^2}{\partial z^2}.$$

Note that
$$\frac{1}{r}\frac{\partial}{\partial r}\left(r\frac{\partial}{\partial r}\right)=\frac{\partial^2}{\partial r^2}+\frac{1}{r}\frac{\partial}{\partial r}.$$

These equations also appear at the back of the *Handbook*.

The Navier–Stokes equation represents a balance of the forces involved in the flow of a viscous fluid. For ease of reference, the separate terms of Equation (2.2) are labelled below:

$$\underset{\text{A}}{\rho\frac{d\mathbf{u}}{dt}} = \underset{\text{B}}{-\boldsymbol{\nabla}p} + \underset{\text{C}}{\rho\mathbf{F}} + \underset{\text{D}}{\mu\nabla^2\mathbf{u}}. \qquad (2.2)$$

The definition of 'viscous' as used in this unit was given towards the end of Subsection 1.3.

Term A:  $\rho\,d\mathbf{u}/dt=\rho\left(\partial\mathbf{u}/\partial t+(\mathbf{u}\cdot\boldsymbol{\nabla})\,\mathbf{u}\right)$ is not really a force at all, but despite this it is often referred to as the 'inertial force'. This term may be recognised as the 'mass × acceleration' term of Newton's Second Law. If the flow is steady, then $\partial\mathbf{u}/\partial t$, which represents the time rate of change of $\mathbf{u}$ at a fixed point in space, is zero. The term $(\mathbf{u}\cdot\boldsymbol{\nabla})\,\mathbf{u}$, the convective acceleration, is non-linear, since it involves a product of $\mathbf{u}$ and its derivatives.

The quantity $\rho\,(\mathbf{u}\cdot\boldsymbol{\nabla})\,\mathbf{u}$ is often called the 'momentum transport term'.

Term B:  $-\boldsymbol{\nabla}p$ is the pressure gradient term, being the non-viscous contribution to the surface forces.

Term C:  $\rho\mathbf{F}$ is the body force, which in this course is assumed to be the force due to the Earth's gravitational field. Other possible body forces (e.g. those arising from electromagnetic effects) are not considered here.

Term D:  $\mu\nabla^2\mathbf{u}$ is the viscous term, which contributes to Newton's Second Law now that viscosity is included in the model.

### Exercise 2.3

Check that the viscous term D has the same dimensions as term A in Equation (2.2).

Observe that if term D in the Navier–Stokes equation (2.2) or (2.3) is ignored, then what remains is *Euler's equation*, as used in *Units 5* and *6* to describe flows for which viscous effects were neglected. Notice, however, that Equation (2.3) will reduce to Euler's equation not only when the coefficient of viscosity, $\mu$, is very small, but also when the appropriate velocity derivatives are negligibly small. Possible simplifications to the Navier–Stokes equation can be achieved by comparing the sizes of the various terms, and this is done in later sections.

See Equation (5.5) of *Unit 5* and Equation (1.1) of *Unit 6*.

## 2.2 Boundary conditions

The equation of motion for viscous flows is given by Equation (2.2) or (2.3), but is this equation enough? Clearly it is not, since the flow of an infinite expanse of viscous fluid will be different in nature from the flow of such a fluid in a confined region, such as a channel or pipe. So, from physical considerations alone, Equation (2.2) must be supplemented with a description of the region in which the viscous fluid is to be found, and boundary conditions are required to complete the mathematical model.

*Unit 5* Subsection 2.3 explained the condition to use if the fluid is in contact with an impermeable boundary (a wall or plate). If the velocity of the fluid immediately adjacent to the wall is $\mathbf{u}$, and if the fluid is not to pass through the wall, which is moving with velocity $\mathbf{U}$, then the normal components of the two velocities, $\mathbf{u}$ and $\mathbf{U}$, must be equal; that is, at each point $P$ on the boundary,

$$\mathbf{u} \cdot \mathbf{n} = \mathbf{U} \cdot \mathbf{n}, \tag{2.5}$$

where $\mathbf{n}$ is the unit normal to the surface at $P$, as shown in Figure 2.1. If the boundary is at rest, then $\mathbf{U} = \mathbf{0}$, and condition (2.5) becomes

$$\mathbf{u} \cdot \mathbf{n} = 0$$

at all points of the boundary. For a simple Cartesian geometry in which the boundary is, say, the plane $z = 0$, the normal component of velocity is just $u_3$, and the condition $\mathbf{u} \cdot \mathbf{n} = 0$ is simply $u_3 = 0$.

This should be familiar territory, since what has been said so far applies to all fluids, regardless of whether or not they are considered to be viscous. However, experimental evidence gives more information where viscous fluids are concerned. It is an observable fact that a Newtonian fluid, no matter how small its viscosity, remains stationary relative to any solid boundary that it is in contact with. This is known as the **no-slip condition**. It says that there is no relative tangential velocity between a boundary and the fluid immediately next to it, which means that at each point of the boundary,

$$\mathbf{u} \times \mathbf{n} = \mathbf{U} \times \mathbf{n}. \tag{2.6}$$

In the case where $\mathbf{U} = \mathbf{0}$, this becomes

$$\mathbf{u} \times \mathbf{n} = \mathbf{0}.$$

The notion underlying the no-slip condition is that the interaction between a fluid particle and an adjacent wall is similar to that which exists between neighbouring fluid particles. Within a fluid there cannot be any discontinuity of velocity. If, therefore, the wall acts like further fluid, the action of viscosity prevents a discontinuity in velocity between wall and fluid; the no-slip condition must apply.

Conditions (2.5) and (2.6) together imply that

$$\mathbf{u} = \mathbf{U}. \tag{2.7}$$

In particular, for a fluid adjacent to a boundary at rest,

$$u_1 = u_2 = u_3 = 0,$$

in Cartesian coordinates. The *total boundary condition* (2.7) states simply that there is no relative motion between a wall and the fluid next to it. However, note that the physical origins of the two parts of Equation (2.7) are quite different. The no-slip condition (2.6) depends essentially on the action of viscosity, while the impermeability condition (2.5) does not.

The continuity equation,

$$\nabla \cdot \mathbf{u} = 0,$$

also holds here.

The mathematics indicates this as well. Equation (2.2) is a differential equation, and such an equation needs further conditions to enable values to be found for any arbitrary constants (see *Unit 2* or Section 1 of the *Revision Booklet*).

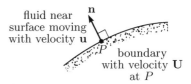

*Figure 2.1*

This is what was called the 'normal boundary condition' in *Unit 5*.

During the first century or so after Newton, however, the kinematic conditions at solid/fluid interfaces were not understood at all. Most authors of the period included 'slip terms' in their solutions to the hydrodynamic equations. As the nineteenth century progressed, more and more experimental evidence piled up in favour of the no-slip condition. It is even found to hold in cases such as mercury on glass, where the fluid does not wet the boundary.

### Exercise 2.4

A viscous fluid flows between infinite parallel plates, given by $z = \pm d$. The lower plate is stationary, and the upper one moves with a velocity which has constant components $U_1$, $U_2$ in the $x$- and $y$-directions, and component zero in the $z$-direction. Write down the components of the fluid velocity, $\mathbf{u}$, on the planes $z = \pm d$.

### Exercise 2.5

A viscous fluid is flowing in a stationary cylindrical pipe of radius $a$. What are the boundary conditions for the fluid velocity in the pipe? (Use cylindrical polar coordinates.)

---

The same argument that is used to establish the no-slip condition for fluid/solid interfaces applies also across fluid/fluid interfaces, so that the velocity is again continuous (but not necessarily zero).

There is a special case of a fluid/fluid interface that requires particular attention here. If a liquid layer (film) flows over a flat horizontal plate under the influence of gravity, it is observed that (to all intents and purposes) the liquid surface is flat and parallel to the plate. Above the liquid is another fluid (its own vapour or air), and so really the flow situation involves both fluids. However, if the upper fluid is a stationary layer of air, for example, then the only stress which the air exerts on the liquid is a normal pressure; the shear stress at the interface is zero. This is described as a *stress-free boundary condition* at the liquid's upper surface. From the argument leading to Equation (1.4), this means that

Stresses are continuous at a boundary or interface.

$$\text{shear stress } = \mu\frac{\partial u_1}{\partial z} = 0 \qquad \text{at the upper surface of the liquid,}$$

for a flow in the horizontal $x$-direction with the $z$-axis vertical.

For the two-dimensional flow shown in Figure 2.2, this means that

$$\frac{\partial u_1}{\partial z} = 0 \qquad \text{on } z = d.$$

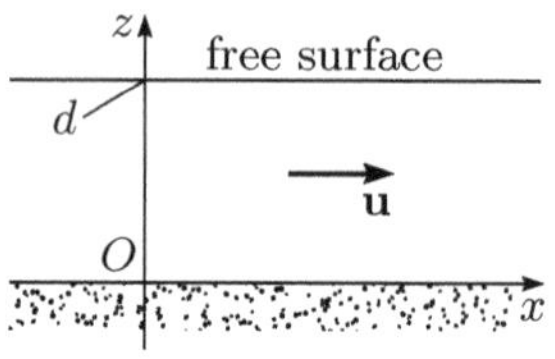

Also, in this case,

$$u_3 = 0 \qquad \text{on } z = d,$$

since $\mathbf{u} \cdot \mathbf{n} = 0$ and $\mathbf{n} = -\mathbf{k}$ here.

*Figure 2.2*

### Exercise 2.6

In Exercise 1.4 you found the general solution of Equation (1.10), for a flow between two infinite horizontal plates a distance $h$ apart, where the pressure gradient $\partial p/\partial x = -C$ is a constant. Assuming that the plates are stationary, and that the lower plate is at $z = 0$, find the particular solution of Equation (1.10) which satisfies the appropriate boundary conditions.

---

There are other types of boundary condition that must be imposed because of the overall physical situation, not just because the model involves fluids. For example, if the fluid has infinite extent (or at least very large extent compared to the dimension of any solid object or disturbance in the flow), then the fluid at large distances from the object can be treated as though the object or disturbance did not exist. Taking the case of a small object in a uniform stream of fluid, flowing with constant speed $U$ in the $x$-direction (see Figure 2.3), an appropriate boundary condition is that $u_1 \to U$ as $x \to \infty$, that is,

$$\lim_{x \to \infty} u_1(x) = U.$$

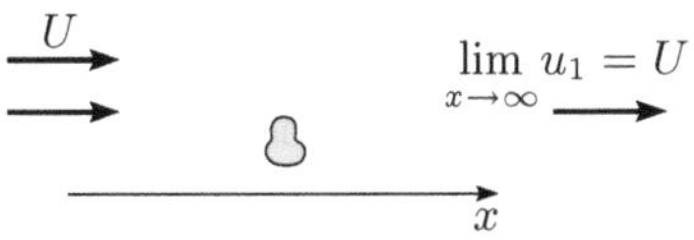

(The same could apply also as $x \to -\infty$.) Also, the mathematical solution should not introduce a physically meaningless situation. For example, if the calculations when working in polar coordinates result in $u_\theta = A/r$, where $A$ is a constant, and $u_\theta$ includes $r = 0$ in its domain, then $A$ must be zero.

The continuity equation, $\boldsymbol{\nabla} \cdot \mathbf{u} = 0$, together with Equations (2.2) and (2.7), form a mathematical model of viscous fluid flow. Remember that a 'viscous' fluid here means a Newtonian fluid of constant density and viscosity.

*Figure 2.3*

The flow of a viscous fluid is modelled by the following equations:

(a)   the continuity equation,

$\boldsymbol{\nabla} \cdot \mathbf{u} = 0;$

(b)   the Navier–Stokes equation,

$\rho\left(\dfrac{\partial \mathbf{u}}{\partial t} + (\mathbf{u} \cdot \boldsymbol{\nabla})\mathbf{u}\right) = -\boldsymbol{\nabla}p + \rho\mathbf{F} + \mu\nabla^2\mathbf{u};$

(c)   the boundary condition

$\mathbf{u} = \mathbf{U}$     on the flow boundary,

where $\mathbf{U}$ is the boundary velocity.

(2.8)

The continuity equation is a partial differential equation for dependent variables $u_1$, $u_2$ and $u_3$. The Navier–Stokes equation is three scalar partial differential equations for dependent variables $u_1$, $u_2$, $u_3$ and $p$.

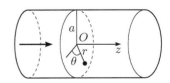

The next question is whether or not this set of equations has a solution. For a few simple geometries (e.g. Exercise 2.6 above) there are exact solutions, and consideration of one of these cases will occupy the remainder of this section.

See the *Media Guide* for more about the Navier–Stokes equations and the flows that they describe.

## 2.3   Pipe flow

This subsection investigates whether the Navier–Stokes equation predicts the results of Hagen and Poiseuille mentioned in Subsection 1.1, namely, that for a viscous fluid flowing along a pipe of circular cross-section, of radius $a$, the volume flow rate varies as $a^4$ and also is proportional to the pressure drop along the pipe.

The model is to be for the flow of fluid in a tube which has a circular cross-section (blood in a blood vessel or water in a pipe). Consider, then, the flow of a viscous fluid, which has had time to settle down, along a long, horizontal, straight, circular pipe of uniform diameter, under the action of a constant difference between the pressures imposed at the two ends of the pipe. (For example, for a long pipe into which fluid is pumped, consider only that portion sufficiently far away from the pump.) The pipe is stationary. It seems sensible to use a cylindrical polar coordinate system, with the positive $z$-axis lying along the axis of the pipe and indicating the direction of flow. The flow is represented diagrammatically in Figure 2.4, where the uniform radius of the pipe is taken to be $a$.

Here, 'has had time to settle down' means that the flow is steady.

In view of the axial symmetry of the situation, and assuming that the forces due to gravity are negligible, the specific orientation of the $\theta = 0$ direction is unimportant. This means that the flow is independent of $\theta$, or in other words that any derivative with respect to $\theta$ is zero.

*Figure 2.4*

More is said later about the neglect of gravity.

179

We start by writing down the general equations for viscous flow in cylindrical polar coordinates, and then use the description of the problem as above to simplify and solve these equations.

The starting point is Equations (2.8).

First consider the boundary conditions. The pipe is stationary, so the result of Exercise 2.5 gives

$$u_r = u_\theta = u_z = 0 \qquad \text{on } r = a.$$

The boundary conditions may appear uninformative, but $u_r = u_\theta = 0$ on $r = a$, together with the facts that the flow has settled down and that the pipe is long, straight and of uniform cross-section, gives us every reason to assume that the only component of $\mathbf{u}$ which is non-zero is $u_z$; that is, $u_r = u_\theta = 0$ everywhere.

Implicitly, $u_r$, $u_\theta$, $u_z$ must also be bounded everywhere inside the pipe.

The continuity equation, $\boldsymbol{\nabla} \cdot \mathbf{u} = 0$, gives

$$\frac{1}{r}\frac{\partial}{\partial r}(r u_r) + \frac{1}{r}\frac{\partial u_\theta}{\partial \theta} + \frac{\partial u_z}{\partial z} = 0.$$

Since $u_r = u_\theta = 0$ everywhere, this reduces to

$$\frac{\partial u_z}{\partial z} = 0.$$

This means that $u_z$ is a function of $r$ and $\theta$, but since the flow is independent of $\theta$, owing to axial symmetry, $u_z$ is a function of $r$ alone; that is, $u_z = u_z(r)$.

There is no $t$-dependence since the flow is steady.

Since $u_r = u_\theta = 0$ everywhere, the Navier–Stokes equation in cylindrical polar coordinates gives

See Equations (2.4).

$$0 = -\frac{\partial p}{\partial r} + \rho F_r, \qquad 0 = -\frac{1}{r}\frac{\partial p}{\partial \theta} + \rho F_\theta, \tag{2.9}$$

Carefully check this reduction of Equations (2.4).

$$\rho\left(\frac{\partial u_z}{\partial t} + u_z\frac{\partial u_z}{\partial z}\right) = -\frac{\partial p}{\partial z} + \rho F_z$$

$$+ \mu\left(\frac{\partial^2 u_z}{\partial r^2} + \frac{1}{r}\frac{\partial u_z}{\partial r} + \frac{1}{r^2}\frac{\partial^2 u_z}{\partial \theta^2} + \frac{\partial^2 u_z}{\partial z^2}\right). \tag{2.10}$$

Using the facts that the flow is steady (so $\partial u_z/\partial t = 0$), that there is symmetry about the central axis of the pipe (so $\partial^2 u_z/\partial \theta^2 = 0$), and that $u_z$ is a function of $r$ alone (so $\partial u_z/\partial z = 0$ and $\partial^2 u_z/\partial z^2 = 0$), Equation (2.10) reduces to

$$0 = -\frac{\partial p}{\partial z} + \rho F_z + \mu\left(\frac{d^2 u_z}{dr^2} + \frac{1}{r}\frac{du_z}{dr}\right). \tag{2.11}$$

Since $u_z$ is a function of $r$ alone,
$$\frac{\partial u_z}{\partial r} = \frac{du_z}{dr}, \text{ etc.}$$

The only body force that is likely to be involved is that due to gravity, which acts downwards and perpendicular to the axis of the horizontal pipe. However, it was assumed above that the effect of gravity is negligible. (For a pipe whose diameter is small compared to its length, this is a reasonable assumption.) Thus

$$F_r = F_\theta = F_z = 0.$$

Equations (2.9) then say that $p$ does not depend on $r$ or on $\theta$; in other words, $p = p(z)$.

In Equation (2.11), $F_z = 0$ and $-\partial p/\partial z$ is a function of $z$ only, while the term involving $\mu$ is a function of $r$ only. Since the latter two terms add to give zero, each must be a constant. Put $-\partial p/\partial z = C$, say, where $C$ is a positive constant. Then Equation (2.11) becomes

$$0 = C + \mu\left(\frac{d^2 u_z}{dr^2} + \frac{1}{r}\frac{du_z}{dr}\right), \tag{2.12}$$

whose solution is subject to the boundary condition $u_z = 0$ on $r = a$ (from earlier), and the constraint that $u_z$ must be finite for $0 \le r \le a$.

Equation (2.12) is a Cauchy–Euler equation, and the general solution is

$$u_z = -\frac{Cr^2}{4\mu} + A\ln r + B,$$

See Exercise 3.7 of *Unit 2*, where this equation was solved (with $k = C/\mu$).

where $A$, $B$ are arbitrary constants. Now, if the mathematical model is to represent a real flow, the velocity must be finite along the $z$-axis, which occurs only if $A = 0$. Using the no-slip condition, $u_z = 0$ on $r = a$, gives $B = Ca^2/(4\mu)$, and so

$$u_z = \frac{C}{4\mu}(a^2 - r^2). \tag{2.13}$$

### Exercise 2.7

Remembering the axial symmetry, what form does the velocity profile take for this flow? Sketch the velocity profile.

Equation (2.13) is now used to find the volume flow rate, and then this is compared with Hagen's and Poiseuille's experimental results.

The volume flow rate is given by $Q = \int_S \mathbf{u} \cdot \mathbf{n}\, dA$; so with $\mathbf{n} = \mathbf{e}_z$, we have

$$
\begin{aligned}
Q &= \int_0^a \int_{-\pi}^{\pi} u_z\, r\, dr\, d\theta \\
&= 2\pi \int_0^a \frac{C}{4\mu}(a^2 - r^2) r\, dr \\
&= \frac{\pi C}{2\mu} \left[ \tfrac{1}{2}a^2 r^2 - \tfrac{1}{4}r^4 \right]_0^a = \frac{\pi C a^4}{8\mu}.
\end{aligned}
$$

Thus

$$Q = \frac{\pi C a^4}{8\mu}. \tag{2.14}$$

Remembering that $-C = dp/dz$ is the (constant) pressure gradient, which is directly proportional to the pressure drop along a fixed length of pipe, Equation (2.14) shows that the volume flow rate or flux varies directly with the pressure drop along the tube and as the fourth power of the radius, $a$. This is the result that Hagen and Poiseuille found on the basis of experiments, and the model predicts the same result. Equation (2.14) is often called the *Hagen–Poiseuille equation*.

Equation (2.13) and Exercise 2.7 indicate that a maximum speed occurs, as expected, along the axis ($r = 0$) of the pipe, and this is given by

$$u_{\max} = \frac{Ca^2}{4\mu}.$$

### Exercise 2.8

An average speed of flow along the pipe can be defined as the volume flow rate divided by the cross-sectional area. Determine this average speed. How is it related to $u_{\max}$?

Flow through pipes was considered in *Unit 6*, where, for an incompressible, *inviscid* fluid,

See *Unit 6* Section 2.

volume flow rate $= u_z \times$ cross-sectional area,

where $u_z$ is uniform.

The volume flow rate in the *viscous* model, from Equation (2.14), is

$$\frac{\pi C a^4}{8\mu} = \frac{Ca^2}{8\mu} \times \pi a^2$$

$$= u_{av} \times \text{cross-sectional area}.$$

See the solution to Exercise 2.8.

Figure 2.5 illustrates the velocity profiles for the two models.

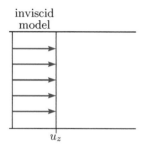 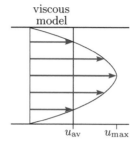

Here a cross-section through the central axis of the pipe is shown in each case.

*Figure 2.5*   Velocity profiles for inviscid and viscous pipe flow

The new mathematical model for viscous fluid flow, given by Equations (2.8), is very encouraging. It overcomes the criticism levelled at the inviscid flow model, in that it predicts parabolic rather than constant velocity profiles for flows through a tank and a pipe, and it shows that Hagen's and Poiseuille's experiments agree with Stokes' theory of viscous fluid flow.

It was predictions such as this, validated by experiment, that led to acceptance of the no-slip condition.

Equations (2.8), and approximations to them, are used in the remainder of this unit. While they are useful in some real flow situations, they apply as a suitable model only to incompressible, Newtonian fluids of constant viscosity.

In the fluid flows observed in real life, there are usually many other features to be taken into account, such as the entry/exit conditions, the roughness and rigidity of the boundaries, the variation of the pressure gradient and the homogeneity of the fluids, which are important enough to affect the validity of the model. The following two exercises end this section with a note of caution.

### Exercise 2.9

At blood-donor clinics it usually takes about 10 minutes for a person to donate half a litre of blood (1 litre $= 10^{-3}\,\mathrm{m}^3$). Suppose that the tube joining the person to the collection point has internal radius 2 mm and length 70 cm. Use the Hagen–Poiseuille equation to estimate the pressure gradient between the person and the collection point. (The viscosity of blood at 20°C is $4.5 \times 10^{-3}\,\mathrm{kg\,m^{-1}s^{-1}}$.) If the collection point is assumed to be at atmospheric pressure, $p_0$, evaluate the excess pressure at the person's arm over $p_0$, and compare your result with the following mean excess pressure estimates for the human body:

$p_{mean} - p_0$ in arteries $\simeq 1.3 \times 10^4$ Pa,

$p_{mean} - p_0$ in veins $\simeq 600$ Pa.

Recall that
$$1\,\mathrm{Pa} = 1\,\mathrm{kg\,m^{-1}s^{-2}}.$$

(Donated blood is usually taken from veins.)

### Exercise 2.10

It takes about 3 seconds to fill a half-litre jug when a water tap is turned on to give a full, steady jet. What time to fill the jug does the Hagen–Poiseuille equation predict, if it is estimated that the pipe joining the water tank to the tap is 10 m long and 15 mm in diameter? The pressure difference between the water tank and the tap is taken to be 0.1 atmosphere ($0.1 \times 1.013 \times 10^5$ Pa). The viscosity of water may be taken as $1.0 \times 10^{-3}$ kg m$^{-1}$s$^{-1}$. Give reasons for any discrepancy in the result.

## End-of-section exercise

### Exercise 2.11

Consider the fully developed flow of a viscous fluid between two large plates, both parallel to the $(x, y)$-plane and a distance $h$ apart, when no pressure gradient is applied. The plates move in the positive $x$-direction with constant speeds, $U_1$ for the lower plate and $U_2$ for the upper plate. Assume that there are no body forces acting on the fluid. Determine the velocity field, and describe the velocity profile.

To say that 'no pressure gradient is applied' means that $\nabla p = \mathbf{0}$.

# 3  Approximating the Navier–Stokes equations

The partial differential equations of viscous fluid flow, the Navier–Stokes equations, are extremely difficult to solve in exact form, and analytic solutions have been found only for rather simple cases. Some flows with relatively simple geometries, for which exact solutions are possible, were investigated in the last section. However, in general, approximations have to be made to the Navier–Stokes equations in order to make progress.

The definition of a 'viscous fluid' was given in Subsection 1.3.

In the course of considering such approximations, an important parameter crops up. This parameter is the Reynolds number, $Re$, which is expressed in terms of some characteristic length, $l$, and speed, $U$, in a flow, and of the viscosity, $\mu$, and density, $\rho$, of the fluid, as

$$Re = \frac{\rho U l}{\mu}.$$

The Reynolds number is dimensionless. It was introduced in *Unit 7* Subsection 4.2, where you saw that in an experiment to investigate the flow of a viscous fluid past a circular cylinder, the various flow configurations depended on the size of the Reynolds number. To demonstrate the importance of the Reynolds number in approximating the Navier–Stokes equations, we begin with a specific problem which can be solved exactly, and for which the key role of the Reynolds number is apparent.

## 3.1   A fluid injection problem

This subsection is concerned with one fluid flow problem, which is stated below. The solution of the problem leads to a discussion of related ideas.

### Problem statement

A viscous fluid, of constant density $\rho$ and coefficient of viscosity $\mu$, flows in the channel formed by two parallel porous plates separated by a distance $h$, as shown in Figure 3.1.

The fluid is pumped in at the left-hand end, and there is a constant pressure gradient, of magnitude $C$, causing the fluid to flow from left to right. Fluid is also forced in through the bottom plate with constant speed $V$ (normal to the plate) and is sucked out through the top plate with the same speed $V$ (again normal to the plate). Find the velocity vector field for this flow, and investigate what happens if the ratio $\rho V h / \mu$ is large.

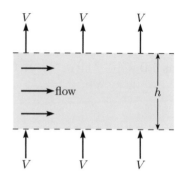

*Figure 3.1*

To start solving this problem, we make the following assumptions.

(i)   *The flow is steady.*   This is a reasonable assumption because the external features that are causing fluid motion, namely the pressure gradient $C$ and the injection speed $V$, remain constant, so that after an initial period, during which the flow pattern is set up, there is no reason for the flow variables to change with time.

(ii)   *The velocity field does not change for different points along the plates.* This means that the plates are sufficiently large to make any edge effects negligible away from the ends. The flow pattern for two different cross-sections transverse to the flow is expected to be the same, and so the flow is two-dimensional and fully developed in the direction from left to right (as in Subsections 1.2 and 1.3).

(iii) *Body forces are negligible.*   This just simplifies the argument, and is a good modelling assumption when the plate separation distance, $h$, is small compared to other lengths.

Define a Cartesian coordinate system, with the $x$-axis along the bottom plate, in the left-to-right direction of motion, and the $z$-axis normal to each plate (see Figure 3.2). The velocity vector field $\mathbf{u}$ has no $y$-component, since the flow is two-dimensional, and so $\mathbf{u} = u_1 \mathbf{i} + u_3 \mathbf{k}$.

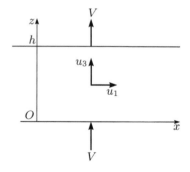

The boundary conditions are that $\mathbf{u} = V \mathbf{k}$ for $z = 0$ and for $z = h$; that is, $u_1 = 0$ and $u_3 = V$ for $z = 0$ and for $z = h$.

Since the fluid is incompressible, the continuity equation is

*Figure 3.2*

$$\nabla \cdot \mathbf{u} = \frac{\partial u_1}{\partial x} + \frac{\partial u_3}{\partial z} = 0. \tag{3.1}$$

Assumption (ii) implies that the velocity field is independent of $x$, so that $\partial u_1 / \partial x = 0$ and $\partial u_3 / \partial x = 0$. Equation (3.1) then reduces to

$$\frac{\partial u_3}{\partial z} = 0,$$

so that $u_3$ is independent of both $x$ and $z$. Hence $u_3$ is a constant value for all points in the flow region. Since $u_3$ takes the value $V$ on the plates,

$$u_3 = V \qquad \text{for } 0 \leq z \leq h \text{ and for all } x.$$

The Navier–Stokes equation, in the absence of body forces, is

See Equation (2.2).

$$\rho \left( \frac{\partial \mathbf{u}}{\partial t} + (\mathbf{u} \cdot \nabla) \mathbf{u} \right) = -\nabla p + \mu \nabla^2 \mathbf{u}. \tag{3.2}$$

This equation can be simplified using assumption (i); for steady flow, we have $\partial \mathbf{u}/\partial t = \mathbf{0}$. The $x$-component of Equation (3.2) then gives

$$\rho \left( u_1 \frac{\partial u_1}{\partial x} + u_3 \frac{\partial u_1}{\partial z} \right) = -\frac{\partial p}{\partial x} + \mu \left( \frac{\partial^2 u_1}{\partial x^2} + \frac{\partial^2 u_1}{\partial z^2} \right). \qquad (3.3)$$

From assumption (ii), we have $\partial u_1/\partial x = 0$, so that $u_1$ is a function of $z$ only, and $\partial^2 u_1/\partial x^2 = 0$. Also, $u_3 = V$. On simplifying and after rearrangement, Equation (3.3) becomes

$$\rho V \frac{du_1}{dz} - \mu \frac{d^2 u_1}{dz^2} = -\frac{\partial p}{\partial x}. \qquad (3.4)$$

Since $u_1 = u_1(z)$, we have
$$\frac{\partial u_1}{\partial z} = \frac{du_1}{dz}, \quad \frac{\partial^2 u_1}{\partial z^2} = \frac{d^2 u_1}{dz^2}.$$

Since $u_3 = V$ (constant), the $z$-component of the Navier–Stokes equation (3.2) reduces to $0 = -\partial p/\partial z$; so there is no pressure gradient in the $z$-direction.

This occurs because body forces have been neglected.

As also $\partial p/\partial t = 0$ and $\partial p/\partial y = 0$, from assumptions (i) and (ii), $p$ and $\partial p/\partial x$ are functions of $x$ only. Hence the right-hand side of Equation (3.4) is a function of $x$ only. The left-hand side is a function of $z$ only, and so each side equals a constant; indeed,

$$\frac{\partial p}{\partial x} = -C \qquad \text{(where } C > 0\text{)}$$

Again $\partial p/\partial x$ is negative because, for fluid to flow in the positive $x$-direction, the pressure must decrease as $x$ increases.

can be deduced from the problem statement. Equation (3.4) becomes

$$\rho V \frac{du_1}{dz} - \mu \frac{d^2 u_1}{dz^2} = C. \qquad (3.5)$$

As noted before, the (no-slip) boundary conditions on the fluid at the plates give $u_1 = 0$ for $z = 0$ and for $z = h$; that is,

$$u_1(0) = u_1(h) = 0. \qquad (3.6)$$

Equations (3.5) and (3.6) provide a boundary-value problem, in which the ordinary differential equation is of second order with constant coefficients.

### Exercise 3.1

Solve the boundary-value problem defined by Equations (3.5) and (3.6).

---

The solution to Exercise 3.1 is

$$u_1 = \frac{C}{\rho V} \left( z - h \, \frac{\exp(\rho V z/\mu) - 1}{\exp(\rho V h/\mu) - 1} \right). \qquad (3.7)$$

It is instructive to investigate what happens for the flow of a liquid with low viscosity. Consider the velocity component $u_1$ given by Equation (3.7). Notice that the coefficient of viscosity, $\mu$, enters into the equation in the combinations $\rho V z/\mu$ and $\rho V h/\mu$. Now the second of these is recognisable as a (dimensionless) *Reynolds number*. Let $Re = \rho V h/\mu$, and then express $\rho V z/\mu$ in terms of this Reynolds number as

The combination $\rho V z/\mu$ is also dimensionless.

$$\frac{\rho V z}{\mu} = Re \, \frac{z}{h},$$

so that Equation (3.7) becomes

$$u_1 = \frac{C}{\rho V} \left( z - h \, \frac{\exp(Re \, z/h) - 1}{\exp(Re) - 1} \right). \qquad (3.8)$$

Figure 3.3 (overleaf) shows sketches of the velocity component $u_1$ against $z$, given by Equation (3.8), for various values of $Re$. (It also shows the straight line $u_1 = Cz/(\rho V)$, the significance of which will become apparent shortly.)

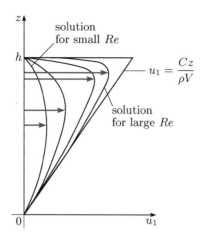

*Figure 3.3*

As this is (the $x$-component of) a velocity profile, the independent variable $z$ is on the vertical axis and the dependent variable $u_1$ on the horizontal axis.

The boundary conditions require the values of $u_1$ at $z = 0$ and at $z = h$ to be zero, and so each of the solution curves begins and ends on the $z$-axis.

As the Reynolds number increases, the value of $z$ at which the maximum value of the velocity component $u_1$ occurs moves nearer to the top plate, at $z = h$. Near the top plate, for large Reynolds numbers, there is a rapid change in the value of $u_1$ from its maximum values (shown by the arrows in Figure 3.3) to zero.

To illustrate the fact that the velocity changes quickly from a non-zero value to zero, for a small change in $z$ close to $z = h$, consider the values $Re = 100$ and $z = 0.9h$. Then the term involving the Reynolds number is

$$\frac{\exp(Re\,z/h) - 1}{\exp(Re) - 1} \simeq 4.5 \times 10^{-5},$$

giving

$$u_1 \simeq \frac{C}{\rho V} \times 0.9h,$$

whereas $u_1 = 0$ at $z = h$.

In fact, with $Re = 100$, the solution for $u_1$ is almost a linear function of $z$ for over 95% of the channel width; see Figure 3.4, which shows the graph of $u_1/(Ch/\rho V)$ against $z/h$, both dimensionless quantities, for $Re = 100$.

For a given fluid of density $\rho$, and fixed values of injection speed, $V$, and plate separation, $h$, increasing the value of the Reynolds number is equivalent to decreasing the value of $\mu$. We shall look at whether Equation (3.8), in the limit as $Re \to \infty$, gives the solution for the inviscid case, $\mu = 0$. Now

$$\frac{\exp(Re\,z/h) - 1}{\exp(Re) - 1} = \frac{\exp(Re\,z/h) - 1}{\exp(Re)(1 - \exp(-Re))}$$

$$= \frac{\exp(-Re(1 - z/h)) - \exp(-Re)}{1 - \exp(-Re)}$$

$$\simeq \exp\left(-Re\left(1 - \frac{z}{h}\right)\right) \qquad \text{for large } Re.$$

Hence if $Re$ is large, Equation (3.8) gives

$$u_1 \simeq \frac{C}{\rho V}\left(z - h\exp\left(-Re\left(1 - \frac{z}{h}\right)\right)\right).$$

Near the bottom plate ($z = 0$), the velocity component is linear in $z$ because $\exp\left(-Re\left(1 - z/h\right)\right) \simeq 0$ if $z/h$ is small compared to 1 (and $Re$ is large). This linear solution, $u_1 = Cz/(\rho V)$, is in fact the solution to the equation of motion (3.5), with $\mu = 0$, that satisfies the boundary condition

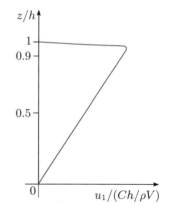

*Figure 3.4*

Note that
$$\exp(-Re) \to 0 \text{ as } Re \to \infty.$$

at $z = 0$. Thus for large values of the Reynolds number,

(i) the fluid velocity component $u_1$ has its maximum value at $z = z_{\max}$, close to the plate $z = h$, and this component rapidly falls to zero between $z = z_{\max}$ and $z = h$;

(ii) the fluid behaves like an inviscid fluid (i.e. with $\mu = 0$) away from this plate (see Figure 3.5, which shows the velocity component profile for large $Re$).

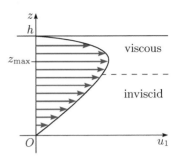

If $\mu = 0$ in Equation (3.5), the mathematical problem reduces to that for the inviscid model,

$$\rho V \frac{du_1}{dz} = C, \tag{3.9}$$

$$u_1(0) = u_1(h) = 0. \tag{3.6}$$

*Figure 3.5*

Mathematically, however, this causes a difficulty. The differential equation here is of first order, but it has two boundary conditions. A first-order differential equation needs only one condition to fully specify a particular solution. So can both conditions be satisfied?

The general solution of Equation (3.9) is

$$u_1 = \frac{Cz}{\rho V} + A, \qquad \text{where } A \text{ is an arbitrary constant.}$$

If $u_1(0) = 0$ is satisfied, then $A = 0$, in which case $u_1(h) = Ch/(\rho V) \neq 0$, and the condition $u_1(h) = 0$ is not satisfied. If we seek instead to satisfy $u_1(h) = 0$, then $A = -Ch/(\rho V)$, in which case $u_1(0) = -Ch/(\rho V) \neq 0$, and the condition $u_1(0) = 0$ is not satisfied.

For a fluid with low viscosity, it is not possible to solve the problem completely just by considering the inviscid model. The reason that the inviscid model fails in the neighbourhood of the plate $z = h$ is that, although $\mu$ might be small, the second-order derivative $d^2u_1/dz^2$ is large in this region, so that the product $\mu\, d^2u_1/dz^2$ is not negligible there.

This narrow region in which $\mu\, d^2u_1/dz^2$ is not really small and cannot be neglected is called a **boundary layer**. In a boundary layer, the viscous term in the Navier–Stokes equation, $\mu\nabla^2\mathbf{u}$, is not small compared with other terms in the equation. Therefore in the boundary layer the full Navier–Stokes equation must be retained, but outside the layer, in what is called the **ideal flow region**, the approximation may be made that the flow is inviscid. The topic of boundary layer theory is considered towards the end of the course. Essentially there has to be 'matching' of the inviscid and viscous solutions at the edge of the boundary layer (i.e. at distance $\delta$, say, from $z = h$ in the fluid injection problem). It is possible to solve the Navier–Stokes equation in the boundary layer by using the fact that the layer is extremely thin. Thus certain variables may vary only slightly across the layer and thus produce approximations which make the boundary layer problem tractable.

See *Unit 13*. There need not be a boundary layer when fluid moves past a solid boundary (there is none here above the plate $z = 0$), though this is unusual. On the other hand, there may be a 'boundary layer' (with a balance between viscous and inertial forces) even far from a solid boundary, as with the motion of a thin jet in otherwise static fluid.

To summarise, this rather mathematical fluid injection problem shows the following major features of many real flows at high Reynolds number.

(i) The inviscid approximation (i.e. putting $\mu = 0$ in the partial differential equations) leads to an improperly posed mathematical problem, for which not all of the boundary conditions can be satisfied.

(ii) There is a region of the flow in which the inviscid approximation provides a good description of the flow.

(iii) There is a thin boundary layer, in which viscosity is important and terms involving second-order velocity derivatives must be retained.

The next subsection proceeds to extend these ideas for the more general Navier–Stokes equations.

## 3.2  Navier–Stokes equations in dimensionless form

In the fluid injection problem, the significance of a large Reynolds number was apparent in the solution for the horizontal velocity component, $u_1$, given by Equation (3.8). For fixed values of $\rho$, $V$ and $h$, increasing $Re$ is equivalent to decreasing $\mu$, and the effect on $u_1$ of letting $Re \to \infty$ was discussed. However, increasing the velocity $V$ may also lead to a large Reynolds number.

Recall that
$$Re = \frac{\rho V h}{\mu}.$$

In general, it will usually not be possible to solve the Navier–Stokes equations and to find an exact expression for the velocity. So it is more natural to look at the outset for large-Reynolds-number approximations to the differential equations themselves.

To do this, we shall write the Navier–Stokes equation in a special form that identifies the significance of the Reynolds number. This involves choosing certain characteristic scales in the flow problem, and writing the flow variables in terms of them. The object is to write the equations of motion in a form where each variable is dimensionless.

To illustrate the procedure, we return to the fluid injection problem and to the differential equation

$$\rho V \frac{du_1}{dz} - \mu \frac{d^2 u_1}{dz^2} = C. \tag{3.5}$$

To write each of the variables in dimensionless form, it is necessary to choose characteristic length and speed scales. In this problem, these scales are immediately obvious; choose $h$ (the plate separation distance) to be a length scale and $V$ (the injection speed) to be a speed scale, and write

$$z^* = \frac{z}{h} \qquad \text{and} \qquad u_1^* = \frac{u_1}{V},$$

where each of the asterisked variables is dimensionless. Substituting for $z$ and $u_1$ in Equation (3.5) gives

$$\rho V \left( \frac{V}{h} \frac{du_1^*}{dz^*} \right) - \mu \left( \frac{V}{h^2} \frac{d^2 u_1^*}{dz^{*2}} \right) = C.$$

Note that
$$\begin{aligned} \frac{du_1}{dz} &= \frac{d}{dz^*}(V u_1^*) \frac{dz^*}{dz} \\ &= \frac{V}{h} \frac{du_1^*}{dz^*}. \end{aligned}$$
Similarly, we have
$$\frac{d^2 u_1}{dz^2} = \frac{V}{h^2} \frac{d^2 u_1^*}{dz^{*2}}.$$

Multiplying through by $h/(\rho V^2)$ and rearranging, we obtain

$$\frac{du_1^*}{dz^*} = \frac{hC}{\rho V^2} + \frac{\mu}{\rho V h} \frac{d^2 u_1^*}{dz^{*2}}. \tag{3.10}$$

On identifying the combination $\rho V h / \mu$ as a Reynolds number, $Re$, the second term on the right-hand side of Equation (3.10) can be written as

$$\frac{1}{Re} \frac{d^2 u_1^*}{dz^{*2}}.$$

### Exercise 3.2

Confirm that the combination $hC/(\rho V^2)$ is dimensionless. (Remember that $-C$ represents the constant pressure gradient, $\partial p / \partial x$.)

Now the Navier–Stokes equation for this problem, in dimensionless form, is

$$\frac{du_1^*}{dz^*} = C^* + \frac{1}{Re} \frac{d^2 u_1^*}{dz^{*2}}, \tag{3.11}$$

where $C^* = hC/(\rho V^2)$ is a dimensionless constant.

The significance of the Reynolds number is now apparent. If the values of $\rho$, $V$, $\mu$ and $h$ are varied individually in a way that keeps $Re$ fixed, then Equation (3.11) does not change. This means that different fluids (different $\mu$ and $\rho$) and different conditions (different $h$ and $V$) can lead to the same equation. However, more significant is the approximation that can be made for large Reynolds number. Provided that $d^2 u_1^*/dz^{*2}$ is not large, Equation (3.11) can be approximated by

$$\frac{du_1^*}{dz^*} = C^*$$

when $Re$ is large. This first-order differential equation is the dimensionless form of Equation (3.9). It provides a good approximation for the horizontal velocity component, $u_1$, in the region away from the boundary $z = h$. It is when the product $(1/Re)\, d^2 u_1^*/dz^{*2}$ is comparable in magnitude with $du_1^*/dz^*$ and $C^*$ that it must be included in the analysis. If $Re$ is large, the term $(1/Re)\, d^2 u_1^*/dz^{*2}$ may become significant near a boundary where $u_1^*$ changes so rapidly that $d^2 u_1^*/dz^{*2}$ is large.

For the analysis of the fluid injection problem, there is no need to approximate the differential equation, because it can be solved exactly. However, the theory above illustrates

(i) the idea of making the equation dimensionless by choosing scales;

(ii) the occurrence of the Reynolds number in the equation of motion.

## *Flow past an object*

Consider now the more general situation of a fluid flowing past an object, where the flow far upstream from the object is a uniform stream with speed $U$, and the only body force is that due to gravity. To write each of the variables in the Navier–Stokes equation in dimensionless form, there is a need here to choose characteristic length, time, speed and pressure scales. The speed $U$ is an obvious speed scale, and to identify a suitable length scale, the geometry of the problem can be used. For example, for the flow past a sphere of diameter $a$, a characteristic length scale could be chosen as $a$.

### *Exercise 3.3*

For each of the following situations, suggest a possible length scale:

(a) the uniform flow past an elliptical cylinder with semi-major axis $a$ and semi-minor axis $b$ (see Figure 3.6);

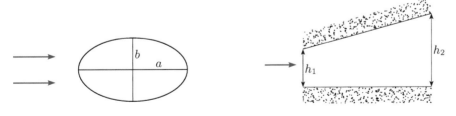

Figure 3.6                     Figure 3.7

(b) the flow in a diverging channel, increasing in width from $h_1$ to $h_2$ (see Figure 3.7).

189

For the flow past an object, consider the $x$-component of the Navier–Stokes equation (2.8b), in the form

$$\frac{\partial u_1}{\partial t} + u_1\frac{\partial u_1}{\partial x} + u_2\frac{\partial u_1}{\partial y} + u_3\frac{\partial u_1}{\partial z}$$

$$= -\frac{1}{\rho}\frac{\partial p}{\partial x} + \frac{\mu}{\rho}\left(\frac{\partial^2 u_1}{\partial x^2} + \frac{\partial^2 u_1}{\partial y^2} + \frac{\partial^2 u_1}{\partial z^2}\right). \tag{3.12}$$

The body force, due to gravity, is taken as $\mathbf{F} = F_3\,\mathbf{k}$; so $F_1 = 0$.

Suppose that a characteristic length scale in the problem is $a$; then write

$$u_1^* = \frac{u_1}{U}, \qquad u_2^* = \frac{u_2}{U}, \qquad u_3^* = \frac{u_3}{U},$$

$$x^* = \frac{x}{a}, \qquad y^* = \frac{y}{a}, \qquad z^* = \frac{z}{a},$$

In some cases, as you will see later, it may be more appropriate to choose different length and speed scales in different directions.

where each of the asterisked variables is dimensionless. It is more difficult to recognise an appropriate time scale and pressure scale from the geometry of the problem; so for the moment we choose arbitrary scales $T$ and $P$, and write

$$t^* = \frac{t}{T} \quad \text{and} \quad p^* = \frac{p}{P}.$$

The subsequent analysis indicates natural choices for $T$ and $P$ in terms of other quantities.

Substituting for the flow variables into Equation (3.12), we obtain

$$\frac{U}{T}\frac{\partial u_1^*}{\partial t^*} + \frac{U^2}{a}\left(u_1^*\frac{\partial u_1^*}{\partial x^*} + u_2^*\frac{\partial u_1^*}{\partial y^*} + u_3^*\frac{\partial u_1^*}{\partial z^*}\right)$$

$$= -\frac{P}{\rho a}\frac{\partial p^*}{\partial x^*} + \frac{\mu U}{\rho a^2}\left(\frac{\partial^2 u_1^*}{\partial x^{*2}} + \frac{\partial^2 u_1^*}{\partial y^{*2}} + \frac{\partial^2 u_1^*}{\partial z^{*2}}\right).$$

For example,

$$\frac{\partial u_1}{\partial x} = \frac{\partial}{\partial x^*}(Uu_1^*)\frac{dx^*}{dx}$$

$$= \frac{U}{a}\frac{\partial u_1^*}{\partial x^*},$$

and so

$$u_1\frac{\partial u_1}{\partial x} = \frac{U^2}{a}u_1^*\frac{\partial u_1^*}{\partial x^*}.$$

Multiplying this equation through by $a/U^2$ gives

$$\frac{a}{UT}\frac{\partial u_1^*}{\partial t^*} + u_1^*\frac{\partial u_1^*}{\partial x^*} + u_2^*\frac{\partial u_1^*}{\partial y^*} + u_3^*\frac{\partial u_1^*}{\partial z^*}$$

$$= -\frac{P}{\rho U^2}\frac{\partial p^*}{\partial x^*} + \frac{\mu}{\rho U a}\left(\frac{\partial^2 u_1^*}{\partial x^{*2}} + \frac{\partial^2 u_1^*}{\partial y^{*2}} + \frac{\partial^2 u_1^*}{\partial z^{*2}}\right). \tag{3.13}$$

Equation (3.13) does not look too different from the original form (3.12), except that there are now combinations of the characteristic scales present as multipliers. In particular, the combination $\rho U a/\mu$ is recognised as a Reynolds number.

### Exercise 3.4

(a) Show that the combinations $a/(UT)$ and $P/(\rho U^2)$ are dimensionless.

(b) Suggest choices for $T$ and for $P$ so that the coefficients of $\partial u_1^*/\partial t^*$ and $\partial p^*/\partial x^*$ in Equation (3.13) have magnitude one.

The solution to Exercise 3.4 illustrates how the characteristic time and pressure scales can be chosen in terms of the length and speed scales which are suggested by the situation. Although the actual choices for $T$ and $P$ are for mathematical convenience, they do have some physical significance as well. For example, the time scale $a/U$ was introduced in *Unit 7* and relates to the convection process.

See Exercise 4.2 of *Unit 7*.

In terms of the chosen dimensionless variables, taking $T = a/U$ and $P = \rho U^2$, the $x$-component of the Navier–Stokes equation (3.13) can now be written as

$$\frac{\partial u_1^*}{\partial t^*} + u_1^* \frac{\partial u_1^*}{\partial x^*} + u_2^* \frac{\partial u_1^*}{\partial y^*} + u_3^* \frac{\partial u_1^*}{\partial z^*}$$

$$= -\frac{\partial p^*}{\partial x^*} + \frac{1}{Re} \left( \frac{\partial^2 u_1^*}{\partial x^{*2}} + \frac{\partial^2 u_1^*}{\partial y^{*2}} + \frac{\partial^2 u_1^*}{\partial z^{*2}} \right). \qquad (3.14)$$

For a flow in which the Reynolds number is large, it is tempting to simplify the analysis by ignoring the final term, with factor $1/Re$, in Equation (3.14). However, the fluid injection problem has shown that care must be taken in the neighbourhood of boundaries, where such an approximation may not be valid.

The above analysis provides an insight into one approach to solving the problem of the flow of a low-viscosity fluid (with high Reynolds number) past an object. Away from the object, the high Reynolds number and relatively small changes in **u** lead to an approximation of the Navier–Stokes equations, namely by those for inviscid flow (in the ideal flow region). The rapid change of velocity in the layer near a solid boundary leads to large velocity gradients, and the full equations need to be solved in this region (the boundary layer). At the interface between these regions, the two solutions are 'matched'.

You can see now that, although the inviscid assumption may appear somewhat unrealistic, there is value in studying the inviscid theory. For many high-Reynolds-number flows, the Navier–Stokes equation can be approximated by that for inviscid flow (Euler's equation) in a large part of the fluid region.

## End-of-section exercise

### Exercise 3.5

Consider the flow of a *compressible* fluid past a sphere of diameter $D$. Suppose that the flow far upstream is a uniform stream with speed $U$. By choosing characteristic length and speed scales, $D$ and $U$, and appropriate time and density scales, write the continuity equation,

$$\frac{\partial \rho}{\partial t} + \boldsymbol{\nabla} \cdot (\rho \mathbf{u}) = 0,$$

in dimensionless form. (Work in Cartesian coordinates.)

191

# 4 Flow with viscous forces dominant

In some circumstances, the effect of the inertial term in the Navier–Stokes equation, $\rho\,(\partial\mathbf{u}/\partial t + (\mathbf{u}\cdot\boldsymbol{\nabla})\mathbf{u})$, can be neglected in comparison with the viscous term, $\mu\nabla^2\mathbf{u}$. This may occur when the Reynolds number is small, perhaps owing to large viscosity. However, it may also happen when the Reynolds number is of moderate size but the inertial terms are of small magnitude owing to the geometry of the flow region. This is the case for the situation considered in Subsection 4.1.

## 4.1 The slider bearing

*Unit 1* mentioned the importance of bearings and the presence of fluid films as agents for reducing the sliding friction between two solid objects which are acted upon by forces tending to push the objects together. There are many different types of bearing. The *slider bearing*, which is the subject of this subsection, is designed as a thrust bearing to support very large loads directed along the axis of a shaft. To carry these loads, the film of fluid (lubricant) between the solid surfaces must develop normal stresses, and the calculation of the pressure distribution and thus the load-carrying capacity of the bearing is necessary.

See *Unit 1* Subsection 1.5.

Typical examples of slider bearings are found in the shafts of screw-propelled ships and in the high-speed turbines of electricity-generating stations. For example, the thrust of a ship's propellers may be transmitted through a series of pads (see Figure 4.1) to the hull of the vessel. Each pad (slider) may be tilted slightly to account for the relative effects of pressure, speed and viscosity, and thus maintain the fluid film between the two surfaces (the slider and its guide) which are in relative motion, and thereby reduce friction (see Figure 4.2, which shows a cross-section of the slider with speed $U$ and the fixed guide). The bearing guide is a flat annulus fixed to the main frame of the ship.

In most lubrication problems, viscous terms in the Navier–Stokes equation dominate completely. The reason is not necessarily that the coefficient of viscosity is large; it may be the case that an extremely small length scale is involved. Figure 4.2 is not drawn to scale; if it were, the gap between the slider and its guide would not be visible. For a pad 200 mm long, the gap would be approximately $2 \times 10^{-2}$ mm. The fact that the thickness of the film is extremely small compared to the lateral dimensions of the bearing has consequences indicated by the dimensionless form of the Navier–Stokes equation.

To illustrate this, a slider bearing with surfaces the size of football fields would have a gap varying from about 1 cm to 2 cm.

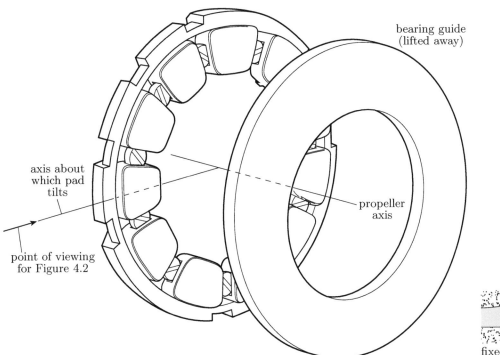

*Figure 4.1* Slider bearing

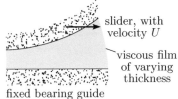

slider, with velocity $U$

viscous film of varying thickness

fixed bearing guide

*Figure 4.2* Section through slider and guide

To formulate a model of the slider bearing, we make the following assumptions.

(i) The lubricant is a viscous fluid; that is, it is a Newtonian fluid with constant density and viscosity.

(ii) The bearing has infinite length into the paper, and the bearing guide is flat, so the model is of two-dimensional flow through a section of the bearing. Taking the flow to be in the $(x, z)$-plane, this implies that $u_2 = 0$ and $\partial/\partial y = 0$.

This assumption ignores the small variations across the pad that are due to different points being at different radial distances from the shaft axis.

(iii) Forces due to gravity can be neglected; so $\mathbf{F} = \mathbf{0}$.

(iv) The flow has settled down and only the steady-state problem is considered; so $\partial/\partial t = 0$.

Choose a Cartesian coordinate system in which the slider is fixed, the $x$-axis being along the bearing guide. Relative to this system, the slider is stationary while the guide moves with constant speed $U$ in the direction of decreasing $x$. Thus the problem is described by Figure 4.3 and Equations (4.1) overleaf, the slider (of length $L$) being represented by the curve $z = h(x)$.

It seems better to let the simpler surface move, keeping the less simple one fixed.

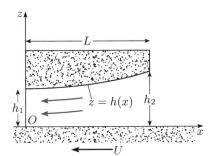

*Figure 4.3*

193

(a)  The continuity equation gives

$$\frac{\partial u_1}{\partial x} + \frac{\partial u_3}{\partial z} = 0.$$

(b)  The Navier–Stokes equation gives

$$\rho\left(u_1\frac{\partial u_1}{\partial x} + u_3\frac{\partial u_1}{\partial z}\right) = -\frac{\partial p}{\partial x} + \mu\left(\frac{\partial^2 u_1}{\partial x^2} + \frac{\partial^2 u_1}{\partial z^2}\right),$$

$$\rho\left(u_1\frac{\partial u_3}{\partial x} + u_3\frac{\partial u_3}{\partial z}\right) = -\frac{\partial p}{\partial z} + \mu\left(\frac{\partial^2 u_3}{\partial x^2} + \frac{\partial^2 u_3}{\partial z^2}\right).$$

(4.1)  *These equations take the four assumptions into account.*

(c)  The boundary conditions are

$$u_1(x,0) = -U, \quad u_3(x,0) = 0 \qquad (0 \le x \le L),$$
$$u_1(x,h(x)) = 0, \quad u_3(x,h(x)) = 0 \qquad (0 \le x \le L).$$

*It is assumed here that the boundary conditions hold at $x = 0$ and at $x = L$, i.e. that there are no 'end effects'. This is reasonable since the length of the slider is large compared with the gap.*

Assume that both ends of the bearing are exposed to a reservoir of surrounding lubricant. Then, except for minor modifications due to the flow around the corners of the bearing face, we have

$$p(0,z) = p(L,z) = p_0 \tag{4.2}$$

as the boundary condition for the pressure.

Now in practice, the gap, $h$, is always much smaller than the length, $L$, and at any point the angle of inclination of the slider face is also small. So $h_1$ and $h_2$ are of similar size, and both are much smaller than $L$.

Equations (4.1) can be made dimensionless using the characteristic lengths $L$ (in the $x$-direction) and $h_1$ (in the $z$-direction). It will also be appropriate to choose different characteristic speeds in the two directions. Clearly $U$ is an appropriate characteristic speed in the $x$-direction, and this gives a time scale $L/U$ for the situation. This time scale in turn indicates the appropriate characteristic speed in the $z$-direction, that is,

*Here $L$ is a characteristic length in the $x$-direction, while $h_1$ (or $h_2$) is a characteristic length in the $z$-direction, and $h_1, h_2 \ll L$.*

$$\frac{h_1}{L/U} = \frac{Uh_1}{L}.$$

On putting

$$x^* = \frac{x}{L}, \qquad z^* = \frac{z}{h_1}, \qquad u_1^* = \frac{u_1}{U}, \qquad u_3^* = \frac{u_3 L}{Uh_1}, \qquad p^* = \frac{p}{P},$$

where $P$ is a characteristic pressure to be determined, the Navier–Stokes equations (4.1b) become

$$\rho\left(\frac{U^2}{L}u_1^*\frac{\partial u_1^*}{\partial x^*} + \frac{U^2 h_1}{Lh_1}u_3^*\frac{\partial u_1^*}{\partial z^*}\right) = -\frac{P}{L}\frac{\partial p^*}{\partial x^*} + \mu\left(\frac{U}{L^2}\frac{\partial^2 u_1^*}{\partial x^{*2}} + \frac{U}{h_1^2}\frac{\partial^2 u_1^*}{\partial z^{*2}}\right),$$

$$\rho\left(\frac{U^2 h_1}{L^2}u_1^*\frac{\partial u_3^*}{\partial x^*} + \frac{U^2 h_1^2}{L^2 h_1}u_3^*\frac{\partial u_3^*}{\partial z^*}\right) = -\frac{P}{h_1}\frac{\partial p^*}{\partial z^*} + \mu\left(\frac{Uh_1}{L^3}\frac{\partial^2 u_3^*}{\partial x^{*2}} + \frac{Uh_1}{Lh_1^2}\frac{\partial^2 u_3^*}{\partial z^{*2}}\right).$$

On multiplying the first of these by $h_1^2/(\rho L U^2)$ and the second by $h_1/(\rho U^2)$, we obtain

$$\frac{h_1^2}{L^2}\left(u_1^*\frac{\partial u_1^*}{\partial x^*} + u_3^*\frac{\partial u_1^*}{\partial z^*}\right) = -\frac{h_1^2}{L^2}\frac{P}{\rho U^2}\frac{\partial p^*}{\partial x^*} + \frac{\mu}{\rho L U}\left(\frac{h_1^2}{L^2}\frac{\partial^2 u_1^*}{\partial x^{*2}} + \frac{\partial^2 u_1^*}{\partial z^{*2}}\right), \tag{4.3}$$

$$\frac{h_1^2}{L^2}\left(u_1^*\frac{\partial u_3^*}{\partial x^*} + u_3^*\frac{\partial u_3^*}{\partial z^*}\right) = -\frac{P}{\rho U^2}\frac{\partial p^*}{\partial z^*} + \frac{\mu}{\rho L U}\left(\frac{h_1^2}{L^2}\frac{\partial^2 u_3^*}{\partial x^{*2}} + \frac{\partial^2 u_3^*}{\partial z^{*2}}\right). \tag{4.4}$$

Now $h_1/L$ is small, while the expressions involving dimensionless variables are expected to be of comparable size to each other. Hence we can deduce from Equation (4.3) that the left-hand side and the term involving $\partial^2 u_1^*/\partial x^{*2}$ are negligible by comparison with the term involving $\partial^2 u_1^*/\partial z^{*2}$.

Making a similar deduction for Equation (4.4), we now have

$$0 = -\frac{h_1^2}{L^2}\frac{P}{\rho U^2}\frac{\partial p^*}{\partial x^*} + \frac{\mu}{\rho LU}\frac{\partial^2 u_1^*}{\partial z^{*2}}, \tag{4.5}$$

$$0 = -\frac{P}{\rho U^2}\frac{\partial p^*}{\partial z^*} + \frac{\mu}{\rho LU}\frac{\partial^2 u_3^*}{\partial z^{*2}}. \tag{4.6}$$

The rightmost terms here have the factor $1/Re$, where $Re = \rho LU/\mu$ need not be small.

What is not clear, at this point, is the relative sizes of the pressure gradient terms, since the pressure scale $P$ has yet to be expressed in terms of the other characteristic scales. We could choose $P = \rho U^2$ (as for the flow past an object, leading to Equation (3.14)). However, in this case *two* characteristic length scales have been identified, $L$ in the $x$-direction and $h_1$ in the $z$-direction; so any choice of the form $P = \rho U^2 (L/h_1)^\alpha$ would also be dimensionally correct.

You showed that $P/(\rho U^2)$ was dimensionless in Exercise 3.4(a).

It turns out that neither term in Equation (4.5) can be ignored. If $\alpha > 2$, then the pressure gradient term would dominate, giving $\partial p/\partial x = 0$. Since $p(0,z) = p(L,z) = p_0$, a constant pressure is predicted, with no rise above the ambient pressure in the fluid reservoir. This is not what is observed in practice; it is the excess pressure generated by this flow that underlies the usefulness of the slider bearing.

For $\alpha > 2$, we would have $\partial p/\partial z = 0$ from Equation (4.6) too, as in the argument for $\alpha = 2$ below.

If $\alpha < 2$, on the other hand, then the pressure gradient term is negligible, and Equation (4.5) corresponds to $\partial^2 u_1/\partial z^2 = 0$. While this can be solved to obtain a profile for $u_1$, the argument leads (as will be seen later) to a contradiction, in that the law of conservation of mass is violated. Hence we are left with $\alpha = 2$, that is, $P = \rho U^2 L^2/h_1^2$.

With this choice, Equation (4.5) becomes

$$0 = -\frac{\partial p^*}{\partial x^*} + \frac{\mu}{\rho LU}\frac{\partial^2 u_1^*}{\partial z^{*2}},$$

which corresponds to the dimensional form

$$0 = -\frac{\partial p}{\partial x} + \mu\frac{\partial^2 u_1}{\partial z^2}. \tag{4.7}$$

Also, Equation (4.6) becomes

$$0 = -\frac{L^2}{h_1^2}\frac{\partial p^*}{\partial z^*} + \frac{\mu}{\rho LU}\frac{\partial^2 u_3^*}{\partial z^{*2}},$$

The dimensionless form has now served its purpose of indicating which terms of the original Navier–Stokes equation can be ignored on account of their comparatively small size.

and here (with $h_1 \ll L$) the first term is clearly dominant. Hence Equation (4.6) corresponds (to a good approximation) to the dimensional form

$$\frac{\partial p}{\partial z} = 0,$$

from which we can deduce that $p = p(x)$.

Equation (4.7) can now be written as

$$\frac{\partial^2 u_1}{\partial z^2} = \frac{1}{\mu}\frac{dp}{dx}, \tag{4.8}$$

in which the right-hand side is a function of $x$ only, while $u_1$ is a function of $x$ and $z$.

Here $dp/dx$ is unknown, but the argument proceeds for the moment as if it were known.

Integrating Equation (4.8) twice with respect to $z$ gives

$$u_1(x,z) = \frac{1}{2\mu}\frac{dp}{dx}z^2 + f(x)\,z + g(x),$$

where $f(x)$ and $g(x)$ are determined by the boundary conditions (4.1c).

These conditions mean that

$$u_1(x, 0) = g(x) = -U$$

and

$$u_1(x, h) = \frac{1}{2\mu}\frac{dp}{dx}h^2 + f(x)\,h + g(x) = 0.$$

Hence

$$f(x) = \frac{1}{h}\left(U - \frac{1}{2\mu}\frac{dp}{dx}h^2\right),$$

and so

$$u_1(x, z) = -U\left(1 - \frac{z}{h}\right) - \frac{h^2}{2\mu}\frac{dp}{dx}\frac{z}{h}\left(1 - \frac{z}{h}\right). \tag{4.9}$$

The load that a bearing carries depends on the pressure, $p(x)$. From Equation (4.9), $dp/dx$ can be expressed in terms of $u_1$. However, the speed $u_1$ is not easy to measure, whereas the volume flow rate is. So we next calculate the volume flow rate, $Q$, for a unit depth of the bearing (into the paper). This gives

$$\begin{aligned}
Q &= \int_0^h u_1\,dz \\
&= \int_0^h\left(-U + \frac{Uz}{h} - \frac{h^2}{2\mu}\frac{dp}{dx}\left(\frac{z}{h} - \frac{z^2}{h^2}\right)\right)dz \\
&= \left[-Uz + \frac{Uz^2}{2h} - \frac{h^2}{2\mu}\frac{dp}{dx}\left(\frac{z^2}{2h} - \frac{z^3}{3h^2}\right)\right]_0^h \\
&= -Uh + \frac{Uh}{2} - \frac{h^2}{2\mu}\frac{dp}{dx}\left(\frac{h}{2} - \frac{h}{3}\right) \\
&= -\frac{Uh}{2} - \frac{h^3}{12\mu}\frac{dp}{dx},
\end{aligned}$$

This integral is calculated at an arbitrary cross-section, $x = $ constant, and applies for each such cross-section.

which can be rearranged to give

$$\frac{dp}{dx} = -\frac{12\mu}{h^3}\left(\tfrac{1}{2}Uh + Q\right), \qquad \text{where } h = h(x). \tag{4.10}$$

Now, it follows from the law of conservation of mass that $Q$ is constant. Integrating Equation (4.10) from 0 to $L$, we obtain

$$p(L) - p(0) = -12\mu\left(\tfrac{1}{2}U\int_0^L \frac{1}{(h(x))^2}\,dx + Q\int_0^L \frac{1}{(h(x))^3}\,dx\right).$$

Using the boundary conditions (4.2), the left-hand side is zero, so that

$$Q = -\tfrac{1}{2}U\int_0^L \frac{1}{(h(x))^2}\,dx \bigg/ \int_0^L \frac{1}{(h(x))^3}\,dx. \tag{4.11}$$

This is the point at which ignoring the $\partial p/\partial x$ term in Equation (4.7) would have led to a contradiction, since $Q = -\tfrac{1}{2}Uh$ cannot be constant with $h$ varying. (It *can* be constant with $h$ fixed, which is the case with parallel plates, considered in Exercises 1.4 and 2.6.)

So the volume flow rate, $Q$, besides being a quantity which is readily measured experimentally, can also be calculated from Equation (4.11), given the geometry of the bearing gap. Exercise 4.1 illustrates this point.

## Exercise 4.1

(a) Find the equation of the straight line describing the slider face, $z = h(x)$, when the face is planar, as shown in Figure 4.4.

(b) Show that the volume flow rate for such a slider bearing is given by

$$Q = -\frac{h_1 h_2}{h_1 + h_2} U.$$

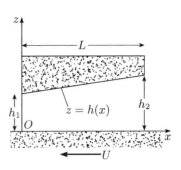

*Figure 4.4*

The case where the slider face is planar is now explored further.

Rewriting Equation (4.10) as

$$\frac{dp}{dx} = -6\mu \left( \frac{U}{h^2} + \frac{2Q}{h^3} \right)$$

and integrating gives

$$p = -6\mu \left( \frac{L}{h_2 - h_1} \right) \left( -\frac{U}{h} - \frac{Q}{h^2} \right) + c,$$

where $c$ is an arbitrary constant. Using the result of Exercise 4.1, this becomes

Note that here
$$\frac{dh}{dx} = \frac{h_2 - h_1}{L},$$
so that, for any function $f(h)$,
$$\int f(h)\, dx = \int f(h) \frac{dx}{dh}\, dh$$
$$= \frac{L}{h_2 - h_1} \int f(h)\, dh.$$

$$p = -\frac{6\mu U L}{h_2 - h_1} \left( -\frac{1}{h} + \frac{h_1 h_2}{h^2(h_2 + h_1)} \right) + c$$

$$= -6\mu U L \left( \frac{-h(h_1 + h_2) + h_1 h_2}{h^2(h_2^2 - h_1^2)} \right) + c.$$

When $x = 0$, $p = p_0$ and $h = h_1$; thus

$$p_0 = -6\mu U L \left( -\frac{1}{h_2^2 - h_1^2} \right) + c = \frac{6\mu U L}{h_2^2 - h_1^2} + c,$$

and so

$$c = p_0 - \frac{6\mu U L}{h_2^2 - h_1^2}.$$

Thus

$$p = p_0 - 6\mu U L \left( \frac{h^2 - h(h_1 + h_2) + h_1 h_2}{h^2(h_2^2 - h_1^2)} \right)$$

$$= p_0 - \frac{6\mu U L(h - h_1)(h - h_2)}{(h_2^2 - h_1^2)h^2}. \tag{4.12}$$

The next exercise asks you to show that the pressure reaches a maximum between 0 and $L$.

## Exercise 4.2

Use Equation (4.10) and the result of Exercise 4.1 to show that, for the planar slider face, the pressure is a maximum where $x = h_1 L/(h_1 + h_2)$. What is the film thickness at this point?

It can be shown that in the right-hand section of the bearing, the pressure increases in the flow direction, and in the left-hand section it decreases. This fact is illustrated in Figure 4.5 (overleaf), which also shows how the velocity profile alters with $x$.

The flow direction here is from right to left.

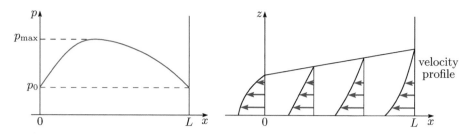

The velocity profile is linear ($\partial^2 u_1/\partial z^2 = 0$) where $p = p_{\max}$ (and $dp/dx = 0$). The curvature of the profile on either side of this point can be deduced from Equation (4.8).

*Figure 4.5*

The total load (per unit depth into the paper) that the bearing can carry against an ambient pressure of $p_0$ is

$$\int_0^L (p - p_0)\, dx.$$

For a planar slider face, $p$ is given by Equation (4.12), and the load is calculated to be

$$\int_0^L (p - p_0)\, dx = \frac{6\mu U L^2}{(h_2 - h_1)^2}\left(\ln\left(\frac{h_2}{h_1}\right) - \frac{2(h_2 - h_1)}{h_2 + h_1}\right). \tag{4.13}$$

There is no need to check the derivation of Equations (4.13) and (4.14).

The slider can to an extent tilt about the axis indicated in Figure 4.1, so as to adjust to the load placed on it. This corresponds to altering the values of $h_1$, $h_2$ in Equation (4.13).

Another quantity of interest is the frictional force arising from motion of the bearing guide. This force generates a torque about the axis of the propeller in Figure 4.1, which counteracts the torque supplied by the engine that turns the shaft. From Equation (1.4), the shear stress at the guide is $\mu\, \partial u_1/\partial z$ evaluated at $z = 0$, and the force per unit depth exerted on the fluid will be

$$\int_0^L \mu \frac{\partial u_1}{\partial z}\bigg|_{z=0} dx.$$

From Equations (4.9) and (4.10), and using the result of Exercise 4.1, the frictional force for a planar slider face is calculated to be

$$\int_0^L \mu \frac{\partial u_1}{\partial z}\bigg|_{z=0} dx = \frac{2\mu U L}{h_2 - h_1}\left(2\ln\left(\frac{h_2}{h_1}\right) - \frac{3(h_2 - h_1)}{h_2 + h_1}\right). \tag{4.14}$$

### Exercise 4.3

Each of Equations (4.13) and (4.14) can be expressed as a function of $h_2/h_1$ multiplied by a factor that involves $\mu$, $U$, $L$ and $h_1$. In this exercise assume that, while parameters may vary, $h_2/h_1$ is fixed.

(a) According to Equation (4.13), how does the magnitude $|\mathbf{N}|$ of the load vary with $\mu$, $U$, $L$ and $h_1$?

(b) According to Equation (4.14), how does the magnitude $|\mathbf{F}|$ of the frictional force vary with $\mu$, $U$, $L$ and $h_1$?

(c) The ratio $|\mathbf{F}|/|\mathbf{N}|$ corresponds to the coefficient of kinetic friction for a dry contact between two surfaces. How does the ratio $|\mathbf{F}|/|\mathbf{N}|$ vary with $\mu$, $U$, $L$ and $h_1$?

(d) Based on these results, what is the most important consideration in designing a slider bearing, so that the greatest load should be carried for given engine power?

(e) Comment on any practical limitations to the answer given in part (d).

Exercise 4.3 indicates that the faster the speed of the slider bearing, or the more viscous the fluid, the greater the load that can be carried; but in either case the friction forces also increase. To achieve the best ratio of load to friction the film of fluid should be as thin as possible, within practical limitations.

The approach to analysing this situation used the steady-state Navier–Stokes equation with zero body forces. By noting that the system has significantly different length scales in the $x$- and $z$-directions, the governing equation was reduced to one which represented a balance between pressure and viscous forces (Equation (4.7)). Despite the simplifications that were made in developing the mathematical model, some interesting conclusions have emerged that are found to correspond with real behaviour.

Lubricants may be liquids or gases. Air lubrication plays an important role in modern computers, providing the thin film that allows the read–write heads of disk drives to function effectively.

A journal bearing, where the shaft rotates in a cylinder and the axes of shaft and cylinder are parallel but not coincident, can be analysed in a similar fashion. There are many applications of this, including disk drives in computers.

Before leaving this topic, there are two further points worthy of comment. You may have noticed that the argument of this subsection called upon neither the continuity equation (4.1a) nor the boundary conditions (4.1c) that relate to $u_3$. In fact, there was no need to estimate an expression for $u_3$ in order to analyse the situation satisfactorily; typical values of $u_3$ will be much smaller than those for $u_1$. Moreover, while Equation (4.1a) has not been applied directly, the assumed constancy of the volume flow rate $Q$ is equivalent to this, since both encapsulate the law of conservation of mass.

Now that $u_1$ is known, an estimate for $u_3$ can be obtained by integrating the continuity equation, but owing to the approximations made, this can exactly satisfy only one of the boundary conditions for $u_3$.

The second point worthy of comment concerns the Reynolds number, which was originally defined in terms of 'typical' length and speed scales. On reaching Equations (4.5) and (4.6), it was pointed out that $Re = \rho L U/\mu$ need not be small. However, $L$ is not the only possible length scale here; it is 'typical' only in the $x$-direction. A typical length scale in the $z$-direction is $h_1$, and this leads to an alternative Reynolds number, $\rho U h_1/\mu$, that is smaller than $Re$ above (by a factor of $h_1/L$). This highlights that the definition of a Reynolds number in terms of characteristic length and speed scales may not always give an unambiguous quantity.

## *Equation of creeping flow*

In this subsection, the full Navier–Stokes equation,

$$\rho\frac{d\mathbf{u}}{dt} = -\boldsymbol{\nabla}p + \rho\,\mathbf{F} + \mu\nabla^2\mathbf{u},$$

See Equation (2.2) on page 176.

was simplified by neglecting the inertial term, $\rho\,d\mathbf{u}/dt$, and the body force term, $\rho\,\mathbf{F}$, in comparison with the other terms. The resulting simplified form, which may be written as

$$\boldsymbol{\nabla}p = \mu\nabla^2\mathbf{u}, \tag{4.15}$$

is called the *equation of creeping motion* or *creeping flow equation*. It is typically associated with flows for which the Reynolds number is small. (For the slider bearing situation, the Reynolds number $\rho U h_1/\mu$ can be considered small, since $h_1 \ll L$, though $\rho L U/\mu$ may not be.)

You have now seen how the steady-state Navier–Stokes equation with no body force,

$$\rho\left(\mathbf{u}\cdot\boldsymbol{\nabla}\right)\mathbf{u}=-\boldsymbol{\nabla}p+\mu\nabla^{2}\mathbf{u}, \tag{4.16}$$

can be approximated in two different ways. Flows with high values for the Reynolds number, $Re$, can be well approximated outside boundary layers by Euler's equation, which is Equation (4.16) with the final viscous term removed.

On the other hand, flows with low $Re$ can be approximated by removing the left-hand side of Equation (4.16), to leave the equation of creeping motion, Equation (4.15). In this case, it may or may not be appropriate to retain the pressure gradient term. For intermediate values of $Re$, both the inertial and viscous terms will need to be taken into account.

There are other technological applications besides bearings where the creeping flow equation can be used satisfactorily, and the next subsection describes one.

## 4.2   Coating processes

Coating processes as used by manufacturing industries arise in a variety of contexts, but, whatever the situation, the basic principle involved is much the same: a thin film of fluid which clings to a roller, sheet or wire is required. There are some fairly obvious examples of processes which need to involve fluids in a thin layer: inks in the printing industry, protective lacquers in the tin-plate industry and emulsions in the photographic industry. In fact, coating processes are needed in the production of all sorts of everyday objects: the layers of adhesive on gummed and transparent plastic tape, PVC coatings on fabrics to produce simulated leathers, fine china-clay coatings to produce high-quality paper, and extremely thin latex coatings on plastic or cellulose food wrappings. The latter coatings are only microns ($10^{-6}$ m) thick, and serve the dual purpose of both making the wrapping material waterproof and giving it an adhesive quality so that the manufacturer or retailer is able to print a description and price of the article onto the wrapping.

The coating process often involves forcing the coating fluid through a thin gap between two rollers, one picking up fluid from a reservoir, and the other carrying some of the fluid away in a thin layer after it emerges from the gap. Flow in the narrow gap can be modelled in a similar way to that seen in Subsection 4.1. Once again, the pressure and viscous terms in the Navier–Stokes equation are more important than the inertial and body force terms, and so the creeping flow equation applies.

However, coating processes need not involve rollers. Wire coating and the coatings on metal welding rods are two such examples. For example, consider the coating of an electric wire which insulates the current-carrying metal from the exterior (and from the user). Here again, a thin, uniform protective layer is required, and a minimal coating thickness is desirable, on the grounds of cost.

In its manufacture, the wire is pulled through a bath of coating liquid and then through a die which 'wipes' the liquid and leaves a coating of the desired thickness on the wire.

A simple model of wire coating would be to consider a cylindrical wire, of radius $r_w$, pulled from a reservoir of coating fluid at atmospheric pressure through a cylindrical die, of radius $r_d$ and length $L$, and emerging as a coated wire of total radius $r_c$. Any edge effects of the coating process can be ignored since the die may be considered to be very long compared to its radius (that is, $r_d \ll L$).

This situation is considered further in Section 5.

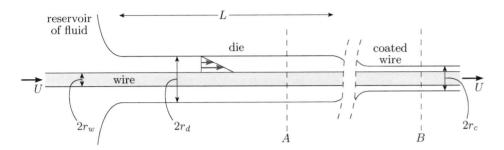

*Figure 4.6*

Figure 4.6 gives a schematic picture of this simple model. It is important to relate the thickness of the coating to the dimensions of the wire and die, by relating the volume flow rates at $A$ and at $B$.

However, the situation described above is rather over-simplified. If there is a large reservoir of coating fluid at one end of the die and only a thin coating emerging on the wire at the other end, some pressure drop is expected across the system. To confine the fluid to the wire on its exit from the die, the latter is more likely to be shaped as in Figure 4.7, with a pressure drop through the die.

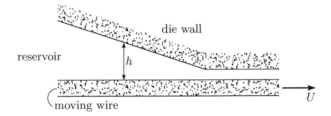

*Figure 4.7*

So some relationship is expected between the fluid layer thickness, $h$, the velocity of the wire, $U$, and the pressure gradient. The importance of the pressure term and a small length scale, $h$ (suggesting $Re \ll 1$), is reminiscent of the assumptions made in formulating and solving the slider bearing problem. In fact, Figure 4.4 and the left-hand side of Figure 4.7 above are really describing a similar problem (especially if, instead of coating a wire, the model is for the coating of a large, flat sheet, with a cross-section of the sheet replacing that of the wire in Figure 4.7).

### Exercise 4.4

Consider the coating of a large, flat sheet of metal, and suppose it may be modelled as shown in Figure 4.7. Choose Cartesian axes in which the die is fixed and the top edge of the plate is moving along the positive $x$-axis with speed $U$, with the $z$-axis perpendicular to the plate. Suppose that there is no pressure change along the straight section of the die, where the die wall is at $z = h_d$. Then (as in Exercise 1.4 with $C = 0$), the fluid velocity within this section of the die is $\mathbf{u} = u_1(z)\,\mathbf{i}$, where $u_1(z) = Az + B$.

(a) Find the values of $A$ and $B$ for which the appropriate boundary conditions on $u_1$ are satisfied, and the corresponding expression for $u_1(z)$.

(b) Express the volume flow rate within the die (per unit depth into the paper) in terms of $h_d$ and $U$.

On emerging from the die, the free surface of the coating fluid is at $z = h_c$, and the fluid velocity is given by $\mathbf{u} = u_1(z)\,\mathbf{i}$, where $u_1(z) = Dz + E$.

(c) Find the values of $D$ and $E$ for which the appropriate boundary conditions on $u_1$ are satisfied. (At the free surface, the shear stress is zero; see the discussion between Exercises 2.5 and 2.6.)

(d) By equating the volume flow rate of fluid after leaving the die with that found in part (b), express $h_c$ in terms of $h_d$.

# End-of-section exercise

### Exercise 4.5

Consider again the steady flow of a viscous fluid along a pipe of circular cross-section (as in Subsection 2.3). Suppose that over a length $L$ of the pipe, the radius (instead of being constant) is a *slowly varying* function of $z$ (see Figure 4.8). This means that the radius $r = a(z)$ varies by a small amount $\varepsilon$ over the length $L$ of pipe, where $\varepsilon \ll L$. Suppose that $V$ is a characteristic speed of the flow, e.g. a mean velocity some distance upstream, where the pipe is uniform.

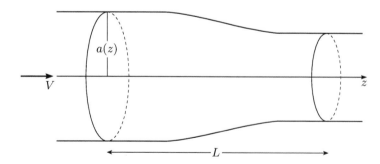

*Figure 4.8*

The $z$-axis lies along the axis of the pipe, and the flow may be assumed symmetric about this axis; that is, $\partial/\partial\theta = 0$ throughout. Assume also that $u_\theta = 0$, and neglect body forces.

(a) Write down the boundary conditions for $\mathbf{u}$, the fluid velocity, on $r = a(z)$. Also, write down the Navier–Stokes equations (in cylindrical polar coordinates) for this flow.

(b) Derive a dimensionless version of the Navier–Stokes equations, using the dimensionless variables

$$r^* = \frac{r}{\varepsilon}, \quad z^* = \frac{z}{L}, \quad u_r^* = \frac{u_r L}{\varepsilon V}, \quad u_z^* = \frac{u_z}{V}, \quad p^* = \frac{p\varepsilon^2}{\rho V^2 L^2}.$$

(The characteristic length, $L$, and speed, $V$, in the $z$-direction give a time scale $L/V$. In this time, motion in the $r$-direction will be of order $\varepsilon$, giving a speed scale $\varepsilon/(L/V) = \varepsilon V/L$ in the $r$-direction.)

(c) Show that (to a good approximation) $\partial p/\partial r = 0$ and so $p = p(z)$.

(d) Show that the remaining Navier–Stokes equation reduces to the equation of creeping motion, in the form

$$\frac{1}{r}\frac{\partial}{\partial r}\left(r\frac{\partial u_z}{\partial r}\right) = \frac{1}{\mu}\frac{dp}{dz}.$$

(e) Solve this equation, applying the boundary conditions from part (a) and any other necessary condition.

(f) Find an expression for the volume flow rate, $Q$, in terms of $\mu$, $a$ and $dp/dz$.

(g) Show that the difference in pressures between two points $z_1$ and $z_2$ on the central axis of the pipe is given by

$$p(z_1) - p(z_2) = \frac{8\mu Q}{\pi}\int_{z_1}^{z_2}\frac{1}{[a(z)]^4}\,dz.$$

# 5   *Modelling fluid flows (audio)*

Suppose that you are given the task of mathematically modelling a flow that occurs in modern technology, perhaps a bearing or coating flow such as described in Section 4. How would you set about the task?

Looking back over the last four sections, you may feel that dealing with a standard 'textbook' flow is something you could master with practice, but that analysing, say, the coating of a wire is quite another matter. Here, you are supported in the modelling of a wire-coating process within an audio session, to show that formulating mathematical descriptions of industrial problems is a task you can begin to tackle. However, note that any such problem which you are expected to attempt in the course will always either have the modelling assumptions (e.g. neglect of gravity) clearly spelt out or be structured to lead you through to a solution.

*When you are ready, start the audio at Track 4 of CD2.*

**1** **Wire moves through three regions**

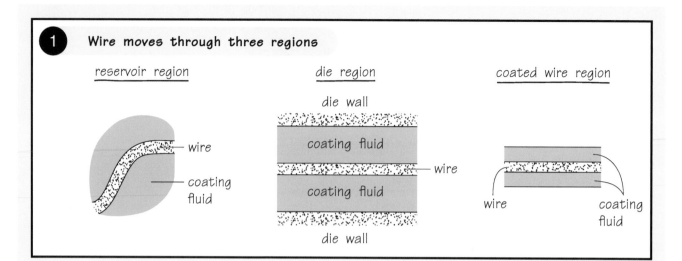

reservoir region                die region                coated wire region

**2** **Making a start on the model**

Assumptions                                             Consequences

1. Wire cylindrical, has uniform radius $r_w$

2. Coated wire cylindrical, has uniform total radius $r_c$          No $\theta$-dependence

3. Die cylindrical, has uniform radius $r_d$

4. Length of die $L \gg$ radius $r_d$                    No edge effects

5. Speed of wire constant, $V$

6. Reservoir and coated wire at same pressure            No pressure gradient
                                                           in $z$-direction

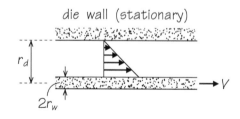

7. Coating fluid Newtonian, with constant density and viscosity

8. Flow has settled down                                No $t$-dependence

9. Body forces are negligible

**Boundary conditions**

(i) When $r = r_d$,   $u_r =$ ▢   $u_\theta =$ ▢   $u_z =$ ▢

(ii) When $r = r_w$,   $u_r =$ ▢   $u_\theta =$ ▢   $u_z =$ ▢

**3**   **The governing equations**

1. Continuity equation

2. Navier–Stokes equation

Refer to the Handbook

Does Subsection 2.3 help?

---

**3A**   **Simplified equations**

$u_r = 0, \quad u_\theta = 0$ everywhere;

$$\frac{1}{r}\frac{\partial}{\partial r}(ru_r) + \frac{1}{r}\frac{\partial u_\theta}{\partial \theta} + \frac{\partial u_z}{\partial z} = 0$$

becomes

$$\frac{\partial u_z}{\partial z} = 0, \text{ so } u_z = u_z(r).$$

Also,

$$\rho\frac{du_z}{dt} = -\frac{\partial p}{\partial z} + \rho F_z + \mu\nabla^2 u_z$$

becomes

$$0 = \mu\left[\frac{d^2 u_z}{dr^2} + \frac{1}{r}\frac{du_z}{dr}\right]$$

(Subsection 2.3)

subject to

$u_z = 0$ on $r = r_d$,

$u_z = V$ on $r = r_w$.

(Frame 2)

---

**4**   **Finding the solution**

Solve equation of motion for $u_z$  $(u_r = u_\theta = 0)$.

General solution: $u_z = $ 

Substituting the boundary conditions in above gives:

$u_z = $

**4A**   **The solution**

Multiplying through by $r^2/\mu$ gives

$$r^2\frac{d^2u_z}{dr^2} + r\frac{du_z}{dr} = 0.$$

Putting $u_z = r^\lambda$ gives $\lambda(\lambda - 1) + \lambda = 0$, so that $\lambda = 0$.

Hence, using Procedure 1.1 of Unit 2,

$$u_z = A\ln r + B \quad (A, B \text{ constants})$$

> general solution

Applying the boundary conditions $u_z(r_d) = 0$ and $u_z(r_w) = V$ gives

$$u_z = \frac{V\ln(r/r_d)}{\ln(r_w/r_d)}.$$

> $$A = \frac{V}{\ln(r_w/r_d)}, \quad B = -\frac{V\ln r_d}{\ln(r_w/r_d)}$$

---

**5**   **Relating the volume flow rates**

die region A

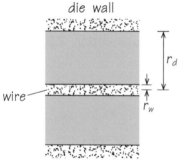

die wall

wire

Volume flow rate $Q_A$
in this region

**?**

coated wire region B

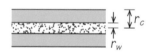

Volume flow rate $Q_B$
in this region

Since fluid density is constant, the continuity
equation can be expressed in the form

Volume flow rate = constant,

that is,        $Q_A = Q_B.$

> Unit 5,
> Subsection 4.3

> Expression for
> volume flow rate in
> Subsection 2.3

> Remember fluid and wire are
> moving together with uniform velocity

Find expressions for $Q_A$ and $Q_B$.

## 5A    Calculating volume flow rates

$$Q_A = \int_{r_w}^{r_d} \int_{-\pi}^{\pi} u_z \, r \, d\theta \, dr = \frac{2\pi V}{\ln(r_w/r_d)} \int_{r_w}^{r_d} \ln\left(\frac{r}{r_d}\right) r \, dr$$

> Integrate first term by parts

$$= \frac{2\pi V}{\ln(r_w/r_d)} \int_{r_w}^{r_d} (r \ln r - r \ln r_d) \, dr$$

$$= \frac{2\pi V}{\ln(r_w/r_d)} \left\{ \left[\tfrac{1}{2}r^2 \ln r\right]_{r_w}^{r_d} - \int_{r_w}^{r_d} \tfrac{1}{2} r \, dr - \left[\tfrac{1}{2}r^2 \ln r_d\right]_{r_w}^{r_d} \right\}$$

$$= \frac{2\pi V}{\ln(r_w/r_d)} \left\{ \tfrac{1}{2} r_d^2 \ln r_d - \tfrac{1}{2}r_w^2 \ln r_w - \left[\tfrac{1}{4}r^2\right]_{r_w}^{r_d} - \tfrac{1}{2}(r_d^2 - r_w^2) \ln r_d \right\}$$

$$= \frac{2\pi V}{\ln(r_w/r_d)} \left\{ \tfrac{1}{4}(r_w^2 - r_d^2) - \tfrac{1}{2}r_w^2 \ln\left(\frac{r_w}{r_d}\right) \right\}$$

$$= \frac{\pi V(r_w^2 - r_d^2)}{2 \ln(r_w/r_d)} - \pi V r_w^2.$$

$$Q_B = V(\pi r_c^2 - \pi r_w^2)$$

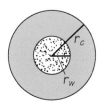

$$= \pi V(r_c^2 - r_w^2).$$

## 6    Deducing the radius of coated wire

Equating $Q_A$ and $Q_B$ for this steady flow gives

$$r_c^2 = \boxed{\phantom{XXXXXXXXXXXXXXXX}}$$

## 6A    Answer

$$r_c^2 = \frac{r_d^2 - r_w^2}{2 \ln(r_d/r_w)}$$

**A possible method of attack**

 Real World

1. Read the description of the problem carefully. It usually helps to make a sketch diagram illustrating the flow.

 Frame 1

2. From the information given, extract the important features, noting any simplifying assumptions.

   Choose a suitable coordinate system. Define your variables and specify the boundary conditions.

 Frame 2

 Mathematical World

3. Write down the governing equations for the flow, and simplify them in accordance with your assumptions.

 Frames 3 and 3A

4. Solve the mathematical problem, which usually consists of differential equations and boundary conditions.

 Frames 4 and 4A

5. Interpret your solution to answer the original problem.

# *Outcomes*

After studying this unit you should be able to:

- understand the concept of viscosity;
- understand what is meant by a Newtonian fluid;
- solve very simple fluid flow problems involving viscosity;
- understand how a special case of the Navier–Stokes equation is derived;
- apply boundary conditions when modelling fluid flows;
- understand the concept of a boundary layer, and say why boundary layers are important in considering fluid flow problems;
- understand why dimensionless forms of the fluid flow equations are useful;
- derive and apply dimensionless fluid flow equations in simple cases;
- follow the derivation of a model for a slider bearing, and understand how the full Navier–Stokes equation may be simplified in order to arrive at this model;
- interpret the solution of a fluid flow problem.

# Solutions to the exercises

## Section 1

### Solution 1.1

(a) Euler's equation for the fluid velocity $\mathbf{u}$ can be written in the form

$$\rho\left(\frac{\partial \mathbf{u}}{\partial t} + (\mathbf{u} \cdot \boldsymbol{\nabla})\,\mathbf{u}\right) = -\boldsymbol{\nabla}p + \rho\,\mathbf{F},$$

where $\rho$ is the density, $p$ is the pressure (so $\boldsymbol{\nabla}p$ is the pressure gradient) and $\mathbf{F}$ is the body force per unit mass. The left-hand side is the 'mass × acceleration' term, $\rho\,d\mathbf{u}/dt$.

(b) A typical body force acting on a fluid is the force due to gravity.

### Solution 1.2

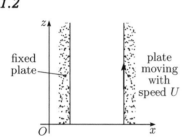

We have $\mathbf{u} = u(x)\,\mathbf{k}$. The viscous fluid is subject to a shear stress in the $z$-direction. The velocity, $\mathbf{u}$, is a function of $x$ only. So the shear stress $\tau$ in the $z$-direction at a point in the fluid has value

$$\tau = \mu \frac{du}{dx},$$

where $\mu$ is the constant coefficient of viscosity. (For an unsteady flow, this would be $\mu\,\partial u/\partial x$, corresponding to Equation (1.4).)

A surface $S$ parallel to the $(y, z)$-plane, with area $A$, experiences a shear force $\tau A\,\mathbf{k}$ due to the fluid to its right, and a shear force $-\tau A\,\mathbf{k}$ due to the fluid to its left.

### Solution 1.3

Consider Equation (1.4). The dimensions of $\tau$ are $\mathrm{M\,L\,T^{-2}}/\mathrm{L^2} = \mathrm{M\,L^{-1}\,T^{-2}}$, and those of $\partial u/\partial z$ are $\mathrm{L\,T^{-1}}/\mathrm{L} = \mathrm{T^{-1}}$; so the dimensions of $\mu$ are $\mathrm{M\,L^{-1}\,T^{-1}}$.

### Solution 1.4

Taking the same coordinate system as in Subsection 1.3, Equation (1.10) is

$$\rho \frac{\partial u_1}{\partial t} = -\frac{\partial p}{\partial x} + \mu \frac{\partial^2 u_1}{\partial z^2}.$$

Since the flow is steady, $\partial u_1/\partial t = 0$, and since the pressure gradient in the $x$-direction is constant, we put $\partial p/\partial x = -C$, where $C > 0$. (A negative constant is chosen here because if the flow is in the positive $x$-direction, fluid will flow from a region of higher pressure to one of lower pressure, and so the pressure

gradient will be negative.) So the equation of motion becomes

$$\frac{d^2 u_1}{dz^2} = -\frac{C}{\mu}.$$

(Steady flow gives $u_1 = u_1(z)$, and so $\partial^2 u_1/\partial z^2 = d^2 u_1/dz^2$.) Integrating this gives

$$u_1 = -\frac{Cz^2}{2\mu} + Az + B,$$

where $A$ and $B$ are arbitrary constants.

### Solution 1.5

Consider an element of fluid in the form of a rectangular block with sides parallel to the $x$-, $y$- and $z$-axes and centre at the point $Q$ $(x, y, z)$. Using the same notation as in Subsection 1.3, referred to the axes given in Figure 1.11, the $x$-component of Newton's Second Law for the fluid element becomes, after division by $\delta x\,\delta y\,\delta z$,

$$\rho \frac{du_1}{dt} = -\frac{p(x + \frac{1}{2}\delta x, z) - p(x - \frac{1}{2}\delta x, z)}{\delta x}$$
$$+ \frac{\tau(x, z + \frac{1}{2}\delta z) - \tau(x, z - \frac{1}{2}\delta z)}{\delta z} + \rho F_1.$$

Taking the limit here as $\delta x \to 0$ and $\delta z \to 0$ gives

$$\rho \frac{du_1}{dt} = -\frac{\partial p}{\partial x} + \frac{\partial \tau}{\partial z} + \rho F_1.$$

Since also $\tau = \mu\,\partial u_1/\partial z$ (Equation (1.4)), this is

$$\rho \frac{du_1}{dt} = -\frac{\partial p}{\partial x} + \mu \frac{\partial^2 u_1}{\partial z^2} + \rho F_1.$$

Furthermore, since $u_2 = u_3 = 0$ and $u_1$ is not a function of $x$, the equation of motion can be written as

$$\rho \frac{\partial u_1}{\partial t} = -\frac{\partial p}{\partial x} + \mu \frac{\partial^2 u_1}{\partial z^2} + \rho F_1. \qquad \text{(S.1)}$$

The $z$-component of Newton's Second Law results similarly in

$$0 = \frac{\sigma(x + \frac{1}{2}\delta x, z) - \sigma(x - \frac{1}{2}\delta x, z)}{\delta x}$$
$$- \frac{p(x, z + \frac{1}{2}\delta z) - p(x, z - \frac{1}{2}\delta z)}{\delta z} + \rho F_3.$$

Taking the limit here as $\delta x \to 0$ and $\delta z \to 0$ gives

$$0 = \frac{\partial \sigma}{\partial x} - \frac{\partial p}{\partial z} + \rho F_3.$$

Now, as shown on page 171, $\sigma = \tau = \mu\,\partial u_1/\partial z$, where $\mu$ is constant and $\partial u_1/\partial z$ does not depend on $x$. Hence $\partial \sigma/\partial x = 0$, and so

$$0 = -\frac{\partial p}{\partial z} + \rho F_3. \qquad \text{(S.2)}$$

Integrating Equation (S.2) with respect to $z$, and rearranging the terms, we have

$$p = \rho F_3\, z + H(x, t),$$

where $H$ is an arbitrary function. Substituting for $p$ into Equation (S.1), and rearranging the terms, gives

$$\rho \frac{\partial u_1}{\partial t} - \mu \frac{\partial^2 u_1}{\partial z^2} - \rho F_1 = -\frac{\partial p}{\partial x} \left( = -\frac{\partial H}{\partial x} \right).$$

The left-hand side is a function of $z$ and $t$ only, and the right-hand side is a function of $x$ and $t$ only. Since they are equal, each must be a function of $t$ only. Thus $-\partial p/\partial x = C(t)$, and so $\partial p/\partial x$ does not vary with $x$ at any instant of time.

## Solution 1.6

This problem is essentially the same as that considered in Subsection 1.3, but with the $x$- and $z$-axes interchanged and with one boundary in motion.

**(a)** True     **(b)** False     **(c)** False

**(d)** False     **(e)** True.

With a constant body force acting in the $z$-direction, these conclusions are unchanged.

# Section 2

## Solution 2.1

In Cartesian coordinates, we have
$$\mathbf{u}\cdot\boldsymbol{\nabla} = u_1\frac{\partial}{\partial x} + u_2\frac{\partial}{\partial y} + u_3\frac{\partial}{\partial z},$$
$$\nabla^2 = \frac{\partial^2}{\partial x^2} + \frac{\partial^2}{\partial y^2} + \frac{\partial^2}{\partial z^2}.$$
The $z$-component of Equation (2.2) is therefore
$$\rho\frac{du_3}{dt} = -\frac{\partial p}{\partial z} + \rho F_3 + \mu\left(\frac{\partial^2 u_3}{\partial x^2} + \frac{\partial^2 u_3}{\partial y^2} + \frac{\partial^2 u_3}{\partial z^2}\right).$$
The left-hand side can also be written as
$$\rho\left(\frac{\partial u_3}{\partial t} + u_1\frac{\partial u_3}{\partial x} + u_2\frac{\partial u_3}{\partial y} + u_3\frac{\partial u_3}{\partial z}\right).$$

## Solution 2.2

From Exercise 2.1, and using a similar result for the $x$-component, the required components are:
$$\rho\left(\frac{\partial u_1}{\partial t} + u_1\frac{\partial u_1}{\partial x} + u_2\frac{\partial u_1}{\partial y} + u_3\frac{\partial u_1}{\partial z}\right)$$
$$= -\frac{\partial p}{\partial x} + \rho F_1 + \mu\left(\frac{\partial^2 u_1}{\partial x^2} + \frac{\partial^2 u_1}{\partial y^2} + \frac{\partial^2 u_1}{\partial z^2}\right) \quad \text{(S.3)}$$
and
$$\rho\left(\frac{\partial u_3}{\partial t} + u_1\frac{\partial u_3}{\partial x} + u_2\frac{\partial u_3}{\partial y} + u_3\frac{\partial u_3}{\partial z}\right)$$
$$= -\frac{\partial p}{\partial z} + \rho F_3 + \mu\left(\frac{\partial^2 u_3}{\partial x^2} + \frac{\partial^2 u_3}{\partial y^2} + \frac{\partial^2 u_3}{\partial z^2}\right).$$
Since $u_2 = u_3 = 0$ and $\partial u_1/\partial x = \partial u_1/\partial y = 0$, these two equations become
$$\rho\frac{\partial u_1}{\partial t} = -\frac{\partial p}{\partial x} + \mu\frac{\partial^2 u_1}{\partial z^2} + \rho F_1 \quad \text{(S.1)}$$
and
$$0 = -\frac{\partial p}{\partial z} + \rho F_3, \quad \text{(S.2)}$$
respectively. These are the equations of motion derived in Solution 1.5.

(A similar argument to that in Subsection 1.3 shows that $\partial p/\partial x$ is at most a function of time.)

Therefore Equation (S.1) is a special case of Equation (S.3), the $x$-component of the Navier–Stokes equation. Similarly, Equation (S.2) is a special case of the $z$-component of the Navier–Stokes equation.

## Solution 2.3

In Exercise 1.3 you showed that $\mu$ has dimensions $\mathrm{M\,L^{-1}T^{-1}}$. Also,
$$[\nabla^2\mathbf{u}] = \frac{[\mathbf{u}]}{\mathrm{L}^2} = \frac{\mathrm{L\,T^{-1}}}{\mathrm{L}^2} = \mathrm{L^{-1}T^{-1}}.$$
Thus term D has dimensions
$$[\mu\nabla^2\mathbf{u}] = \mathrm{M\,L^{-2}T^{-2}}.$$
The dimensions of term A are
$$\left[\frac{\text{mass} \times \text{acceleration}}{\text{volume}}\right] = \frac{\mathrm{M\,L\,T^{-2}}}{\mathrm{L}^3} = \mathrm{M\,L^{-2}T^{-2}},$$
which is the same as for the viscous term.

## Solution 2.4

The fluid velocity at $z = d$ is $\mathbf{u} = U_1\,\mathbf{i} + U_2\,\mathbf{j}$.

The lower plate is stationary, so at $z = -d$ the fluid velocity is $\mathbf{u} = \mathbf{0}$.

## Solution 2.5

Let cylindrical polar coordinates be defined as in the figure.

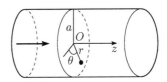

Since the pipe is stationary, the fluid in contact with the boundary is stationary; that is, $\mathbf{u} = \mathbf{0}$ at $r = a$, or $\mathbf{u}(a, \theta, z) = \mathbf{0}$. Alternatively, using cylindrical polar velocity components, this can be written as
$$u_r = u_\theta = u_z = 0 \qquad \text{on } r = a.$$

## Solution 2.6

Solution 1.4 gave
$$u_1 = -\frac{Cz^2}{2\mu} + Az + B,$$
where $-C$ is the constant pressure gradient, and $A$ and $B$ are arbitrary constants.

The boundary conditions for $u_1(z)$ here are $u_1(0) = 0$ and $u_1(h) = 0$; so
$$0 = B \qquad \text{and} \qquad 0 = -\frac{Ch^2}{2\mu} + Ah + B,$$
giving $A = Ch/(2\mu)$ and $B = 0$. The required particular solution is therefore
$$u_1 = \frac{Cz(h - z)}{2\mu}.$$

## Solution 2.7

Plotting $u_z$ against $r$ for Equation (2.13), the resulting curve is a parabola, independent of $z$, and so the velocity profile takes the form shown below (a paraboloid) at any point along the pipe.

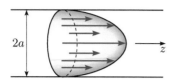

## Solution 2.8

The average speed across the pipe is
$$u_{av} = \frac{\text{volume flow rate}}{\text{cross-sectional area}} = \frac{\pi C a^4}{8\mu\,\pi a^2} = \frac{Ca^2}{8\mu},$$
so
$$u_{max} = \frac{Ca^2}{4\mu} = 2u_{av}.$$

## Solution 2.9

Time taken $= 10$ minutes $= 600$ s.

Volume collected $= 0.5 \times 10^{-3}\,\mathrm{m^3}$.

The volume flow rate is
$$Q = \frac{\text{volume collected}}{\text{time taken}} = \frac{10^{-5}}{12}\,\mathrm{m^3\,s^{-1}}.$$
The Hagen–Poiseuille equation gives
$$Q = \frac{\pi C a^4}{8\mu},$$
so the pressure gradient is
$$C = \frac{8\mu Q}{\pi a^4} = \frac{8 \times 4.5 \times 10^{-3} \times 10^{-5}}{12\pi(2 \times 10^{-3})^4}$$
$$= \frac{4.5 \times 10^4}{24\pi} = 5.968 \times 10^2\,\mathrm{Pa\,m^{-1}}.$$
This is the gradient over a 0.7 m length of tube. The pressure at the person's arm is then estimated to be
$$p_0 + 0.7C.$$
Compared to atmospheric pressure, the excess pressure at the arm is
$$0.7C \simeq 418\,\mathrm{Pa},$$
which compares in magnitude with the value of $p_{mean} - p_0$ given for veins, but does not give a close estimate.

There are many reasons why the Hagen–Poiseuille equation does not accurately model this flow. Some reasons are listed here, but you may think of others.

(i)   The pressure gradient is not constant. The pressure changes as the heart beats.

(ii)  The flow is not steady. Again, this varies with time as the heart beats. A simple model would be to assume a sinusoidal flow rate.

(iii) The tube is not necessarily rigid, straight or horizontal.

(iv)  The entry conditions are very different from simple tube flow (a needle enters the arm, etc.).

(v)   Blood is neither a homogeneous nor a Newtonian fluid.

(vi)  All values are rough estimates.

## Solution 2.10

From the Hagen–Poiseuille equation, the volume flow rate is
$$Q = \frac{\pi C a^4}{8\mu} = \frac{\pi \times 0.1 \times 1.013 \times 10^5 \times (7.5 \times 10^{-3})^4}{10 \times 8 \times 1.0 \times 10^{-3}}$$
$$= \frac{\pi \times 1.013 \times 7.5^4 \times 10^{-6}}{8}.$$
Therefore the estimated time to fill the jug is
$$\frac{\text{volume}}{Q} = \frac{0.5 \times 10^{-3} \times 8}{\pi \times 1.013 \times 7.5^4 \times 10^{-6}} \simeq 0.4\,\mathrm{s}.$$
There are many reasons for the discrepancy, some of which are as follows.

(i)   The flow is not laminar.

(ii)  The pipe is not smooth, horizontal or straight.

(iii) The entry and exit situations are not modelled correctly.

(iv)  All values are rough estimates.

## Solution 2.11

Choose a Cartesian coordinate system, as shown in the figure below, with the plates lying in the planes $z = 0$ and $z = h$.

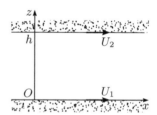

Equations (2.8) are
$$\nabla \cdot \mathbf{u} = 0, \tag{S.4}$$
$$\rho\left(\frac{\partial \mathbf{u}}{\partial t} + (\mathbf{u} \cdot \nabla)\,\mathbf{u}\right) = -\nabla p + \rho\,\mathbf{F} + \mu\nabla^2\mathbf{u}, \tag{S.5}$$
$$\mathbf{u} = \mathbf{U} \quad \text{on the boundaries.} \tag{S.6}$$
Assume that the flow is steady (since nothing is time-dependent); so $\partial \mathbf{u}/\partial t = \mathbf{0}$.

Assume that the plates are infinite in extent and that the flow is two-dimensional, with no variation in the $y$-direction. Then $u_2 = 0$ and $\partial \mathbf{u}/\partial y = \mathbf{0}$. Also, the flow is fully developed in the $x$-direction (see page 169); so $\partial \mathbf{u}/\partial x = \mathbf{0}$, and
$$\mathbf{u} = u_1(z)\,\mathbf{i} + u_3(z)\,\mathbf{k}.$$
The continuity equation (S.4) becomes $du_3/dz = 0$, and since $u_3 = 0$ on both boundaries, we have $u_3 = 0$ everywhere and $\mathbf{u} = u_1(z)\,\mathbf{i}$. Also
$$\nabla p = \mathbf{0} \quad \text{(there is no applied pressure gradient)},$$
$$\mathbf{F} = \mathbf{0} \quad \text{(there are no body forces)}.$$
The $x$-component of Equation (S.5) then gives
$$\frac{d^2 u_1}{dz^2} = 0 \quad \text{(the other components give } 0 = 0).$$

On integrating, we obtain

$$u_1 = Az + B,$$

where $A$, $B$ are arbitrary constants. The boundary conditions (S.6) are

$$\mathbf{u} = U_1\,\mathbf{i} \quad \text{on } z = 0, \qquad \mathbf{u} = U_2\,\mathbf{i} \quad \text{on } z = h,$$

that is,

$$u_1(0) = U_1, \qquad u_1(h) = U_2.$$

Hence $B = U_1$ and $A = (U_2 - U_1)/h$. So

$$u_1 = \frac{U_2 - U_1}{h}z + U_1.$$

The velocity field is

$$\mathbf{u} = \left(\frac{U_2 - U_1}{h}z + U_1\right)\mathbf{i},$$

and the velocity profile is a straight line as in the figure below, which shows the two cases $U_2 > U_1$ and $U_2 < U_1$.

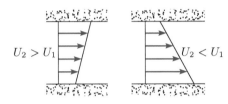

# Section 3

## Solution 3.1

Equation (3.5) can be written as

$$\mu\frac{d^2u_1}{dz^2} - \rho V\frac{du_1}{dz} = -C, \tag{S.7}$$

which has auxiliary equation

$$\mu\lambda^2 - \rho V\lambda = 0,$$

with roots $\lambda = 0$ and $\lambda = \rho V/\mu$. Thus the complementary function for Equation (S.7) is

$$A + B\exp\left(\frac{\rho V z}{\mu}\right),$$

where $A$, $B$ are arbitrary constants.

A particular solution of Equation (S.7) is

$$u_1 = \frac{Cz}{\rho V},$$

and so the general solution is

$$u_1 = A + B\exp\left(\frac{\rho V z}{\mu}\right) + \frac{Cz}{\rho V}.$$

The boundary conditions, $u_1(0) = u_1(h) = 0$, require

$$0 = A + B, \qquad 0 = A + B\exp\left(\frac{\rho V h}{\mu}\right) + \frac{Ch}{\rho V},$$

from which

$$A = -B, \qquad B = \frac{Ch}{\rho V}\bigg/\left(1 - \exp\left(\frac{\rho V h}{\mu}\right)\right).$$

The general solution is therefore

$$u_1 = \frac{C}{\rho V}\left(z - h\,\frac{\exp(\rho V z/\mu) - 1}{\exp(\rho V h/\mu) - 1}\right).$$

## Solution 3.2

We have

$$\left[\frac{hC}{\rho V^2}\right] = \frac{[h]\,[C]}{[\rho]\,[V]^2} = \frac{(\mathrm{L})(\mathrm{M}\,\mathrm{L}^{-2}\mathrm{T}^{-2})}{(\mathrm{M}\,\mathrm{L}^{-3})(\mathrm{L}\,\mathrm{T}^{-1})^2}$$

$$= 1, \qquad \text{as required.}$$

## Solution 3.3

(a) There are two possibilities: $a$ and $b$. Intuition suggests that defining a Reynolds number in terms of $a$ would be sensible for the component of the equation of motion in the direction of the uniform flow.

(b) Significant length scales here are $h_1$ and $h_2$, although other possibilities are $h_2 - h_1$ and $\frac{1}{2}(h_1 + h_2)$. (Guidance will be given whenever there is such a choice to be made. A completely different length scale in this case could be the distance between the ends of the channel.)

## Solution 3.4

(a) We have

$$\left[\frac{a}{UT}\right] = \frac{[a]}{[U]\,[T]} = \frac{\mathrm{L}}{(\mathrm{L}\,\mathrm{T}^{-1})\,\mathrm{T}}$$

$$= 1, \qquad \text{as required,}$$

and

$$\left[\frac{P}{\rho U^2}\right] = \frac{[P]}{[\rho]\,[U]^2} = \frac{\mathrm{M}\,\mathrm{L}^{-1}\mathrm{T}^{-2}}{(\mathrm{M}\,\mathrm{L}^{-3})(\mathrm{L}\,\mathrm{T}^{-1})^2}$$

$$= 1, \qquad \text{as required.}$$

(b) The choice $T = a/U$ gives

$$\frac{a}{UT} = 1,$$

and the choice $P = \rho U^2$ gives

$$\frac{P}{\rho U^2} = 1.$$

## Solution 3.5

The continuity equation for a compressible fluid is

$$\frac{\partial\rho}{\partial t} + \boldsymbol{\nabla}\cdot(\rho\mathbf{u}) = 0,$$

or

$$\frac{\partial\rho}{\partial t} + \rho\left(\frac{\partial u_1}{\partial x} + \frac{\partial u_2}{\partial y} + \frac{\partial u_3}{\partial z}\right)$$

$$+ u_1\frac{\partial\rho}{\partial x} + u_2\frac{\partial\rho}{\partial y} + u_3\frac{\partial\rho}{\partial z} = 0. \tag{S.8}$$

Choose $D$ and $U$ to be length and speed scales; also choose $T$ and P (capital $\rho$) to be time and density scales, and write

$$u_1^* = \frac{u_1}{U}, \qquad u_2^* = \frac{u_2}{U}, \qquad u_3^* = \frac{u_3}{U},$$

$$x^* = \frac{x}{D}, \qquad y^* = \frac{y}{D}, \qquad z^* = \frac{z}{D},$$

$$t^* = \frac{t}{T}, \qquad \rho^* = \frac{\rho}{\mathrm{P}}.$$

Equation (S.8) becomes

$$\frac{P}{T}\frac{\partial \rho^*}{\partial t^*} + \frac{PU}{D}\rho^*\left(\frac{\partial u_1^*}{\partial x^*} + \frac{\partial u_2^*}{\partial y^*} + \frac{\partial u_3^*}{\partial z^*}\right)$$

$$+ \frac{PU}{D}\left(u_1^*\frac{\partial \rho^*}{\partial x^*} + u_2^*\frac{\partial \rho^*}{\partial y^*} + u_3^*\frac{\partial \rho^*}{\partial z^*}\right) = 0. \qquad \text{(S.9)}$$

Dividing through by $P/T$, and choosing $T = D/U$, Equation (S.9) becomes

$$\frac{\partial \rho^*}{\partial t^*} + \rho^*\left(\frac{\partial u_1^*}{\partial x^*} + \frac{\partial u_2^*}{\partial y^*} + \frac{\partial u_3^*}{\partial z^*}\right)$$

$$+ u_1^*\frac{\partial \rho^*}{\partial x^*} + u_2^*\frac{\partial \rho^*}{\partial y^*} + u_3^*\frac{\partial \rho^*}{\partial z^*} = 0.$$

(Any density scale will do.)

# Section 4

## Solution 4.1

**(a)** If the slider face is straight, then (from Figure 4.4) the relevant equation is

$$z = \frac{h_2 - h_1}{L}x + h_1$$

$$= mx + c \qquad \text{(say)}.$$

**(b)** The volume flow rate $Q$ is (from Equation (4.11)) obtained from the integrals

$$\int_0^L \frac{1}{(h(x))^2}\,dx \qquad \text{and} \qquad \int_0^L \frac{1}{(h(x))^3}\,dx.$$

From part (a), the first of these is

$$\int_0^L \frac{1}{(mx + c)^2}\,dx = \left[-\frac{1}{m(mx + c)}\right]_0^L$$

$$= -\frac{1}{m(mL + c)} - \left(-\frac{1}{mc}\right)$$

$$= \frac{L}{c(mL + c)},$$

and the second is

$$\int_0^L \frac{1}{(mx + c)^3}\,dx = \left[-\frac{1}{2m(mx + c)^2}\right]_0^L$$

$$= -\frac{1}{2m(mL + c)^2} - \left(-\frac{1}{2mc^2}\right)$$

$$= \frac{L(2c + mL)}{2c^2(mL + c)^2}.$$

Thus, from Equation (4.11), we have

$$Q = -\tfrac{1}{2}U\int_0^L \frac{1}{(h(x))^2}\,dx \bigg/ \int_0^L \frac{1}{(h(x))^3}\,dx$$

$$= -\tfrac{1}{2}U \frac{L}{c(mL + c)}\frac{2c^2(mL + c)^2}{L(2c + mL)}$$

$$= -\frac{Uc(mL + c)}{mL + 2c}.$$

Putting $m = (h_2 - h_1)/L$ and $c = h_1$ from part (a), this becomes

$$Q = -\frac{h_1 h_2}{h_1 + h_2}U.$$

## Solution 4.2

From Equation (4.10), $dp/dx = 0$ when

$$Q = -\tfrac{1}{2}Uh.$$

The result of Solution 4.1 gives

$$Q = -\frac{h_1 h_2}{h_1 + h_2}U,$$

so that the value of $h$ (the film thickness) when $dp/dx = 0$ is

$$h = -\frac{2Q}{U} = \frac{2h_1 h_2}{h_1 + h_2}.$$

Since $p > p_0$ for $h_1 < h < h_2$, from Equation (4.12), this value of $h$ is the thickness of the film when the pressure is a *maximum*. (Evaluating $d^2 p/dx^2$ for $Q = -\tfrac{1}{2}Uh$ confirms this.)

To find the corresponding value of $x$, substitute $h = 2h_1 h_2/(h_1 + h_2)$ into the equation of the slider face,

$$z = h(x) = \frac{h_2 - h_1}{L}x + h_1.$$

Thus

$$\frac{2h_1 h_2}{h_1 + h_2} = \frac{h_2 - h_1}{L}x + h_1,$$

from which

$$x = \frac{L}{h_2 - h_1}\left(\frac{2h_1 h_2}{h_1 + h_2} - h_1\right) = \frac{h_1 L}{h_1 + h_2}.$$

This is where the pressure is a maximum.

## Solution 4.3

**(a)** Equation (4.13) for the load $|\mathbf{N}|$ can be written as

$$|\mathbf{N}| = \frac{\mu U L^2}{h_1^2}\,f\!\left(\frac{h_2}{h_1}\right).$$

Hence the load that can be carried rises with increases in the viscosity $\mu$, the slider speed $U$ and the slider length $L$, and with decreases in the film thickness $h_1$.

**(b)** Equation (4.14) for the frictional force $|\mathbf{F}|$ can be expressed as

$$|\mathbf{F}| = \frac{\mu U L}{h_1}\,g\!\left(\frac{h_2}{h_1}\right).$$

The conclusions concerning variation of $|\mathbf{F}|$ with changes in $\mu$, $U$, $L$ and $h_1$ are the same as for $|\mathbf{N}|$ in part (a).

**(c)** From parts (a) and (b), we have

$$\frac{|\mathbf{F}|}{|\mathbf{N}|} = \frac{\mu U L}{h_1}\frac{h_1^2}{\mu U L^2}\,k\!\left(\frac{h_2}{h_1}\right) = \frac{h_1}{L}\,k\!\left(\frac{h_2}{h_1}\right),$$

where $k = g/f$. This 'coefficient of friction' does not depend on the viscosity $\mu$ or the slider speed $U$, but only on the geometric dimensions of the fluid film. The ratio $|\mathbf{F}|/|\mathbf{N}|$ can be lowered by widening the slider or by reducing the thickness of the film.

**(d)** Apart from frictional losses elsewhere, the torque produced by the engine will be balanced in the steady state by the torque caused by the friction force at the slider. To maximise $|\mathbf{N}|$, it seems from part (c) that $L/h_1$ should be made as large as possible. Hence, for a given slider length $L$, the slider should be designed with as thin a fluid film as possible.

**(e)** If the film thickness is too thin, the model may not be appropriate, because:

(i) the fluid may no longer be considered as Newtonian when the film thickness approaches molecular size;

(ii) even a supposedly smooth surface has some roughness, and the bearing surfaces may no longer be sufficiently smooth.

The designer should aim to reduce the film thickness to the least possible value, such that the model is still applicable.

## Solution 4.4

**(a)** The boundary conditions are

$$u_1(0) = U \qquad \text{and} \qquad u_1(h_d) = 0;$$

so $B = U$ and $Ah_d + B = 0$, that is, $A = -U/h_d$. Thus within the die,

$$u_1(z) = U\left(1 - \frac{z}{h_d}\right).$$

**(b)** The volume flow rate (per unit depth) within the die is

$$Q = \int_0^{h_d} u_1(z)\,dz$$

$$= U\int_0^{h_d}\left(1 - \frac{z}{h_d}\right)dz$$

$$= U\left[z - \frac{z^2}{2h_d}\right]_0^{h_d} = \tfrac{1}{2}Uh_d.$$

**(c)** The boundary conditions after emerging from the die are

$$u_1(0) = U \qquad \text{and} \qquad \frac{du_1}{dz}(h_c) = 0;$$

so $E = U$ and $D = 0$. Hence after leaving the die,

$$u_1(z) = U,$$

and the fluid moves like a rigid body.

**(d)** The volume flow rate after leaving the die is

$$Q = \int_0^{h_c} u_1(z)\,dz = Uh_c.$$

Since $Q$ must be the same as in part (b), we have

$$h_c = \tfrac{1}{2}h_d.$$

Hence the thickness of the coating that emerges from the die is half that of the fluid layer within the die.

## Solution 4.5

**(a)** The boundary conditions on $r = a(z)$ are

$$u_r = u_\theta = u_z = 0 \qquad \text{(see Exercise 2.5)}.$$

With $u_\theta = 0$ and $\partial/\partial\theta = 0$ everywhere, and with no body forces, the Navier–Stokes equations are

$$\rho\left(u_r\frac{\partial u_r}{\partial r} + u_z\frac{\partial u_r}{\partial z}\right)$$

$$= -\frac{\partial p}{\partial r} + \mu\left(\frac{1}{r}\frac{\partial}{\partial r}\left(r\frac{\partial u_r}{\partial r}\right) - \frac{u_r}{r^2} + \frac{\partial^2 u_r}{\partial z^2}\right), \quad \text{(S.10)}$$

$$\rho\left(u_r\frac{\partial u_z}{\partial r} + u_z\frac{\partial u_z}{\partial z}\right)$$

$$= -\frac{\partial p}{\partial z} + \mu\left(\frac{1}{r}\frac{\partial}{\partial r}\left(r\frac{\partial u_z}{\partial r}\right) + \frac{\partial^2 u_z}{\partial z^2}\right). \quad \text{(S.11)}$$

**(b)** Using the given dimensionless variables, the dimensionless forms of Equations (S.10) and (S.11) are

$$\frac{\varepsilon V^2}{L^2}\rho\left(u_r^*\frac{\partial u_r^*}{\partial r^*} + u_z^*\frac{\partial u_r^*}{\partial z^*}\right) = -\frac{\rho V^2 L^2}{\varepsilon^3}\frac{\partial p^*}{\partial r^*}$$

$$+\mu\left(\frac{V}{L\varepsilon}\frac{1}{r^*}\frac{\partial}{\partial r^*}\left(r^*\frac{\partial u_r^*}{\partial r^*}\right) - \frac{V}{L\varepsilon}\frac{u_r^*}{r^{*2}} + \frac{\varepsilon V}{L^3}\frac{\partial^2 u_r^*}{\partial z^{*2}}\right), \quad \text{(S.12)}$$

$$\frac{V^2}{L}\rho\left(u_r^*\frac{\partial u_z^*}{\partial r^*} + u_z^*\frac{\partial u_z^*}{\partial z^*}\right) = -\frac{\rho V^2 L}{\varepsilon^2}\frac{\partial p^*}{\partial z^*}$$

$$+\mu\left(\frac{V}{\varepsilon^2}\frac{1}{r^*}\frac{\partial}{\partial r^*}\left(r^*\frac{\partial u_z^*}{\partial r^*}\right) + \frac{V}{L^2}\frac{\partial^2 u_z^*}{\partial z^{*2}}\right). \quad \text{(S.13)}$$

**(c)** On multiplying Equation (S.12) by $\varepsilon^3/(\rho V^2 L^2)$, we obtain

$$\frac{\varepsilon^4}{L^4}\rho\left(u_r^*\frac{\partial u_r^*}{\partial r^*} + u_z^*\frac{\partial u_r^*}{\partial z^*}\right) = -\frac{\partial p^*}{\partial r^*}$$

$$+\frac{\varepsilon^2}{L^2}\frac{\mu}{\rho V L}\left(\frac{1}{r^*}\frac{\partial}{\partial r^*}\left(r^*\frac{\partial u_r^*}{\partial r^*}\right) - \frac{u_r^*}{r^{*2}} + \frac{\varepsilon^2}{L^2}\frac{\partial^2 u_r^*}{\partial z^{*2}}\right).$$

With $\varepsilon \ll L$, this becomes $0 = -\partial p^*/\partial r^*$. Hence Equation (S.10) may be reduced to $\partial p/\partial r = 0$, indicating that $p = p(z)$.

**(d)** On multiplying Equation (S.13) by $\varepsilon^2/(\rho V^2 L)$, we have

$$\frac{\varepsilon^2}{L^2}\left(u_r^*\frac{\partial u_z^*}{\partial r^*} + u_z^*\frac{\partial u_z^*}{\partial z^*}\right) = -\frac{\partial p^*}{\partial z^*}$$

$$+\frac{\mu}{\rho V L}\left(\frac{1}{r^*}\frac{\partial}{\partial r^*}\left(r^*\frac{\partial u_z^*}{\partial r^*}\right) + \frac{\varepsilon^2}{L^2}\frac{\partial^2 u_z^*}{\partial z^{*2}}\right).$$

With $\varepsilon \ll L$, this becomes

$$0 = -\frac{\partial p^*}{\partial z^*} + \frac{\mu}{\rho V L}\frac{1}{r^*}\frac{\partial}{\partial r^*}\left(r^*\frac{\partial u_z^*}{\partial r^*}\right).$$

Hence Equation (S.11) reduces to

$$0 = -\frac{\partial p}{\partial z} + \frac{\mu}{r}\frac{\partial}{\partial r}\left(r\frac{\partial u_z}{\partial r}\right).$$

From part (c), this can be written as

$$\frac{1}{r}\frac{\partial}{\partial r}\left(r\frac{\partial u_z}{\partial r}\right) = \frac{1}{\mu}\frac{dp}{dz}, \qquad \text{as required.}$$

**(e)** Multiplying by $r$ and then integrating with respect to $r$ gives

$$r\frac{\partial u_z}{\partial r} = \frac{1}{2\mu}\frac{dp}{dz}r^2 + f(z).$$

Dividing now by $r$ and integrating with respect to $r$ once more, we obtain

$$u_z(r,z) = \frac{1}{4\mu}\frac{dp}{dz}r^2 + f(z)\ln r + g(z),$$

where $f$ and $g$ are arbitrary functions. Now $u_z$ must have a finite value at $r = 0$, so $f(z) = 0$. The boundary condition $u_z(a,z) = 0$ then gives

$$g(z) = -\frac{a^2}{4\mu}\frac{dp}{dz}.$$

Hence

$$u_z(r,z) = \frac{1}{4\mu}\frac{dp}{dz}\left(r^2 - a^2\right).$$

**(f)** The volume flow rate is

$$Q = \int_{-\pi}^{\pi} \int_{0}^{a(z)} u_z(r, z)\, r\, dr\, d\theta$$

$$= \frac{2\pi}{4\mu} \frac{dp}{dz} \int_{0}^{a(z)} (r^3 - a^2 r)\, dr$$

$$= \frac{\pi}{2\mu} \frac{dp}{dz} \left[\tfrac{1}{4}r^4 - \tfrac{1}{2}a^2 r^2\right]_0^a = -\frac{\pi a^4}{8\mu} \frac{dp}{dz}.$$

**(g)** The pressure gradient is

$$\frac{dp}{dz} = -\frac{8\mu Q}{\pi a^4}, \qquad \text{where } a = a(z).$$

Thus the pressure difference is given by

$$p(z_1) - p(z_2) = \frac{8\mu Q}{\pi} \int_{z_1}^{z_2} \frac{1}{[a(z)]^4}\, dz.$$

# Index